# GUIDANCE, NAVIGATION, TRACKING, and SPACE PHYSICS

VOLUME III of Ballistic Missile and Space Technology

# BALLISTIC MISSILE and SPACE TECHNOLOGY

*Edited by* DONALD P. LeGALLEY

VOLUME I

Bioastronautics and Electronics and Invited Addresses

VOLUME II

Propulsion and Auxiliary Power Systems

VOLUME III

Guidance, Navigation, Tracking, and Space Physics

VOLUME IV

Re-entry and Vehicle Design

# GUIDANCE, NAVIGATION, TRACKING, and SPACE PHYSICS

## VOLUME III of Ballistic Missile and Space Technology

Proceedings of the Fifth Symposium on Ballistic Missile and Space Technology, held in Los Angeles, California, in August, 1960

Sponsored by Headquarters, Air Force Ballistic Missile Division, Space Technology Laboratories, Inc., and Aerospace Corporation

EDITOR

**Donald P. LeGalley**

*Space Technology Laboratories, Inc., Los Angeles, California*

ACADEMIC PRESS
New York and London • 1960

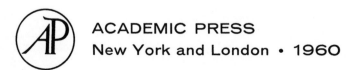

ACADEMIC PRESS INC.
111 FIFTH AVENUE
NEW YORK 3, N. Y.

*United Kingdom Edition*
Published by
ACADEMIC PRESS INC. (LONDON) LTD.
17 OLD QUEEN STREET, LONDON S.W. 1

*Library of Congress Catalog Card Number 60-16987*

PRINTED IN THE UNITED STATES OF AMERICA

## CONTRIBUTORS

Bernard Arrow, The Martin Company, Denver Division, Denver, Colorado

Richard H. Battin, Instrumentation Laboratory, Massachusetts Institute of Technology, Cambridge 39, Massachusetts

Frederick L. Beckner, Military Physics Research Laboratory, The University of Texas, Austin, Texas

J. L. Brenner, Stanford Research Institute, Menlo Park, California

Joseph P. Frazier, General Electric Company, Syracuse, New York

W. F. Holst, Lincoln Laboratory, Massachusetts Institute of Technology, Lexington, Massachusetts

Jean I. F. King, Missile and Space Vehicle Department, General Electric Company, Philadelphia, Pennsylvania

John M. Lambert, General Electric Company, Syracuse, New York

D. L. Lovenvirth, Lincoln Laboratory, Massachusetts Institute of Technology, Lexington, Massachusetts

D. S. Merrilees, Douglas Aircraft Co., Inc., Missiles and Space Systems Engineering, Santa Monica, California

Paul A. Penzo, Space Technology Laboratories, Inc., Los Angeles 45, California

Bernard Raab, Republic Aviation Corporation, Missile Systems Division, Mineola, New York

Alan Rosen, Space Technology Laboratories, Inc., Los Angeles 45, California

S. Rubin, Stanford Research Institute, Menlo Park, California

C. G. Sauer, Jr., Jet Propulsion Laboratory,
California Institute of Technology,
Pasadena, California

Edward Smith, Space Technology Laboratories, Inc.,
Los Angeles 45, California

S. D. Softky, Stanford Research Institute,
Menlo Park, California

Otto R. Spies, Burroughs Research Center,
Paoli, Pennsylvania

D. G. Stechert, The Martin Company, Denver Division,
Denver, Colorado

J. C. Walker, Douglas Aircraft Co., Inc.,
Missiles and Space Systems Engineering,
Santa Monica, California

Robert R. Wolfe, The Martin Company, Denver Division,
Denver, Colorado

G. O. Young, Hughes Research Laboratories and
University of Southern California

# PREFACE

The first Symposium on ballistic missile technology, jointly sponsored by Headquarters, AFBMD and The Ramo-Wooldridge Corporation, was held at the suggestion of Simon Ramo in June of 1956. The second Symposium followed in June of 1957, the third in July of 1958, the fourth in August of 1959, and the fifth in August of 1960. AFBMD and the Space Technology Laboratories, Inc. sponsored the fourth Symposium while the Aerospace Corporation joined in the sponsorship of the fifth. The first two Symposia were planned and coordinated by Duane Roller, the third and fourth by Charles T. Morrow and associates in AFBMD and STL, and the fifth by a Steering Committee, of which Charles T. Morrow was the Chairman. Dr. Morrow was joined, in an editorial capacity, by Donald P. LeGalley in 1959 and by Colonel Lawrence D. Ely, USAF, (Ret.) in 1960. Beginning in 1959, the scope of the Symposia was enlarged to include work being done in the field of space technology.

The purpose of these Symposia has been to provide a free exchange of technical information and ideas among the engineers and scientists working on the United States ballistic missile and space programs. In many technical fields, such as hypersonics, aerodynamic heating, material structures, propulsion, communications, computers, bio-astronautics, guidance, etc., scientific and technical developments have occurred so rapidly that a free exchange of information and ideas is essential. The sessions of the various Symposia, together with publication of the classified papers in the Transactions and the unclassified papers in the Proceedings, have provided this exchange on a national scale.

The Fifth Symposium on Ballistic Missile and Space Technology was held at the University of Southern California on August 29-31, 1960, and was attended by over 1000 scientists and engineers from all parts of the nation. In addition to the several introductory, keynote, and luncheon addresses by invited speakers, 125 technical papers, both classified and unclassified, were presented in 25 sessions. The Proceedings contain the 74 unclassified papers presented at the Symposium and organized into four volumes as follows:

| | | |
|---|---|---|
| Volume | I - | Bioastronautics and Electronics, and Invited Addresses |
| Volume | II - | Propulsion and Auxiliary Power Systems |
| Volume | III - | Guidance, Navigation, Tracking, and Space Physics |
| Volume | IV - | Re-entry and Vehicle Design |

The manuscripts for the Fifth Symposium were requested in advance of the Symposium. A total of 255 manuscripts were received and submitted to a Program Committee for review and selection for the final program. The Program Committee, with assistance from many AFBMD and STL staff members, reviewed these manuscripts for content, suitability, and interest, and selected 125 for presentation at the Symposium. Unfortunately, many excellent papers had to be rejected because of the limitation of time and space. The members of the Program Committee are listed below:

Program Committee
Donald P. LeGalley, Chairman

| | | |
|---|---|---|
| G. D. Bagley | J. F. Chalmers | C. T. Morrow |
| E. K. Blum | M. U. Clauser | R. B. Muchmore |
| R. Bromberg | R. D. DeLauer | Capt. B. W. Pinc |
| J. R. Burnett | L. G. Ludwig | G. E. Solomon |

In addition to the work of the Program Committee, the editor wishes gratefully to acknowledge the assistance of members of the staff of the STL Office of Scientific and Engineering Relations. In particular, Colonel Ely has reviewed the manuscripts dealing with re-entry and vehicle design (Volume IV), and Mrs. Mildred R. Smith, Senior Publications Writer, has reviewed each manuscript and has made corrections and changes which have contributed greatly to the uniformity of format and the published appearance of the 74 papers.

Space Technology Laboratories, Inc. Donald P. LeGalley
September, 1960

CONTENTS

# GUIDANCE AND NAVIGATION

# A COMPARISON OF FIXED AND VARIABLE TIME OF ARRIVAL NAVIGATION FOR INTERPLANETARY FLIGHT

Richard H. Battin
Instrumentation Laboratory
Massachusetts Institute of Technology
Cambridge 39, Massachusetts

## Abstract

Two types of self-contained navigation schemes are contrasted for the case of an unmanned spacecraft launched from Earth and established in a free-fall solar orbit destined to contact either Venus or Mars. A statistical study of the navigation errors and velocity corrections is made for several different trajectories using a three-dimensional model of the Solar System. It is shown that if a certain degree of flexibility is permitted in the arrival time at the destination planet, both the position accuracy and total velocity correction required can be improved by as much as a factor of two.

## 1. Introduction

As the scope of interplanetary ventures broadens, the need for self-sufficiency in spacecraft operations will become apparent. Self-contained navigation systems operating without radiation contact with the Earth will provide the only answer to the problem of spacecraft guidance for all but the most elementary kind of missions.

A general scheme for self-contained interplanetary navigation has been described (1). The process involves a sequence of velocity corrections at a number of preselected check-points based on deviations in position from a planned trajectory. Position determination is made by on-board optical measurements of angles between lines of sight to various celestial objects and of the apparent angular diameters of planets. The translation of positional errors into required velocity corrections is made by the spacecraft computer. Then, in turn, the microrocket propulsion system alters the velocity of the vehicle under direct control of the computer.

A somewhat different navigation theory will be described in this paper and the effectiveness of the two schemes will be contrasted. In the new approach the primary objective will be that of minimizing the fuel consumption of the microrocket system without degrading the over-all accuracy of the mission. The reduction in fuel requirements is accomplished by permitting the time of contact with the target planet to be a variable chosen in such a way that the velocity correction at any check-point will have the smallest possible magnitude. Just as in the fixed-time-of-arrival navigation scheme, the spaceship is controlled in the vicinity of a reference interplanetary trajectory. When the main propulsion stages of the booster rocket are completed, the vehicle proceeds in a solar orbit with an inaccuracy in the initial velocity attributable to injection guidance errors. At each of a number of check-points during the flight, positional deviations from the precomputed reference trajectory are determined from celestial observations. From these data velocity corrections are computed. By allowing a certain degree of flexibility in the exact time of arrival at the destination planet, only a fraction of the velocity correction needed to direct the vehicle toward the reference arrival point need be applied.

The objective here is first to derive an expression for the appropriate velocity correction in terms of positional deviations from a reference path which is suitable for use by the spaceship. Following this, explicit expressions for the velocity corrections in terms of both the measurement and accelerometer errors are determined. Then, for the purpose of an error analysis of guidance accuracy, the final position and velocity errors are related to the measurement and accelerometer errors.

After the theoretical development a statistical study of the navigation errors and the microrocket fuel requirements is made, using a three-dimensional model of the Solar System. For this analysis several different trajectories are subjected to a systematic study to determine the relationship between the total required velocity corrections and the navigational accuracy.

## 2. The Fundamental Navigation Equation

Let $\underline{r}_s(t)$ and $\underline{v}_s(t)$ denote the position and velocity vectors of the spaceship in an inertial coordinate system with origin at the Sun, and let $\underline{g}(\underline{r}_s, t)$ denote the gravitational acceleration at position $\underline{r}_s$ and time t. Then

$$\frac{d\underline{r}_s}{dt} = \underline{v}_s \quad , \quad \frac{d\underline{v}_s}{dt} = \underline{g}(\underline{r}_s, t) \tag{1}$$

are the basic equations of motion of the spaceship except for those brief periods during which propulsion is applied.

Let the vectors $\underline{r}_o(t)$ and $\underline{v}_o(t)$ represent the position and velocity at time t associated with the prescribed reference trajectory, and define

$$\delta\underline{r}(t) = \underline{r}_s(t) - \underline{r}_o(t) \quad , \quad \delta\underline{v}(t) = \underline{v}_s(t) - \underline{v}_o(t) \tag{2}$$

Then, the deviations $\delta r$ and $\delta v$ may be approximately related by means of the linearized differential equations:

$$\frac{d(\delta\underline{r})}{dt} = \delta v \quad , \quad \frac{d(\delta\underline{v})}{dt} = R_o(\underline{r}_o, t)\,\delta\underline{r} \tag{3}$$

where $R_o(\underline{r}_o, t)$ is a matrix whose elements are the partial derivatives of the components of $g(\underline{r}_o, t)$ with respect to the components of $\underline{r}_o$.

A particularly useful fundamental set of solutions of Eq. (3) may be developed in the following way. Let $T_L$ and $T_A$ be, respectively, the time of launch and the time of arrival at the destination planet. Then, define the matrices R(t), R*(t), V(t), V*(t) as the solutions of the matrix differential equations

$$\frac{dR}{dt} = V \quad , \quad \frac{dR^*}{dt} = V^*$$

$$\frac{dV}{dt} = R_o R \quad , \quad \frac{dV^*}{dt} = R_o R^* \tag{4}$$

which satisfy the initial conditions

$$R(T_L) = 0 \quad , \quad R^*(T_A) = 0$$

$$V(T_L) = I \quad , \quad V^*(T_A) = I \tag{5}$$

Here O and I denote, respectively, the zero and identity matrix. If we now write

$$\delta\underline{r}(t) = R(t)\underline{c} + R^*(t)\underline{c}^* \tag{6}$$

$$\delta\underline{v}(t) = V(t)\underline{c} + V^*(t)\underline{c}^* \tag{7}$$

where $\underline{c}$ and $\underline{c}^*$ are arbitrary constant vectors, it follows that these expressions satisfy the perturbation differential equations, Eq. (3), and contain precisely the required number of unspecified constants to meet any valid set of initial or boundary conditions.

Assume that measured positional deviations $\delta\tilde{\underline{r}}_{n-1}$ and $\delta\tilde{\underline{r}}_n$ from corresponding reference values are available at the times $T_{n-1}$ and $T_n$ of two successive fixes. Then Eq. (6) may be written twice with $T_{n-1}$ and $T_n$ substituted for t. Solving this set for $\underline{c}$ and $\underline{c}^*$ and substituting these values into Eq. (7), we have†

$$\delta\tilde{\underline{v}}_n^- = (B_n + B_n^*)\,\delta\tilde{\underline{r}}_n + (\Gamma_n + \Gamma_n^*)\,\delta\tilde{\underline{r}}_{n-1} \tag{8}$$

where we have used the notation $R_n \equiv R(T_n)$, etc., and defined, for convenience, the matrices

$$A_n = R_{n-1} R_n^{-1}, \qquad C_n = V_n R_n^{-1}$$
$$\Gamma_n = C_n (A_n - A_n^*)^{-1}, \qquad B_n = -\Gamma_n A_n^* \tag{9}$$

with similar definitions for $A_n^*$, $C_n^*$, $\Gamma_n^*$, $B_n^*$ obtained from Eq. (9) by replacing all starred matrices by the corresponding unstarred ones and conversely.

Equation (8) provides a means of estimating the spaceship velocity at time $T_n$ from positional information at times $T_n$ and $T_{n-1}$. For fixed-time-of-arrival navigation there must be added to this velocity a calculated velocity increment $\tilde{\underline{\Delta}}_n$ to arrive at the point $\underline{r}_0(T_A)$ at the time $T_A$. If the spaceship arrives at the reference point from its present position, there will be a velocity deviation $\delta\tilde{\underline{v}}(T_A)$ upon arrival which is related to $\delta\tilde{\underline{r}}_n$ by

$$\delta\tilde{\underline{r}}_n = R_n^*\,\delta\tilde{\underline{v}}(T_A)$$

The corresponding velocity deviation at time $T_n$,

$$V_n^*\,\delta\tilde{\underline{v}}(T_A) = V_n^* R_n^{*-1}\,\delta\tilde{\underline{r}}_n = C_n^*\,\delta\tilde{\underline{r}}_n$$

is precisely that which must be established at time $T_n$. Hence, the fixed-time-of-arrival required velocity correction is given by

$$\tilde{\underline{\Delta}}_n = C^*_n\,\delta\tilde{\underline{r}}_n - \delta\tilde{\underline{v}}_n^- = H_n\,\delta\tilde{\underline{r}}_n - P_n\,\delta\tilde{\underline{r}}_{n-1} \tag{10}$$

where the matrices $H_n$ and $P_n$ are defined by

$$H_n = C_n^* - (B_n + B_n^*), \qquad P_n = \Gamma_n + \Gamma_n^* \tag{11}$$

---

† The superscripts - and + are used to distinguish the velocity just prior to a correction from the velocity immediately following the correction.

In order to calculate the variable-time-of-arrival required velocity correction, let us consider the effect of changing the arrival time $T_A$ by a small amount $\delta T$. Let $\underline{r}_p(t)$ and $\underline{v}_p(t)$ be, respectively, the position and velocity vectors of the target planet. Then the new point of contact will be $\underline{r}_p(T_A + \delta T)$, and associated therewith will be a somewhat different reference path. Let $\delta \underline{v}_o(T_L)$ be the vector change in launch velocity from the old reference trajectory which is needed to establish the spaceship in the new reference path. From the definition of the R matrix, it follows that at time $T_A$ the spaceship position will be

$$\underline{r}_o(T_A) + R_A \, \delta \underline{v}_o(T_L)$$

At a time $\delta T$ later the spaceship position will be

$$\underline{r}_o(T_A) + R_A \, \delta \underline{v}_o(T_L) + \underline{v}_o(T_A)\, \delta T$$

and the corresponding planet position will be

$$\underline{r}_p(T_A) + \underline{v}_p(T_A)\, \delta T$$

Assuming contact to be made at time $T_A + \delta T$, these positions are the same and we may solve for $\delta \underline{v}_o(T_L)$ to obtain

$$\delta \underline{v}_o(T_L) = - R_A^{-1} \underline{v}_R(T_A)\, \delta T \tag{12}$$

where

$$\underline{v}_R(T_A) = \underline{v}_s(T_A) - \underline{v}_p(T_A) \tag{13}$$

is the velocity of the spaceship relative to the planet at the nominal arrival time $T_A$.

Now at the $n^{th}$ check point, the vector differences in position $\delta \underline{r}_o(T_n)$ and velocity $\delta \underline{v}_o(T_n)$ between the old and new reference trajectories are simply

$$\delta \underline{r}_o(T_n) = R_n \, \delta \underline{v}_o(T_L) \quad , \quad \delta \underline{v}_o(T_n) = V_n \, \delta \underline{v}_o(T_L)$$

Hence, from Eq. (12)

$$\delta \underline{r}_o(T_n) = - R_n R_A^{-1} \underline{v}_R(T_A)\, \delta T \tag{14}$$

$$\delta \underline{v}_o(T_n) = - V_n R_A^{-1} \underline{v}_R(T_A)\, \delta T \tag{15}$$

Let the measured deviation in position from the old reference path be $\delta \underline{\tilde{r}}_n$, while $\partial \underline{\tilde{r}}_n$ is the corresponding deviation from the new reference path. Then

$$\partial \underline{\tilde{r}}_n = \delta \underline{\tilde{r}}_n - \delta \underline{\tilde{r}}_o(T_n) \tag{16}$$

With similar definitions for velocity deviations, we have

$$\partial \tilde{\underline{v}}_n = \delta \tilde{\underline{v}}_n - \delta \underline{v}_o (T_n) \tag{17}$$

By following the same arguments which led to Eq. (10) we find that the velocity correction $\tilde{\underline{\Delta}}'_n\,(\delta T)$ to reach the new point of contact is

$$\tilde{\underline{\Delta}}'_n(\delta T) = C_n^* \delta \tilde{\underline{r}}_n - \partial \tilde{\underline{v}}_n \tag{18}$$

Using Eqs. (16), (17), (14), (15), and (10), we may write this in the form

$$\tilde{\underline{\Delta}}'_n(\delta T) = \tilde{\underline{\Delta}}_n - \underline{\nu}_n \delta T \tag{19}$$

where, for convenience, we have defined the vector $\underline{\nu}_n$ by

$$\underline{\nu}_n = \Lambda_n R_A^{-1} \underline{v}_R (T_A) \tag{20}$$

and the matrix $\Lambda_n$ by

$$\Lambda_n = V_n - C_n^* R_n \tag{21}$$

With the object of picking $\delta T$ so as to minimize the magnitude of $\tilde{\underline{\Delta}}'_n\,(\delta T)$, clearly the best choice is that which will render $\tilde{\underline{\Delta}}'_n\,(\delta T)$ normal to $\underline{\nu}_n$. Calling this value $\delta \tilde{T}_A$, we have, from Eq. (19),

$$\delta \tilde{T}_A = \frac{\tilde{\underline{\Delta}}_n \cdot \underline{\nu}_n}{\underline{\nu}_n \cdot \underline{\nu}_n} \tag{22}$$

As a consequence, the velocity correction $\tilde{\underline{\Delta}}'_n$ of smallest magnitude which will accomplish the mission is simply related to $\tilde{\underline{\Delta}}_n$ by

$$\tilde{\underline{\Delta}}'_n = M_n \tilde{\underline{\Delta}}_n \tag{23}$$

The matrix $M_n$ is defined by†

$$M_n = I - \underline{\nu}_n \underline{\nu}_n^T / \underline{\nu}_n \cdot \underline{\nu}_n \tag{24}$$

and is a projection operator.

## 3. Analysis of the Velocity Correction

In order to provide a basis for the selection of checkpoints, we will derive a relationship which will show explicitly how the velocity correction at time $T_n$ is related to the initial velocity errors at launch, the errors associated with the positional fix, and the errors in establishing the desired

† The superscript T on a matrix is used to denote the matrix transpose.

velocity corrections at the previous check-points. For this purpose let $\tilde{\underline{\Delta}}'_n$ and $\underline{\eta}_n$ denote, respectively, the actual velocity applied at time $T_n$ and the error made in the application of the desired correction $\tilde{\underline{\Delta}}'_n$. Thus

$$\tilde{\underline{\Delta}}'_n = \underline{\Delta}'_n + \underline{\eta}_n \tag{25}$$

Similarly, we define $\underline{\epsilon}_n$ and $\underline{\delta}_n$, respectively, as the vector difference between the inferred and actual position and velocity deviations at time $T_n$, i. e.,

$$\delta\tilde{\underline{r}}_n = \delta\underline{r}_n + \underline{\epsilon}_n \quad , \quad \delta\tilde{\underline{v}}_n^- = \delta\underline{v}_n^- + \underline{\delta}_n \tag{26}$$

Therefore, it follows from Eqs. (25) and (10) that

$$\underline{\Delta}'_n + \underline{\eta}_n = M_n\,[C_n^*(\delta\underline{r}_n + \underline{\epsilon}_n) - (\delta\underline{v}_n^- + \underline{\delta}_n)] \tag{27}$$

However, from Eqs. (8) and (26) we have

$$\underline{\delta}_n = (B_n + B_n^*)\underline{\epsilon}_n + (\Gamma_n + \Gamma_n^*)\underline{\epsilon}_{n-1} \tag{28}$$

Thus, Eq. (27) may be written as

$$\underline{\Delta}'_n = M_n(C_n^*\delta\underline{r}_n - \delta\underline{v}_n^-) + M_n(H_n\underline{\epsilon}_n - P_n\underline{\epsilon}_{n-1}) - \underline{\eta}_n \tag{29}$$

It now remains to express $C_n^*\,\delta\underline{r}_n - \delta\underline{v}_n^-$ in terms of the error vectors at the present and previous check-points.

To this end we note that at time $T_n^-$ we have

$$C_n^*\delta\underline{r}_n - \delta\underline{v}_n^- = -\Lambda_n\,\underline{c}$$

which is obtained by premultiplying Eq. (6) by $C_n^*$ and subtracting Eq. (7) with $t = T_n^-$. The constant vector $\underline{c}$ is determined from Eqs. (6) and (7) with $t = T_{n-1}^*$. We find

$$\underline{c} = -\Lambda_{n-1}^{-1}(C_{n-1}^*\,\delta\underline{r}_{n-1} - \delta\underline{v}_{n-1}^+) \tag{30}$$

Noting that

$$\delta\underline{v}_{n-1}^+ = \delta\underline{v}_{n-1}^- + \underline{\Delta}'_{n-1}$$

we have

$$C_n^*\delta\underline{r}_n - \delta\underline{v}_n^- = \Lambda_n\,\Lambda_{n-1}^{-1}(C_{n-1}^*\,\delta\underline{r}_{n-1} - \delta\underline{v}_{n-1}^- - \underline{\Delta}'_{n-1}) \tag{31}$$

Equation (31) may be used as a recursion formula so that by successive applications we have

$$C_n^*\delta\underline{r}_n - \delta\underline{v}_n^- = -\Lambda_n\sum_{k=0}^{n-1}\Lambda_k^{-1}\,\underline{\Delta}'_k \tag{32}$$

if we define

$$\underline{\Delta}'_o = \delta\underline{v}(T_L) = -\underline{\eta}_o$$

as the error in the initial launch velocity. Thus, Eq. (29) becomes

$$\underline{\Delta}'_n = M_n (H_n \underline{\epsilon}_n - P_n \underline{\epsilon}_{n-1}) - \underline{\eta}_n - M_n \Lambda_n \sum_{k=0}^{n-1} \Lambda_k^{-1} \underline{\Delta}'_k \qquad (33)$$

and $\underline{\Delta}'_n$ is expressed recursively in terms of all previous measurement and accelerometer errors.

In order to express $\underline{\Delta}'_n$ directly in terms of the errors, let us consider the following.

Lemma: If a sequence of vectors $\underline{a}_0, \underline{a}_1, \ldots, \underline{a}_n$ is defined by

$$\underline{a}_0 = \underline{b}_0$$

$$\underline{a}_1 = \underline{b}_1 + \psi_1 \Omega_0 \underline{a}_0$$

$$\vdots \qquad (34)$$

$$\underline{a}_n = \underline{b}_n + \psi_n \sum_{k=0}^{n-1} \Omega_k a_k \qquad n \geq 2$$

where $\underline{b}_0, \ldots, \underline{b}_n; \psi_1, \ldots, \psi_n;$ and $\Omega_0, \ldots, \Omega_{n-1}$ are arbitrary sequences of vectors and matrices, then

$$\underline{a}_n = \underline{b}_n + \psi_n \Omega_{n-1} b_{n-1} + \psi_n \sum_{k=0}^{n-2} \prod_{j=n-1}^{k+1} (I + \Omega_j \psi_j) \Omega_k \underline{b}_k \qquad n \geq 2 \quad (35)$$

Proof: If we define

$$\underline{d}_n = \sum_{k=0}^{n-1} \Omega_k \underline{a}_k \qquad n \geq 2 \qquad (36)$$

then we have

$$\underline{a}_n = \underline{b}_n + \psi_n \underline{d}_n$$

and it is sufficient to show that

$$\underline{d}_n = \Omega_{n-1} \underline{b}_{n-1} + \sum_{k=0}^{n-2} \prod_{j=n-1}^{k+1} (I + \Omega_j \psi_j) \Omega_k b_k \qquad n \geq 2 \qquad (37)$$

For this purpose we note that, from the definitions of $\underline{d}_n$ and $\underline{a}_n$, we have

$$\underline{d}_{n+1} = \underline{d}_n + \Omega_{n-1}\underline{a}_{n-1}$$

$$= \underline{d}_n + \Omega_{n-1}(\underline{b}_{n-1} + \psi_{n-1}\underline{d}_n)$$

$$= (I + \Omega_{n-1}\psi_{n-1})\underline{d}_n + \Omega_{n-1}\underline{b}_{n-1}$$

as a difference equation for $\underline{d}_n$. Furthermore, it is a simple matter to verify that $\underline{d}_n$, as given by Eq. (37), is the solution. For n = 2, Eq. (37) yields

$$\underline{d}_2 = \Omega_1\underline{b}_1 + (I + \Omega_1\psi_1)\,\Omega_0\underline{b}_0$$

which is clearly the same as that obtained from Eq. (36), using the definitions of $\underline{a}_0$ and $\underline{a}_1$. Hence, the lemma is proved.

---

We may apply the lemma to the problem at hand by making the following identifications:

$$\underline{a}_n \sim \underline{\Delta}'_n \quad , \quad \psi_n \sim -M_n\Lambda_n$$

$$\underline{b}_n \sim M_n(H_n\underline{\epsilon}_n - P_n\underline{\epsilon}_{n-1}) - \underline{\eta}_n \quad , \quad \Omega_k \sim \Lambda_k^{-1}$$

Then if we define

$$X_{k,n} = \begin{cases} I & \text{for } k = n-1 \\ \prod_{j=n-1}^{k+1} (I - \Lambda_j^{-1}M_j\Lambda_j) & \text{for } k \leq n-2 \end{cases} \tag{38}$$

we may use Eq. (35) to write Eq. (33) in the form

$$\underline{\Delta}'_n = M_n(H_n\underline{\epsilon}_n - P_n\underline{\epsilon}_{n-1}) - \underline{\eta}_n - M_n\Lambda_n\sum_{k=0}^{n-1} X_{k,n}\Lambda_k^{-1}[M_k(H_k\underline{\epsilon}_k - P_k\underline{\epsilon}_{k-1}) - \underline{\eta}_k] \tag{39}$$

In the summation indicated in Eq. (39), all terms for $k \leq n-2$ have as a factor

$$M_n\Lambda_n(I - \Lambda_{n-1}^{-1}M_{n-1}\Lambda_{n-1})$$

Using Eqs. (20) and (24), this factor may be written as

$$M_n \Lambda_n \Lambda_{n-1}^{-1} \underline{\nu}_{n-1} \underline{\nu}_{n-1}^T \Lambda_{n-1} / \underline{\nu}_{n-1} \cdot \underline{\nu}_{n-1}$$

$$= M_n \Lambda_n \Lambda_{n-1}^{-1} \Lambda_{n-1} R_A^{-1} \underline{v}_R (T_A) \underline{v}_R^T (T_A) R_A^{T-1} \Lambda_{n-1}^T \Lambda_{n-1} / \underline{\nu}_{n-1} \cdot \underline{\nu}_{n-1}$$

$$= M_n (\Lambda_n R_A^{-1} \underline{v}_R (T_A) \underline{v}_R^T (T_A) R_A^{T-1} \Lambda_n^T) \Lambda_n^{T-1} \Lambda_{n-1}^T \Lambda_{n-1} / \underline{\nu}_{n-1} \cdot \underline{\nu}_{n-1}$$

$$= M_n \underline{\nu}_n \underline{\nu}_n^T \Lambda_n^{T-1} \Lambda_{n-1}^T \Lambda_{n-1} / \underline{\nu}_{n-1} \cdot \underline{\nu}_{n-1}$$

$$= M_n (I - M_n) \Lambda_n^{T-1} \Lambda_{n-1}^T \Lambda_{n-1} \left( \frac{\underline{\nu}_n \cdot \underline{\nu}_n}{\underline{\nu}_{n-1} \cdot \underline{\nu}_{n-1}} \right)$$

Now, since $M_n$ is a projection operator it follows that

$$M_n (I - M_n) = 0$$

Hence, all terms in Eq. (39) for $k \leq n - 2$ are identically zero, and we may write

$$\underline{\Delta}_n' = M_n H_n \underline{\epsilon}_n - (M_n P_n + M_n \Lambda_n \Lambda_{n-1}^{-1} M_{n-1} H_{n-1}) \underline{\epsilon}_{n-1}$$
$$+ M_n \Lambda_n \Lambda_{n-1}^{-1} M_{n-1} P_{n-1} \underline{\epsilon}_{n-2} - \underline{\eta}_n + M_n \Lambda_n \Lambda_{n-1}^{-1} \underline{\eta}_{n-1} \quad (40)$$

This relationship expresses explicitly the velocity impulse actually applied at time $T_n$ in terms of present and previous measurement errors as well as errors in controlling the applied velocity. It is interesting to note that the corresponding expression for fixed-time-of-arrival navigation is obtained from Eq. (40) by replacing the matrices $M_n$ and $M_{n-1}$ by the identity matrix.

## 4. Navigation Error Analysis

The effects of an initial velocity error, together with imperfect velocity corrections applied at the various checkpoints, will be: (1) a velocity deviation from the reference value at the destination planet; (2) a positional error or miss distance; and (3) a change from the scheduled arrival time. For use in the statistical analysis of guidance accuracy, we shall now develop appropriate expressions for each of these quantities in terms of the various measurement and accelerometer errors.

### a) Velocity Deviation

We write Eqs. (6) and (7) for $t = T_n$ with $\delta \underline{r}(T_n) = 0$ and $\delta \underline{v}(T_n) = \underline{\Delta}_n'$, and solve for $\underline{c}$ and $\underline{c}^*$ to obtain

$$\underline{c} = \Lambda_n^{-1} \underline{\Delta}'_n \quad , \quad \underline{c}^* = \Lambda_n^{*-1} \underline{\Delta}'_n$$

Then if, $\delta \underline{v}_n(T_A)$ is the velocity deviation at time $T_A$ due to the velocity impulse at time $T_n$, it follows from Eq. (7) that

$$\delta \underline{v}_n(T_A) = V(T_A)\underline{c} + \underline{c}^*$$

(Note that $V^*(T_A)$ is the identity matrix.) Now assuming N check-points, the total effect, obtained by superposition, is expressible as

$$\delta \underline{v}(T_A) = \sum_{n=0}^{N} [V(T_A) - R_n^{*-1} R_n] \Lambda_n^{-1} \underline{\Delta}'_n \tag{41}$$

where $\underline{\Delta}'_0$ is the initial velocity error at launch. By means of Eq. (40), $\delta \underline{v}(T_A)$ may be expressed in terms of the errors $\underline{\epsilon}$ and $\underline{\eta}$.

b) Positional Error

In order to determine the positional deviation at the time of arrival, we use Eqs. (6) and (30) in the form

$$\delta \underline{r}(T_A) = R_A \Lambda_N^{-1} (\delta \underline{v}_N^- - C_N^* \delta \underline{r}_N + \underline{\Delta}'_N) \tag{42}$$

Then by substituting from Eq. (32) with n = N, we obtain

$$\delta \underline{r}(T_A) = R_A \sum_{k=0}^{N} \Lambda_k^{-1} \underline{\Delta}'_k \tag{43}$$

Only the component of $\delta \underline{r}(T_A)$ perpendicular to the direction of relative motion between the vehicle and the target planet is of interest in determining the actual miss distance. The other component along the direction of motion is more nearly responsible for an error in the scheduled arrival time. Denoting the actual miss distance vector by $\delta \underline{r}_a$, we have

$$\delta \underline{r}_a = M_a \delta \underline{r}(T_A) \tag{44}$$

where the matrix $M_a$ is a projection operator

$$M_a = I - \underline{v}_R(T_A)\underline{v}_R^T(T_A)/\underline{v}_R(T_A) \cdot \underline{v}_R(T_A) \tag{45}$$

It would seem at first that the miss distance at the target planet is a function of measurement and velocity correction errors at all of the previous check-points. Indeed, as can be seen from Eq. (43), the positional deviation from the reference arrival point does depend on all past errors; but only the measurement errors at the last two check-points, together with the last accelerometer error, affect the component $\delta \underline{r}_a$. For the proof we use Eq. (33) with n = N to write Eq. (43) in the form

$$\delta \underline{r}(T_A) = R_A \Lambda_N^{-1} M_N (H_N \underline{\epsilon}_N - P_N \underline{\epsilon}_{N-1}) - R_A \Lambda_N^{-1} \underline{\eta}_N + R_A (I - \Lambda_N^{-1} M_N \Lambda_N) \sum_{k=0}^{N-1} \Lambda_k^{-1} \underline{\Delta}_k' \tag{46}$$

When we apply the projection operator $M_a$ to this vector, the coefficient of the indicated summation can be shown to vanish identically. For if we use the definitions (20) and (24), we have

$$M_a R_A (I - \Lambda_N^{-1} M_N \Lambda_N)$$

$$= M_a R_A \Lambda_N^{-1} \underline{\nu}_N \underline{\nu}_N^T \Lambda_N / \underline{\nu}_N \cdot \underline{\nu}_N$$

$$= M_a R_A \Lambda_N^{-1} \Lambda_N R_A^{-1} \underline{v}_R (T_A) \underline{v}_R^T (T_A) R_A^{T-1} \Lambda_N^{T-1} \Lambda_N / \underline{\nu}_N \cdot \underline{\nu}_N$$

$$= M_a (I - M_a) R_A^{T-1} \Lambda_N^{T-1} \Lambda_N \left( \frac{\underline{v}_R (T_A) \cdot \underline{v}_R (T_A)}{\underline{\nu}_N \cdot \underline{\nu}_N} \right)$$

and from the definition (45) of $M_a$ it follows that

$$M_a (I - M_a) = 0$$

Thus, the appropriate expression for the miss distance at the target planet is simply

$$\delta \underline{r}_a = M_a R_A \Lambda_N^{-1} [M_N (H_N \underline{\epsilon}_N - P_N \underline{\epsilon}_{N-1}) - \underline{\eta}_N] \tag{47}$$

c) Change in the Scheduled Time of Arrival

From Eq. (22) it is seen that at each check-point the optimum difference in arrival time from the nominal value $T_A$ depends on the velocity correction $\underline{\tilde{\Delta}}_n$ which would be required to carry the vehicle to the nominal point of arrival $\underline{r}_p(T_A)$. If, at each of the previous check-points, the corrections have been of the variable time of arrival type, then $\underline{\tilde{\Delta}}_n$ will be a function of all previous measurement and velocity correction errors. The precise relationship is obtained as follows.

From Eqs. (10) and (26) we have

$$\underline{\tilde{\Delta}}_n = (C_n^* \delta \underline{r}_n - \delta \underline{v}_n^-) + H_n \underline{\epsilon}_n - P_n \underline{\epsilon}_{n-1}$$

and substituting from Eq. (32) gives

$$\underline{\tilde{\Delta}}_n = H_n \underline{\epsilon}_n - P_n \underline{\epsilon}_{n-1} - \Lambda_n \sum_{k=0}^{n-1} \Lambda_k^{-1} \underline{\Delta}'_k \tag{48}$$

where $\underline{\Delta}'_k$ is expressed in terms of the $\underline{\epsilon}$'s and $\underline{\eta}$'s according to Eq. (40). The final indicated change in the scheduled arrival time is obtained from Eq. (22) with n = N. We find

$$\delta \tilde{T}_A = (\underline{\nu}_N \cdot \underline{\nu}_N)^{-1} \left\{ \underline{\nu}_N^T \left[ H_N \underline{\epsilon}_N - P_N \underline{\epsilon}_{N-1} - \Lambda_N \sum_{k=0}^{N-1} \Lambda_k^{-1} \underline{\Delta}'_k \right] \right\} \tag{49}$$

## 5. Numerical Results and Conclusions

Four trajectories were selected for use as samples in analyzing the fixed and variable-time-of-arrival navigation schemes. These trajectories, which were determined using the methods described in (2), are illustrated in Figs. 1 through 4 and their basic characteristics are summarized in Table 1. Each of these trajectories is attainable from a circular coasting orbit from Canaveral. In the table is given the launch azimuth from Canaveral together with the latitude and longitude on the Earth's surface at which injection into orbit is to occur. The illustrations show the orbits of the spacecraft and the planets Venus, Earth, and Mars. The paths are shown as solid lines when the orbital plane is above the plane of the ecliptic and broken lines when below. The launch and arrival positions are marked with the corresponding dates. The configuration of the spacecraft and the planets is shown for one instant of time during midcourse on the date indicated in the figures. A shaded circle is used to show the position of the Earth at the time of contact with the target planet.

The method of analysis closely parallels the approach taken in (1) and is entirely statistical in nature. A number of check-points is postulated at which positional deviations from the reference path are determined from celestial observations of the type described in (1).

For our present study, in order to increase the attainable accuracy in the determination of spacecraft position, the number of admissible celestial objects was enlarged and the strategies by which pairs of them could be selected were generalized. The Moon was added to the collection of observable objects within the Solar System and the number of available stars was increased to ten. In order of brightness those chosen are as follows:

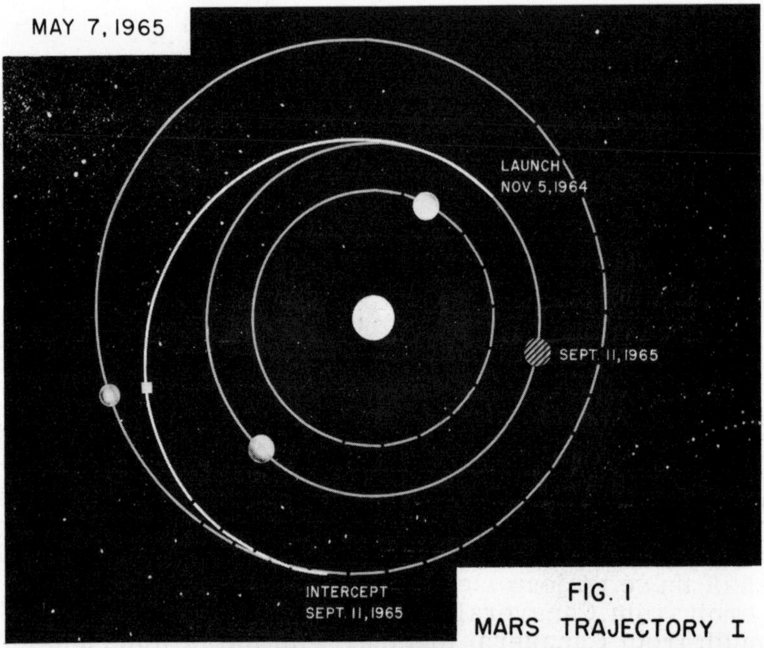


FIG. 1
MARS TRAJECTORY I

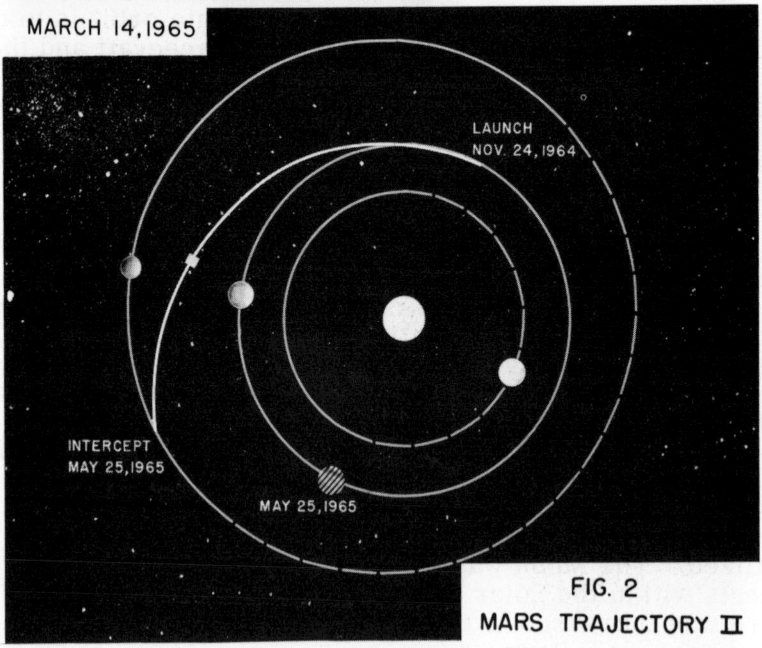


FIG. 2
MARS TRAJECTORY II

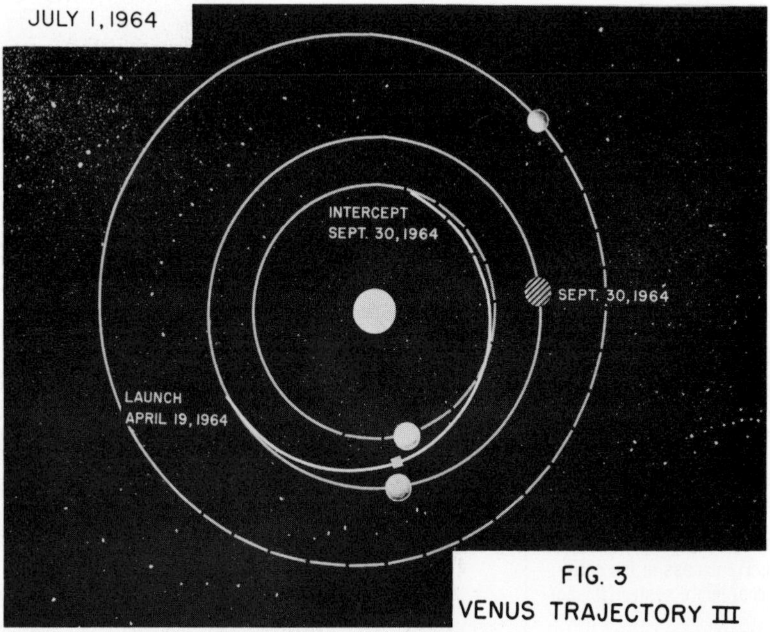


FIG. 3
VENUS TRAJECTORY III

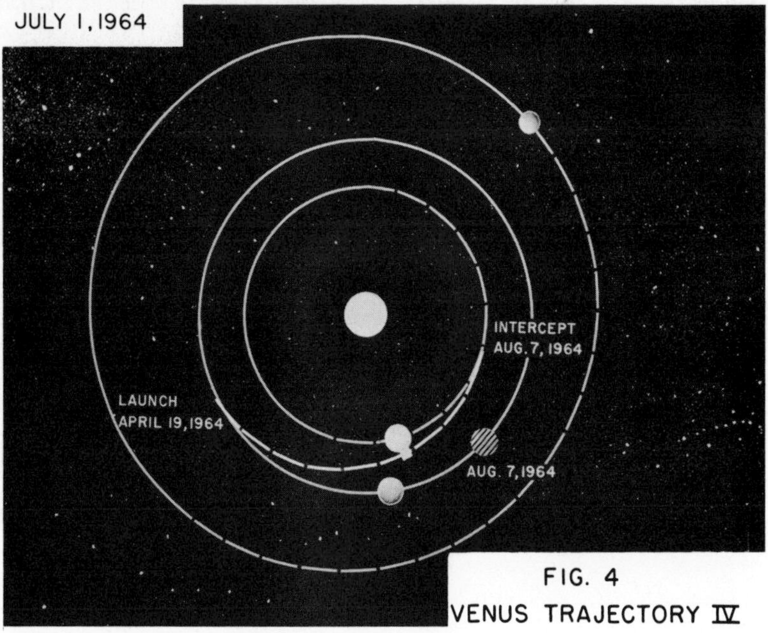


FIG. 4
VENUS TRAJECTORY IV

Table 1. Trajectory data.

| | Earth to Mars | | Earth to Venus | |
|---|---|---|---|---|
| | I | II | III | IV |
| Time of departure | Nov. 5, 1964 | Nov. 24, 1964 | Apr. 19, 1964 | Apr. 19, 1964 |
| Time of flight (years) | 0.85 | 0.50 | 0.45 | 0.30 |
| Injection velocity (ft/sec) | 37,484 | 38,583 | 37,410 | 38,826 |
| Hyperbolic velocity excess at earth (ft/sec) | 9968 | 13,526 | 9688 | 14,206 |
| Components of hyperbolic velocity excess in the ecliptic coordinate system (ft/sec) | −8478<br>4288<br>3016 | −12,788<br>3633<br>2493 | −2582<br>9324<br>510 | 3678<br>11,471<br>−7529 |
| Semi-major axis (a.u.) | 1.24466 | 1.40745 | 0.84580 | 0.87093 |
| Eccentricity | 0.20788 | 0.30040 | 0.18806 | 0.17330 |
| Hyperbolic velocity excess at destination planet (ft/sec) | 9135 | 25,261 | 18,357 | 13,339 |
| Distance from earth at time of contact (a.u.) | 1.79539 | 1.07767 | 0.95173 | 0.53476 |
| Launch azimuth from Cape Canaveral (deg) | 100 | 110 | 100 | 100 |
| Longitude of injection point (deg) | 125 E | 144 E | 128 E | 1 E |
| Latitude of injection point (deg) | 16 S | 5 N | 15 S | 10 S |

| | Magnitude | | Magnitude |
|---|---|---|---|
| Sirius | -1.58 | Arcturus | 0.24 |
| Canopus | -0.86 | Rigel | 0.34 |
| Alpha Centauri | 0.06 | Procyon | 0.48 |
| Vega | 0.14 | Achernar | 0.60 |
| Capella | 0.21 | Beta Centauri | 0.86 |

At each instant of time along the sample trajectories various combinations of celestial measurements were considered in an effort to reduce the uncertainty in spacecraft position. The standard deviation of the measurement errors was assumed to be 0.05 milliradians or 10.3 seconds of arc and the clock was assumed to drift at a constant rms rate of one part in 100,000. The best obtained rms position and time errors as a function of time from launch are presented in Tables 2 through 5. †

In order to test the concept of variable-time-of-arrival navigation, a number of complete statistical simulations were made using different combinations of times for velocity corrections. The postulated guidance errors were

(1) an RMS injection velocity error of 40 feet per second and

(2) an RMS error in applying any desired velocity correction of 1%.

The injection velocity error corresponds to burn-out of the main propulsion. Therefore, it is necessary to apply a magnification factor of $[1 + (v_{esc}/v_R)^2]$ to the mean-squared injection velocity error to obtain the mean-squared velocity error after escape. Here $v_{esc}$ and $v_R$ are, respectively, the escape velocity and the excess hyperbolic velocity of the spacecraft.

For the clock error it was assumed that between the times of two consecutive fixes the clock is drifting at a constant rate, where the rate is random, and statistically independent of any previous drift.

In each of the navigation simulations four separate fixes and associated velocity corrections were made. The times selected as check-points were chosen in the following way for each trajectory. From the possible times of fix, as

† The notation NO 2ND PLANET in the Tables indicates that the line-of-sight to only one planet was more than 15 degrees away from the Sun-line. Thus, a fix strategy involving more than one planet is not possible if 15 degrees is used as the threshold of visibility.

Table 2. Celestial fix position and time errors.
Mars trajectory Nov. 5, 1964
$V_{RE}$ = 9968 ft/sec $V_{RM}$ = 9135 ft/sec

| Time (years) | RMS Position Error (miles) | RMS Time Error (hours) | Time (years) | RMS Position Error (miles) | RMS Time Error (hours) |
|---|---|---|---|---|---|
| 0.001 | 10 | 0.0000 | 0.425 | 2926 | 0.0359 |
| 0.002 | 14 | 0.0002 | 0.450 | 3267 | 0.0380 |
| 0.003 | 20 | 0.0003 | 0.475 | 3742 | 0.0401 |
| 0.004 | 28 | 0.0004 | 0.500 | 4233 | 0.0419 |
| 0.005 | 39 | 0.0004 | 0.525 | 4950 | 0.0436 |
| 0.006 | 51 | 0.0005 | 0.550 | 5802 | 0.0452 |
| 0.007 | 67 | 0.0006 | 0.575 | 6689 | 0.0464 |
| 0.008 | 87 | 0.0007 | 0.600 | 6796 | 0.0500 |
| 0.009 | 112 | 0.0008 | 0.625 | 6812 | 0.0520 |
| 0.010 | 143 | 0.0009 | 0.650 | 6733 | 0.0543 |
| 0.025 | 1292 | 0.0022 | 0.675 | 5854 | 0.0586 |
| 0.050 | 2430 | 0.0044 | 0.700 | 5081 | 0.0594 |
| 0.075 | 2899 | 0.0066 | 0.725 | 4396 | 0.0589 |
| 0.100 | 3453 | 0.0088 | 0.750 | 3885 | 0.0571 |
| 0.125 | 4026 | 0.0109 | 0.775 | 3612 | 0.0545 |
| 0.150 | 3757 | 0.0129 | 0.800 | 6137 | 0.0670 |
| 0.175 | 6414 | 0.0151 | 0.825 | 6049 | 0.0689 |
| 0.200 | 5049 | 0.0170 | 0.840 | 2890 | 0.0617 |
| 0.225 | 7644 | 0.0200 | 0.841 | 2422 | 0.0607 |
| 0.250 | NO 2ND PLANET | | 0.842 | 1964 | 0.0600 |
| 0.275 | NO 2ND PLANET | | 0.843 | 1537 | 0.0594 |
| 0.300 | 2400 | 0.0254 | 0.844 | 1156 | 0.0590 |
| 0.325 | 2339 | 0.0274 | 0.845 | 837 | 0.0588 |
| 0.350 | 2382 | 0.0295 | 0.846 | 596 | 0.0587 |
| 0.375 | 2486 | 0.0316 | 0.847 | 444 | 0.0587 |
| 0.400 | 2633 | 0.0338 | 0.848 | 379 | 0.0586 |

Table 3. Celestial fix position and time errors.
Mars trajectory Nov. 24, 1964
$V_{RE}$ = 13,526 ft/sec $V_{RM}$ = 25,261 ft/sec

| Time (years) | RMS Position Error (miles) | RMS Time Error (hours) | Time (years) | RMS Position Error (miles) | RMS Time Error (hours) |
|---|---|---|---|---|---|
| 0.001 | 10 | 0.0001 | 0.250 | NO 2ND PLANET | |
| 0.002 | 9 | 0.0002 | 0.275 | 2719 | 0.0234 |
| 0.003 | 11 | 0.0003 | 0.300 | 2634 | 0.0255 |
| 0.004 | 21 | 0.0004 | 0.325 | 2799 | 0.0277 |
| 0.005 | 49 | 0.0004 | 0.350 | 2999 | 0.0298 |
| 0.006 | 119 | 0.0005 | 0.375 | 3326 | 0.0320 |
| 0.007 | 318 | 0.0006 | 0.400 | 3772 | 0.0341 |
| 0.008 | 564 | 0.0007 | 0.425 | 4373 | 0.0365 |
| 0.009 | 450 | 0.0008 | 0.450 | 5107 | 0.0382 |
| 0.010 | 376 | 0.0009 | 0.475 | 6019 | 0.0400 |
| 0.025 | 764 | 0.0022 | 0.490 | 6517 | 0.0420 |
| 0.050 | 3407 | 0.0044 | 0.491 | 6463 | 0.0421 |
| 0.075 | 3289 | 0.0066 | 0.492 | 6345 | 0.0421 |
| 0.100 | 3434 | 0.0087 | 0.493 | 6112 | 0.0422 |
| 0.125 | 4899 | 0.0109 | 0.494 | 5679 | 0.0423 |
| 0.150 | 6800 | 0.0130 | 0.495 | 4931 | 0.0423 |
| 0.175 | 6138 | 0.0149 | 0.496 | 3808 | 0.0424 |
| 0.200 | 8097 | 0.0174 | 0.497 | 2475 | 0.4248 |
| 0.225 | NO 2ND PLANET | | 0.498 | 1318 | 0.0408 |

Table 4. Celestial fix position and time errors.
Venus trajectory Apr. 19, 1964
$V_{RE}$ = 9688 ft/sec $V_{RV}$ = 18,357 ft/sec

| Time (years) | RMS Position Error (miles) | RMS Time Error (hours) | Time (years) | RMS Position Error (miles) | RMS Time Error (hours) |
|---|---|---|---|---|---|
| 0.001 | 19 | 0.0001 | 0.225 | 1870 | 0.0190 |
| 0.002 | 10 | 0.0002 | 0.250 | 1765 | 0.0208 |
| 0.003 | 9 | 0.0003 | 0.275 | 1793 | 0.0224 |
| 0.004 | 12 | 0.0004 | 0.300 | 1865 | 0.0238 |
| 0.005 | 17 | 0.0004 | 0.325 | 1962 | 0.0249 |
| 0.006 | 24 | 0.0005 | 0.350 | 3650 | 0.0285 |
| 0.007 | 33 | 0.0006 | 0.375 | 2939 | 0.0259 |
| 0.008 | 44 | 0.0007 | 0.400 | 2354 | 0.0277 |
| 0.009 | 55 | 0.0008 | 0.425 | 2143 | 0.0239 |
| 0.010 | 68 | 0.0009 | 0.440 | 2857 | 0.0329 |
| 0.025 | 604 | 0.0022 | 0.441 | 2902 | 0.0329 |
| 0.050 | 1990 | 0.0044 | 0.442 | 2856 | 0.0330 |
| 0.075 | 4337 | 0.0066 | 0.443 | 2729 | 0.0330 |
| 0.100 | 5531 | 0.0088 | 0.444 | 2486 | 0.0328 |
| 0.125 | 7301 | 0.0109 | 0.445 | 2103 | 0.0325 |
| 0.150 | 12,768 | 0.0131 | 0.446 | 1607 | 0.0321 |
| 0.175 | 21,517 | 0.0149 | 0.447 | 1090 | 0.0317 |
| 0.200 | 2272 | 0.0170 | 0.448 | 668 | 0.0300 |

Table 5. Celestial fix position and time errors.
Venus trajectory Apr. 19, 1964
$V_{RE}$ = 14,206 ft/sec $V_{RV}$ = 13,339 ft/sec

| Time (years) | RMS Position Error (miles) | RMS Time Error (hours) | Time (years) | RMS Position Error (miles) | RMS Time Error (hours) |
|---|---|---|---|---|---|
| 0.001 | 10 | 0.0001 | 0.150 | 1100 | 0.0129 |
| 0.002 | 14 | 0.0002 | 0.175 | 1026 | 0.0150 |
| 0.003 | 22 | 0.0003 | 0.200 | 1053 | 0.0170 |
| 0.004 | 34 | 0.0004 | 0.225 | 1343 | 0.0188 |
| 0.005 | 49 | 0.0004 | 0.250 | 1875 | 0.0203 |
| 0.006 | 68 | 0.0005 | 0.275 | 2596 | 0.0219 |
| 0.007 | 91 | 0.0006 | 0.290 | 2440 | 0.0241 |
| 0.008 | 116 | 0.0007 | 0.291 | 2266 | 0.0241 |
| 0.009 | 145 | 0.0008 | 0.292 | 2030 | 0.0241 |
| 0.010 | 177 | 0.0009 | 0.293 | 1733 | 0.0241 |
| 0.025 | 1675 | 0.0022 | 0.294 | 1389 | 0.0240 |
| 0.050 | 3817 | 0.0044 | 0.295 | 1032 | 0.0240 |
| 0.075 | 1983 | 0.0066 | 0.296 | 701 | 0.0239 |
| 0.100 | 1545 | 0.0087 | 0.297 | 439 | 0.0240 |
| 0.125 | 1277 | 0.0109 | 0.298 | 277 | 0.0241 |

listed in Tables 2 through 5, four subsets of times were picked. Then the fix times for each navigation run were selected, one from each group, by a random choice.

The result of each run is represented by a point in the Figs. 5 through 8 where the final position error in miles has been plotted against total velocity correction in feet per second. The envelope of these points is shown in the figures and may be used as one of the principal criteria in planning a mission. This curve expresses the ultimate precision attainable for the trajectory as far as optimizing the miss distance with respect to total velocity correction. The detailed history of each navigation run lying along the envelope curve is presented in Tables 6 through 9.

Mars trajectory I is superior to II with respect to navigation accuracy. One can perhaps correlate this result with the fact that the velocity relative to Mars at arrival is much less for I than for II. The same thesis is borne out when Venus trajectory III is compared with IV.

The distribution of points in Fig. 7 for Venus trajectory III is so widely scattered that it is impossible to recognize any envelope curve from the available data.

As a result of this study the conclusions are immediate. For either navigation scheme it is clear that, in general, position accuracy can be improved only at the expense of extra fuel. Furthermore, the superiority of the variable-time-of-arrival navigation scheme is more than two-fold with regard to both position accuracy and total velocity correction required. For a one-way planetary mission, its advantages seem far to over-balance any potential difficulties which could result from an uncertainty in the exact time of rendezvous with the destination planet.

## Acknowledgment

The author wishes to acknowledge many profitable discussions with Dr. J. Halcombe Laning during the progress of this study and to express his sincere appreciation for a number of fruitful suggestions.

This report was prepared under Project 55-171, Division of Sponsored Research, Massachusetts Institute of Technology, sponsored by the National Aeronautics and Space Administration through contract NASw-130; it was published under the auspices of DSR Project 52-156, sponsored by the Ballistic Missile Division of the Air Research and Development Command through USAF contract AF 04(647)-303.

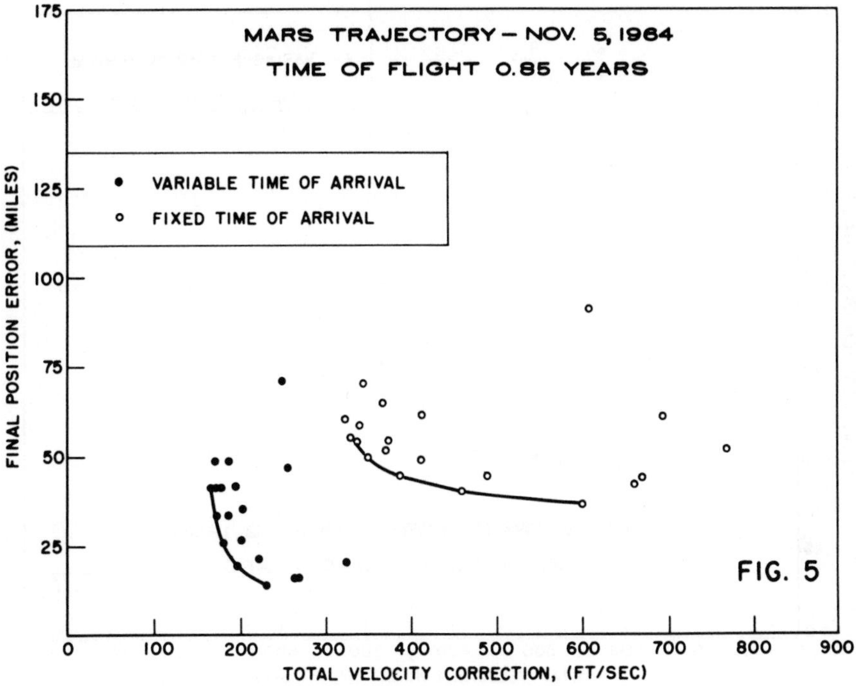
MARS TRAJECTORY – NOV. 5, 1964
TIME OF FLIGHT 0.85 YEARS
VARIABLE TIME OF ARRIVAL
FIXED TIME OF ARRIVAL
FINAL POSITION ERROR, (MILES)
TOTAL VELOCITY CORRECTION, (FT/SEC)
0
100
200
300
400
500
600
700
800
900
25
50
75
100
125
150
175

FIG. 5

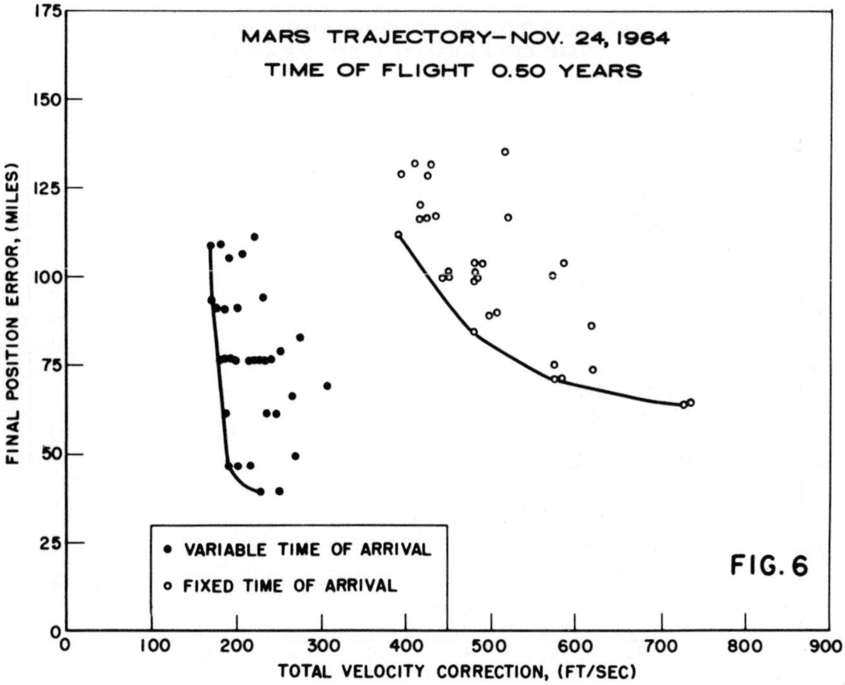
MARS TRAJECTORY–NOV. 24, 1964
TIME OF FLIGHT 0.50 YEARS
VARIABLE TIME OF ARRIVAL
FIXED TIME OF ARRIVAL
FINAL POSITION ERROR, (MILES)
TOTAL VELOCITY CORRECTION, (FT/SEC)
0
100
200
300
400
500
600
700
800
900
25
50
75
100
125
150
175

FIG. 6

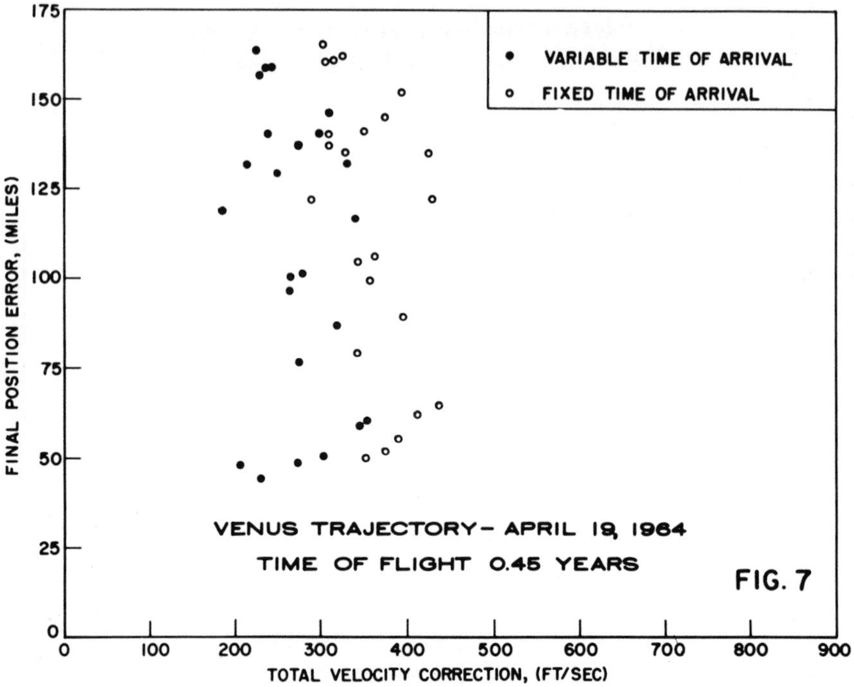
VARIABLE TIME OF ARRIVAL
FIXED TIME OF ARRIVAL
VENUS TRAJECTORY— APRIL 19, 1964
TIME OF FLIGHT 0.45 YEARS
FINAL POSITION ERROR, (MILES)
TOTAL VELOCITY CORRECTION, (FT/SEC)
0
25
50
75
100
125
150
175
100
200
300
400
500
600
700
800
900

FIG. 7

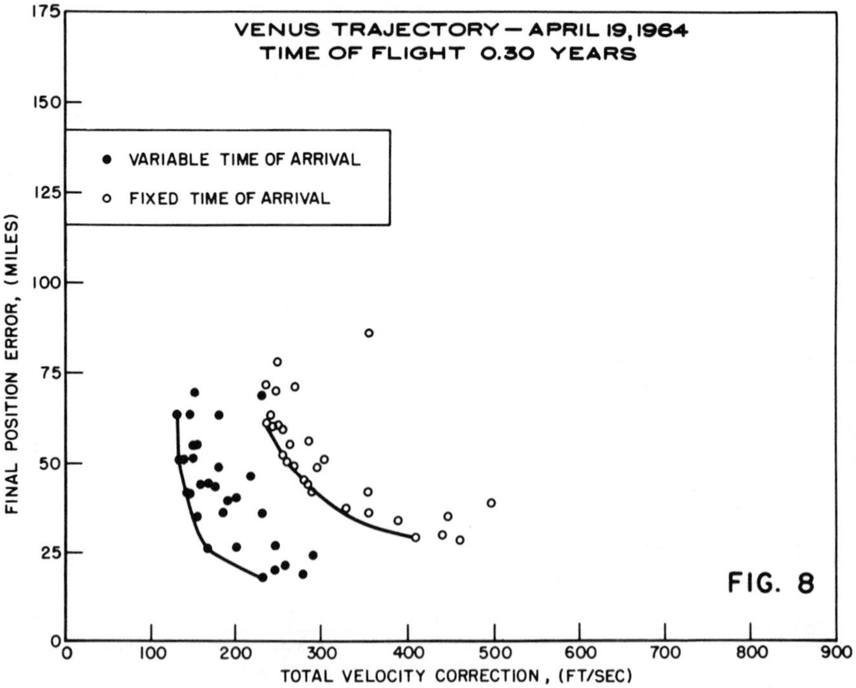
VENUS TRAJECTORY — APRIL 19, 1964
TIME OF FLIGHT 0.30 YEARS
VARIABLE TIME OF ARRIVAL
FIXED TIME OF ARRIVAL
FINAL POSITION ERROR, (MILES)
TOTAL VELOCITY CORRECTION, (FT/SEC)
0
25
50
75
100
125
150
175
100
200
300
400
500
600
700
800
900

FIG. 8

Table 6. Mars trajectory Nov. 5, 1964.
$V_{RE}$ = 9968 ft/sec $V_{RM}$ = 9135 ft/sec

| Variable Time of Arrival Navigation | | | | Fixed Time of Arrival Navigation | | | |
|---|---|---|---|---|---|---|---|
| Time of Fix | RMS Velocity Correction | Final Velocity Error | Final Position Error | Time of Fix | RMS Velocity Correction | Final Velocity Error | Final Position Error |
| 0.001 | 126 | | | 0.004 | 156 | | |
| 0.425 | 4 | | | 0.300 | 7 | | |
| 0.775 | 14 | | | 0.775 | 42 | | |
| 0.844 | 23 | | | 0.843 | 117 | | |
| Total | 167 | 239 | 41 | Total | 322 | 113 | 61 |
| 0.004 | 127 | | | 0.002 | 155 | | |
| 0.375 | 2 | | | 0.400 | 9 | | |
| 0.775 | 11 | | | 0.775 | 30 | | |
| 0.845 | 31 | | | 0.844 | 135 | | |
| Total | 172 | 240 | 33 | Total | 328 | 127 | 55 |
| 0.002 | 126 | | | 0.005 | 157 | | |
| 0.375 | 2 | | | 0.300 | 7 | | |
| 0.775 | 11 | | | 0.775 | 42 | | |
| 0.846 | 39 | | | 0.844 | 132 | | |
| Total | 179 | 241 | 26 | Total | 337 | 127 | 54 |
| 0.006 | 129 | | | 0.004 | 156 | | |
| 0.400 | 3 | | | 0.375 | 8 | | |
| 0.775 | 13 | | | 0.775 | 28 | | |
| 0.847 | 50 | | | 0.845 | 157 | | |
| Total | 195 | 243 | 19 | Total | 349 | 149 | 49 |
| 0.005 | 128 | | | 0.002 | 155 | | |
| 0.325 | 2 | | | 0.375 | 8 | | |
| 0.775 | 13 | | | 0.775 | 28 | | |
| 0.848 | 85 | | | 0.846 | 195 | | |
| Total | 228 | 253 | 14 | Total | 385 | 186 | 44 |
| | | | | 0.006 | 157 | | |
| | | | | 0.400 | 10 | | |
| | | | | 0.775 | 30 | | |
| | | | | 0.847 | 263 | | |
| | | | | Total | 460 | 254 | 40 |
| | | | | 0.005 | 157 | | |
| | | | | 0.325 | 7 | | |
| | | | | 0.775 | 35 | | |
| | | | | 0.848 | 401 | | |
| | | | | Total | 600 | 392 | 36 |

Table 7. Mars trajectory Nov. 24, 1964
$V_{RE}$ = 13,526 ft/sec $V_{RM}$ = 25,261 ft/sec

| Variable Time of Arrival Navigation | | | | Fixed Time of Arrival Navigation | | | |
|---|---|---|---|---|---|---|---|
| Time of Fix | RMS Velocity Correction | Final Velocity Error | Final Position Error | Time of Fix | RMS Velocity Correction | Final Velocity Error | Final Position Error |
| 0.003 | 95 | | | 0.001 | 116 | | |
| 0.025 | 5 | | | 0.025 | 6 | | |
| 0.400 | 37 | | | 0.350 | 38 | | |
| 0.494 | 34 | | | 0.494 | 231 | | |
| Total | 170 | 132 | 93 | Total | 391 | 227 | 112 |
| 0.001 | 95 | | | 0.001 | 116 | | |
| 0.025 | 5 | | | 0.100 | 9 | | |
| 0.350 | 24 | | | 0.350 | 43 | | |
| 0.494 | 54 | | | 0.495 | 276 | | |
| Total | 177 | 135 | 91 | Total | 444 | 268 | 100 |
| 0.004 | 95 | | | 0.002 | 116 | | |
| 0.025 | 5 | | | 0.025 | 6 | | |
| 0.400 | 39 | | | 0.400 | 61 | | |
| 0.495 | 40 | | | 0.496 | 298 | | |
| Total | 179 | 134 | 77 | Total | 481 | 292 | 84 |
| 0.002 | 95 | | | 0.001 | 116 | | |
| 0.025 | 5 | | | 0.025 | 6 | | |
| 0.400 | 36 | | | 0.425 | 78 | | |
| 0.496 | 50 | | | 0.497 | 374 | | |
| Total | 185 | 136 | 61 | Total | 574 | 365 | 72 |
| 0.001 | 95 | | | 0.003 | 116 | | |
| 0.025 | 5 | | | 0.075 | 9 | | |
| 0.425 | 45 | | | 0.400 | 82 | | |
| 0.497 | 51 | | | 0.498 | 520 | | |
| Total | 196 | 139 | 46 | Total | 727 | 507 | 64 |
| 0.004 | 95 | | | | | | |
| 0.025 | 5 | | | | | | |
| 0.425 | 51 | | | | | | |
| 0.498 | 75 | | | | | | |
| Total | 226 | 152 | 39 | | | | |

Table 8. Venus trajectory Apr. 19, 1964
$V_{RE}$ = 9688 ft/sec $V_{RV}$ = 18,357 ft/sec

| Variable Time of Arrival Navigation | | | | Fixed Time of Arrival Navigation | | | |
|---|---|---|---|---|---|---|---|
| Time of Fix | RMS Velocity Correction | Final Velocity Error | Final Position Error | Time of Fix | RMS Velocity Correction | Final Velocity Error | Final Position Error |
| 0.006 | 131 | | | 0.006 | 161 | | |
| 0.225 | 5 | | | 0.225 | 7 | | |
| 0.400 | 22 | | | 0.400 | 26 | | |
| 0.443 | 28 | | | 0.443 | 98 | | |
| Total | 186 | 125 | 117 | Total | 292 | 92 | 122 |
| 0.002 | 129 | | | 0.002 | 159 | | |
| 0.200 | 6 | | | 0.200 | 8 | | |
| 0.400 | 38 | | | 0.400 | 44 | | |
| 0.447 | 57 | | | 0.447 | 140 | | |
| Total | 231 | 137 | 44 | Total | 350 | 133 | 49 |

Table 9. Venus trajectory Apr. 19, 1964
$V_{RE}$ = 14,206 ft/sec $V_{RV}$ = 13,339 ft/sec

| Variable Time of Arrival Navigation | | | | Fixed Time of Arrival Navigation | | | |
|---|---|---|---|---|---|---|---|
| Time of Fix | RMS Velocity Correction | Final Velocity Error | Final Position Error | Time of Fix | RMS Velocity Correction | Final Velocity Error | Final Position Error |
| 0.003 | 92 | | | 0.004 | 112 | | |
| 0.175 | 5 | | | 0.100 | 6 | | |
| 0.250 | 7 | | | 0.225 | 23 | | |
| 0.293 | 24 | | | 0.294 | 98 | | |
| Total | 128 | 116 | 63 | Total | 238 | 89 | 61 |
| 0.002 | 92 | | | 0.004 | 112 | | |
| 0.150 | 4 | | | 0.125 | 5 | | |
| 0.250 | 9 | | | 0.250 | 23 | | |
| 0.294 | 28 | | | 0.295 | 119 | | |
| Total | 133 | 117 | 51 | Total | 259 | 108 | 50 |
| 0.001 | 91 | | | 0.001 | 111 | | |
| 0.150 | 5 | | | 0.100 | 6 | | |
| 0.250 | 9 | | | 0.200 | 17 | | |
| 0.295 | 34 | | | 0.296 | 144 | | |
| Total | 139 | 118 | 41 | Total | 279 | 136 | 45 |
| 0.005 | 93 | | | 0.001 | 111 | | |
| 0.125 | 5 | | | 0.075 | 8 | | |
| 0.250 | 14 | | | 0.225 | 38 | | |
| 0.296 | 42 | | | 0.296 | 131 | | |
| Total | 154 | 120 | 35 | Total | 288 | 121 | 42 |
| 0.006 | 93 | | | 0.001 | 111 | | |
| 0.150 | 6 | | | 0.075 | 8 | | |
| 0.250 | 9 | | | 0.225 | 38 | | |
| 0.297 | 56 | | | 0.298 | 252 | | |
| Total | 164 | 125 | 26 | Total | 409 | 241 | 29 |
| 0.003 | 92 | | | 0.001 | 111 | | |
| 0.075 | 8 | | | 0.025 | 13 | | |
| 0.250 | 37 | | | 0.225 | 97 | | |
| 0.298 | 90 | | | 0.298 | 237 | | |
| Total | 227 | 139 | 18 | Total | 459 | 229 | 28 |

## References


1. Battin, Richard H., and Laning, J. H. Jr., "A Navigation Theory for Round-Trip Reconnaissance Missions to Venus and Mars", Proceedings of the Fourth AFBMD/STL Symposium on Ballistic Missile and Space Technology, Pergamon Press, 1960.

2. Battin, Richard H., "The Determination of Round-Trip Planetary Reconnaissance Trajectories", Journal of the Aero-Space Sciences, Sept. 1959.

# ADVANCED RADAR INFORMATION EVALUATION SYSTEM - ARIES

D.L. Lovenvirth and W. F. Holst
Massachusetts Institute of Technology
Lincoln Laboratory
Lexington, Massachusetts

## Abstract

A flexible system of 709 computer programs has been developed to investigate satellite-orbit data-processing schemes. Simulating redundant measurements made by a specified radar on a population of random satellite orbits, this system can be used to find an optimal scheme amongst a given set of data processors, as well as to investigate a number of related problems. Initially we have chosen one particular processing technique: averaging the raw data consisting of range, range rate, azimuth, elevation and time, then pairing the resulting average points to obtain sets of Keplerian elements which are in turn averaged to provide mean estimates of the elements. We are attempting to optimize this technique as a function of its parameters: the length of the averaging interval, the time between points in a pairing and the time between pairings. The effects of various kinds of radar errors upon this processor are being investigated. The criterion of optimality used is the error between the simulated true and predicted positions during several time intervals following the last time of sighting.

## Introduction

The problem of determining the future position of a satellite from a short time sequence of noisy, redundant radar data is a complex one. Its complexity may be considered as arising from four rather broad (in some cases overlapping) areas:

1. The characteristics of the radar or radars of interest.
2. The characteristics of the satellite population which can be observed by the radar.
3. The properties and types of noise corrupting the radar data.
4. The method or methods available for processing the data.

With such a wide variety of variables in our problem it seems reasonable to break it up into a number of smaller, related problems. We might ask, for example:

1. What is the sensitivity of predicted position to each orbital elements?
2. What is the best technique for computing predicted position?
3. What procedure should be used to process the radar data to obtain a best estimate of the orbital elements?
4. How do the radar errors propagate?
5. Given a particular processing scheme, it is extreme accuracy more critical in some radar measurements than in others?

The purpose of this paper is to describe a flexible system of computer programs which has been designed to investigate these problems. It is hoped that this system, called ARIES, will provide some of the answers, and at the same time indicate possible paths to follow in seeking analytic solutions. The need for such an approach is obvious. While the above questions may be posed analytically, and (with sufficient simplifying assumptions) perhaps be solved analytically, it is apparent that a long period of investigation would be requisite. This is unfortunate simply because results are needed in the more immediate future with regard to choosing data-processing techniques and designing radars. The ARIES is capable of giving answers now, yet is flexible enough to be used to investigate and compare new and more sophisticated prediction and processing schemes later, without the necessity of rewriting the entire program system.

## General Structure of ARIES

ARIES presently consists of five IBM 709 computer programs. The first of these is a self-contained data generating program. The remaining four have been written in modular form in such a way that any one of them may be replaced by another, similarly functioning program without changing the remaining segments of the system. The structure of ARIES is shown in Figure 1.

The first ARIES program, GROPE, is given the radar site location, the radar coverage and the data rate. Additional inputs are the size of the random satellite population desired, along with limits on the number of data points per satellite and bounds on the size of semimajor axis and perigee distance. The output, in addition to a BCD tape, is a binary tape containing a set of Keplerian orbital elements and a block of noise-free position and velocity data for each satellite generated.

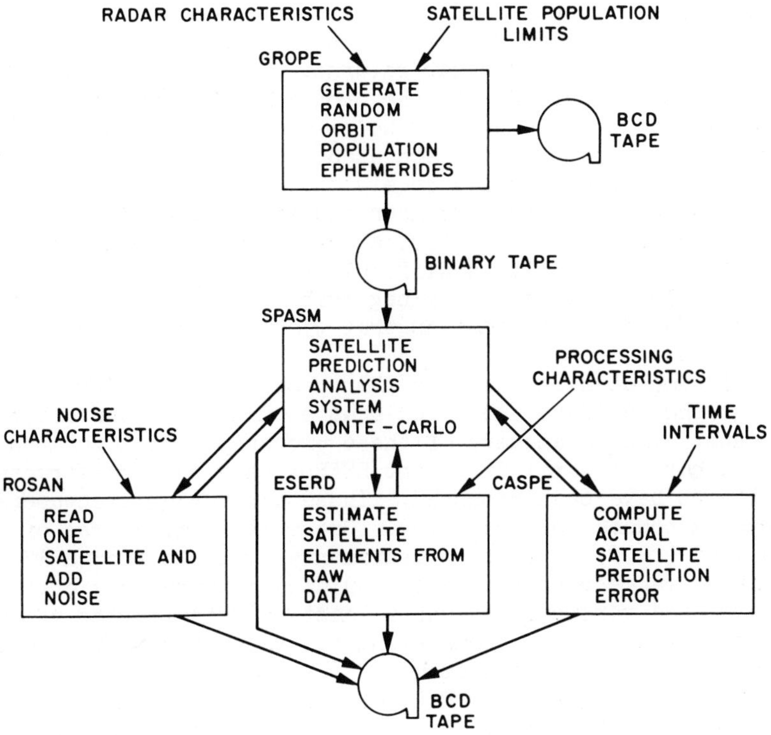


Fig. 1. Structure of ARIES.

These sets of ($r$, $\alpha$, $\beta$, $\dot{r}$, $\dot{\alpha}$, $\dot{\beta}$, $t$) measurements have been obtained from the corresponding orbital elements and are used as input to the remaining four programs.

SPASM functions as a control program for the rest of the system. It directs the flow of data through each of the other three programs. The noise-free data is fed first to ROSAN, which converts it to simulated raw radar data by adding pseudo-random errors to one or more of the radar quantities. The choise of error distributions can be specified, within certain limitations, by input cards.

It must be emphasized at this point that ROSAN does not introduce any spurious radar returns. The present version of ARIES is not concerned with the problems of correlation or deghosting. When we speak of noise in this paper we refer only to the random errors which are used to degrade the GROPE data. Hence "noise-free" implies solely that the ROSAN error distributions specified have zero mean and standard deviations. Further sources of system "noise" are computer round-off and truncation errors. It is difficult to estimate their effects, but we believe that they are negligible compared to the effects of the radar data degradation that will be deliberately introduced.

The simulated raw data is then processed by ESERD, which smooths the raw data and calculates estimates of the orbital elements. The parameters of these processes are regulated by input cards. Several different ESERDs have been constructed and others have been proposed. Those already written use an averaging scheme for smoothing. One of them makes use of the simulated ($r$, $\alpha$, $\beta$, $\dot{r}$, $t$) measurements, while a second ESERD estimates range rate from the simulated measurements of range. Contemplated versions include a least-squares fitting of data, and an approximation scheme using two sets of range, azimuth, elevation and time measurements.

The last program, CASPE, operates upon the ESERD estimates of the orbital elements. It calculates various statistics, extrapolates the satellite position over a desired time interval, and produced measures of system performance which can be used to compare one system configuration with another.

The five programs just described make use of a set of utility subroutines and tables called the CELMEC (Celestial Mechanics) Compool. These subroutines perform the necessary coordinate and time transformations and the computation of the satellite orbital elements in a Keplerian system. By thus separating the more common types of mathematical computations from the main parts of the system programs, additional flexibility has been gained.

## Current System Functions

In its present form ARIES can be used to answer several of the problems mentioned earlier, in a number of ways. For example, given a set of data-processing techniques, a particular radar configuration, and a variety of noise characteristics, ARIES can evaluate the relative effectiveness of these techniques over large random satellite populations. Alternatively, given a radar and a particular processing scheme, which has been suggested by ease of execution or some of the reasons suggested above, we can use ARIES to optimize the parameters involved in this processing technique.

Other applications suggest themselves, all of which are relatively easy to implement because of the manner in which the simulation system functions have been kept separate from one another. One can investigate, for example, the effect of small errors in radar measurements upon the estimation of the orbital elements. With the present version of AIRES, which essentially makes use of a Keplerian model, ignoring the effects of oblateness and drag, one can study the propagation of error over time intervals of reasonable length. By reasonable, we mean that interval of time within which such additional factors would perturb the predicted "true" and estimated motions to approximately the same degree.

It seems worthwhile at this point to mention in greater detail the functions which the first currently planned runs of ARIES will perform.

### GROPE

The characteristics of the radar to be simulated are shown in Figure 2. Using this radar information, GROPE will be used to generate several random satellite populations. The number of simulated data points per satellite, $N_D$, will lie in the interval $4 \leq N_D \leq 20$. The data rate simulated will be three per minute, corresponding to the azimuth scan rate of this hypothetical radar. (This study will not, at least initially, be concerned with the implied preprocessing of the pulse-to-pulse data but only with the scan-to-scan data.)

GROPE generates each satellite by choosing a position $(r, \alpha, \beta)$ at random within the radar coverage. It then derives a velocity vector at this point using randomly chosen values of semimajor axis (a) and eccentricity (e) picked from intervals satisfying the dynamical constraints. The dynamical constraints are imposed by specifying a maximum semimajor axis and a minimum perigee distance. For the present set of production runs these have been set at 6883.5 nautical miles for the maximum semimajor axis, and 3545.0 nautical miles for the

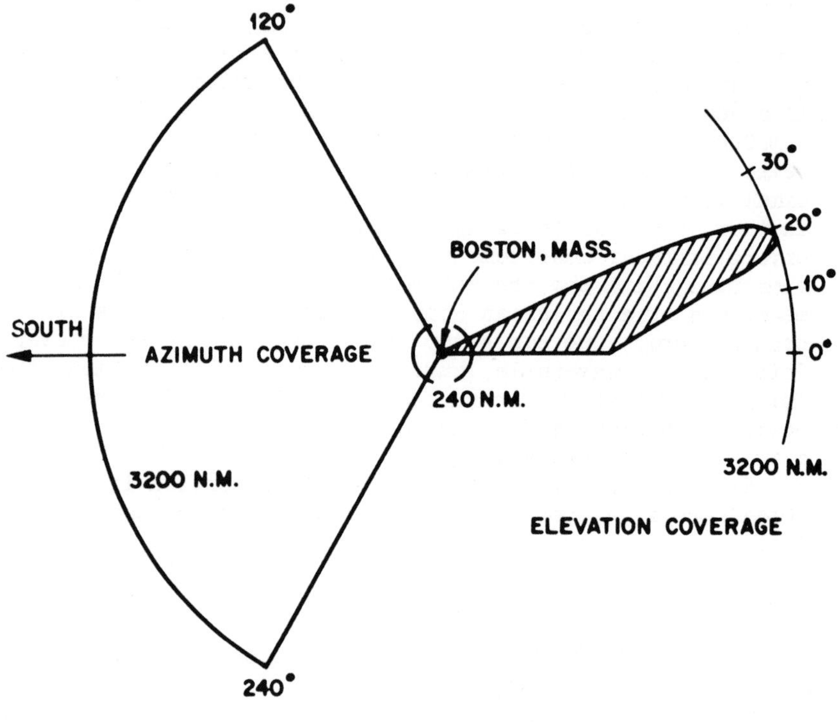


Fig. 2. Radar Coverage Simulated In ARIES.

minimum perigee distance. Using the Keplerian model, radar data is generated forward and backward along its orbit until either the data moves out of radar coverage or the limits on the number of data points are exceeded. Because of the radar coverage volume and the satellite characteristics specified for the current series of ARIES runs, the values of a and e for the satellite populations generated in these runs lie in the following intervals: $0.0 \leq e \leq 0.5$; $3545.0$ n.m. $\leq a \leq 6883.5$ n.m..

The GROPE program can also function in a non-random mode. That is, GROPE will generate radar data for a particular given set of Keplerian orbital elements, relative to a specific radar. For many types of error studies it is convenient to examine the performance of a system with respect to a particular orbit. This is especially true when there is actually a satellite in such an orbit, for we are then in a position to compare the output of ARIES with results obtained from actual tracking of the satellite. However, any conclusions drawn from such studies are strongly dependent upon the particular orbit chosen. In designing the present version of ARIES, we wanted to be able to obtain results which would allow us to characterize the complete radar and processing system in a general way. To do this we have to determine how well the system can operate upon all the satellites that the radar can possibly detect.

It is for this reason that the GROPE program's random mode begins its satellite simulation by choosing points at random from the given radar coverage volume. If we denote by $\{0_\infty\}$ the set of all satellites observable by the simulated radar, then we are interested in the general characteristics of our system over this set. By starting with points in the radar coverage volume, GROPE generates a population of N satellites such that

$$\{0_N\} \subset \{0_\infty\} \tag{1}$$

If we are interested in a number of system performance characteristics $\pi_1, \pi_2, \ldots, \pi_m$, we compute then as

$$\pi_i \{0_N\}, \quad i = 1, 2, \ldots, m \tag{2}$$

and assume that they are a good approximation to

$$\pi_i \{0_\infty\}, \quad i = 1, 2, \ldots, m \tag{3}$$

In this way we tend to minimize the dependence of our results upon particular orbit characteristics.

ROSAN

The current version of ROSAN will add noise to the radar data as shown in Figure 3a. Here $\epsilon(N)$ is a sample from a probability distribution characterized by N. The sample values $\epsilon(N)$ are generated in two stages. First a multiplicative congruential process (1) of the form

$$x_{n+1} = kx_n \pmod{2^{35}} \tag{4}$$

is used to generate N pseudo-random, independent, uniformly distributed numbers $y_1, y_2, \ldots, y_N$ over the interval (0,1). The quantity

$$z = \sum_{i=1}^{N} y_i \tag{5}$$

is then calculated. It can be shown (2) that the distribution of z is given by

$$f_N(z) = \frac{1}{(N-1)!}\left[z^{N-1} - \binom{N}{1}(z-1)^{N-1} + \binom{N}{2}(z-2)^{N-1} - + \cdots\right] \tag{6}$$

where $0 < z < N$ and the summation is continued as long as z, z-1, etc., are positive. In order to obtain distributions which have zero mean and unit standard deviation, we apply a linear transformation to z, and calculate $\epsilon(N)$ by

$$\epsilon(N) = \sqrt{3N}\ (2z - N)/N \tag{7}$$

Some examples of the distributions of $\sigma_Q\ \epsilon(N)$ are shown in Figure 3b.

The numbers $\mu_Q$, $\sigma_Q$, and N may be specified by card input for each radar quantity Q, such as $r$, $\dot{r}$, $\alpha$, $\beta$, etc. Later versions of ROSAN may modify this noise generator to the form shown in Figure 3c. This would allow one to take into account the greater inaccuracies associated with the lower effective signal-to-noise ratios characterizing radar data from targets near the limits of coverage.

ESERD

For our initial runs it was thought best to confine our attention to one particular scheme of smoothing and estimation. This scheme is illustrated in Figure 4. The first version of ESERD smooths the simulated raw data by averaging the data over successive time intervals of length $(\lambda-1)\Delta t$, where $\Delta t$ is the

**PART a**

$$Q^* = Q + \mu_Q + \sigma_Q \epsilon(N)$$

**PART b**

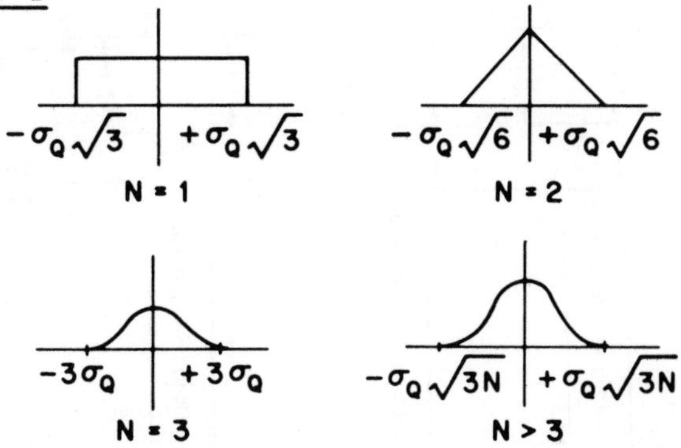


AS N INCREASES, DISTRIBUTION APPROACHES GAUSSIAN.

**PART c**

$$Q^* = Q + \mu_Q(Q) + \sigma_Q(Q)\,\epsilon(N,Q)$$

Fig. 3. Error Generation in ROSAN.

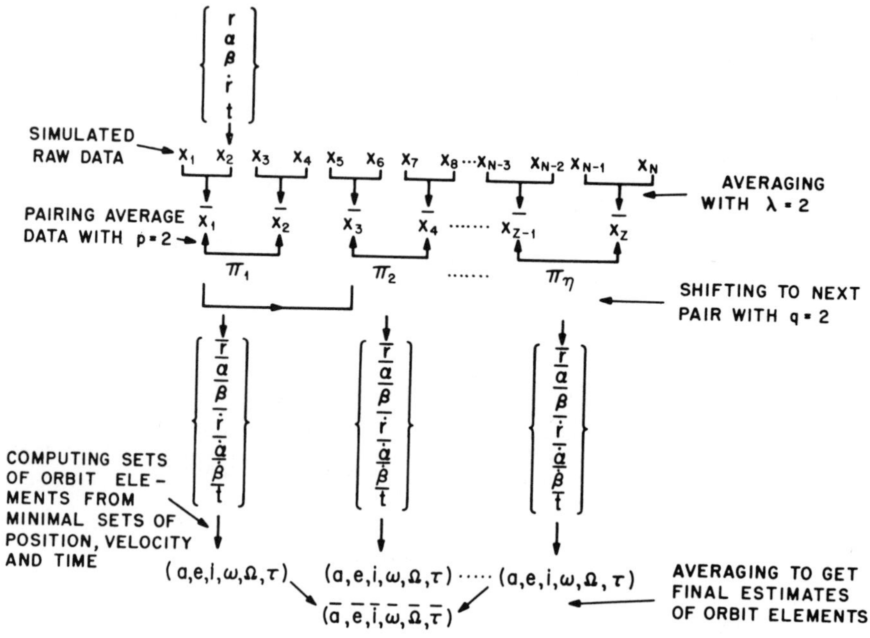


Fig. 4. Averaging and Estimation Procedure in ESERD 1: $(\lambda, p, q) = (2, 2, 2)$.

constant time spacing between data points, and $\lambda \geq 1$ is an integer parameter. If a satellite is given by N raw data points, there will be $Z = [N/\lambda]$ average data points.* We now take pairs of these average points. The points in a pair are separated by a time interval of length $(p-1)\Delta t$ where $p \geq 2$ is an integer. Given one pair of average points we choose the first point of the next pair by shifting over in time an amount $q\Delta t$ ($q$ an integer $\geq 1$) from the first point in the most recent pair already obtained.

The first ARIES runs will be used to optimize the averaging process with respect to the three parameters defined above, for the given radar system. These parameters are

1. The length of the raw data averaging interval, $\lambda$.
2. The time between points in a pairing, p.
3. The time between successive pairings, q.

If the pairing parameters are defined as above, there will be

$$\eta = \left[\frac{Z - p + q}{q}\right] \tag{8}$$

pairings, where Z is the number of average data points, as defined previously, and the subscripts of the first and second average data points in the $i^{th}$ pairing are given respectively by

$$\left.\begin{aligned} j &= 1 + (i-1)q \\ k &= j + p-1 \end{aligned}\right\} \quad i = 1, 2, \ldots, \eta \tag{9}$$

Each pairing gives rise to a position and velocity estimate at an intermediate point, determined from

$$\overline{Q} = \frac{Q_i + Q_j}{2} \qquad Q = r, \dot{r}, \alpha, \beta, t \tag{10}$$

$$\dot{Q} = \frac{Q_j - Q_i}{t_j - t_i} \qquad Q = \alpha, \beta \tag{11}$$

A check is made on the apparent energy to assure that the average data represents a closed orbit. If the energy condition is not satisfied, the pair of average data points is thrown out, and the next pair considered. If all pairs are disqualified no further computations for this satellite are made, but a record

*[ ] denotes here "largest integer contained in".

is kept of the number of such cases. The Keplerian orbital elements for each of these intermediate points are averaged to provide a mean estimate of this satellite's elements. This ESERD utilizes the simulated range, azimuth, elevation, range rate and time measurements that are generated by GROPE and degraded by ROSAN.

CASPE

The ESERD estimates of the orbital elements together with their true values (available from GROPE) are then used by CASPE to calculate the vector difference in position, in an inertial XYZ coordinate system, at a number of times in a given interval. These times are chosen relative to the last time of sighting for each satellite. This is done so that averages of position error for each such fixed time, taken over the entire simulated population, will be meaningful. Such averages indicate how position error grows with time. In our extrapolation of the "true" and "estimated" position we are neglecting possible perturbations of the Keplerian orbits, assuming that this will have only small influence on the relative performance of the alternate data-processing procedures studied. Later versions of CASPE may include correction procedures for such effects.

The choice of a measure of performance for the ARIES depends, of course, upon the class of problems which will be studied. Initially we are concerned with predicting the future position of a satellite at some time following the last sighting. It is simple, therefore, to use as a performance measure the magnitude of the position error vector between the true and estimated predicted positions of a satellite.

For a fixed value of time, the position errors $d_\nu(t_0)$, $\nu = 1, 2, \ldots, N$, obtained by operating on the population of N random satellites, may be treated as N sample values of a random variable $D(t_0)$ possessing a distribution $f(D(t_0))$. It is this distribution, for each $t_0$, that characterizes the system performance over the entire satellite population.

As a single number to characterize each distribution we use the sample mean

$$\overline{d(t_0)} = \frac{1}{N} \sum_{\nu=1}^{N} d_\nu(t_0) \qquad (12)$$

Aside from ease of calculation, the sample mean has the sensitivity that we would like to have in investigating system performance. Unlike the sample median, for example, it will reflect more readily extremes in prediction accuracy.

Finally, in order to give some gross indication of performance over an entire time interval, we calculate for convenience the quantity

$$D_I = \frac{1}{\nu_0} \sum_{j=1}^{\nu_0} \overline{d(t_j)}, \quad I = \{t_1 \leq t_j \leq t_{\nu_0}\} \tag{13}$$

Sample standard deviations calculated along with the means enable us to derive confidence intervals for the true population means.

### Program Operation

Program operating times for ARIES necessarily depend upon the parameter values specified and the amount of printout required. These times are mostly a function of satellite population size and the average number of data points per satellite. Ranges of values of operating time required per satellite, as a function of average number of data points per satellite ($\overline{N}_D$), are shown in Figure 5.* Because of the data rate scheduled for the current set of ARIES computer runs, the value of $\overline{N}_D$ is quite low now.

## ARIES Results to Date

The scheduled ARIES production runs may be conveniently divided into two groups. The first group of runs has as its objectives the determination of

1. The performance of the processing and prediction portions of ARIES in a noise-free environment.
2. The best (statistically) population size to use in any given series of computer runs.

The second group will measure the effects of noise upon processing and prediction. The parameters to be chosen for these runs will be dependent upon the results of the first group.

At the time of this writing, the scheduled computer runs have not been completed. Some noise-free runs have been made, examples of which are shown in Figures 6, 7, 8 and 9. A number of sets of processing parameter values were considered. Their effect was noted over an interval of time extending from zero to fourteen hours after last time of sighting for each

*These are program operating times on an IBM 709 computer.

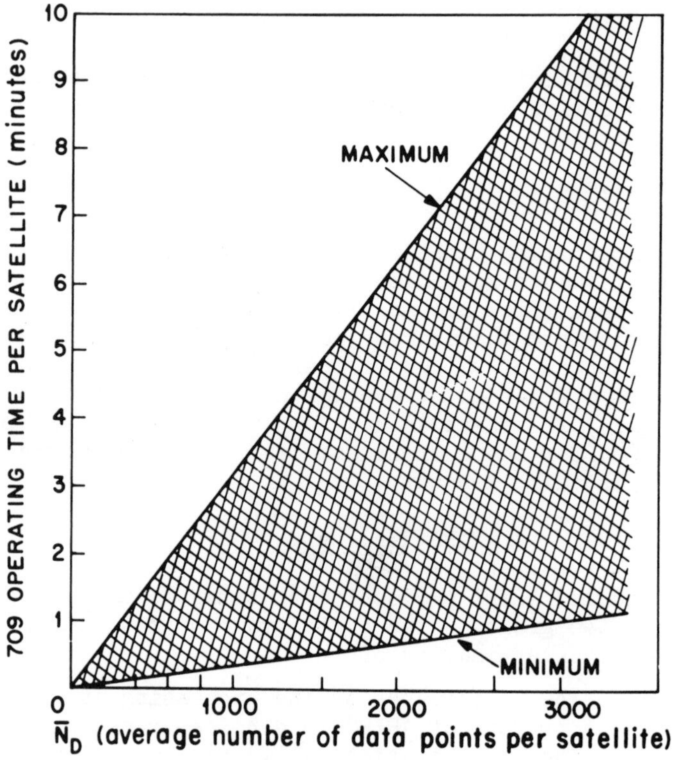


Fig. 5. Operating Time per Satellite as a Function of Average Number of Data Points per Satellite.

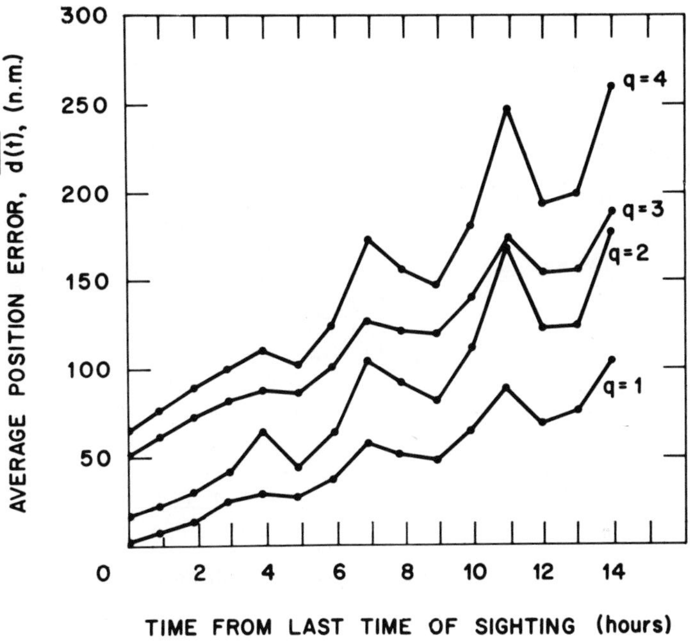


Fig. 6. Average Position Error as a Function of Time from Last Time of Sighting as Shift Parameter q Increases .....NOISE FREE $(\lambda, p) = (1, 2)$ $N_S = 100$ .

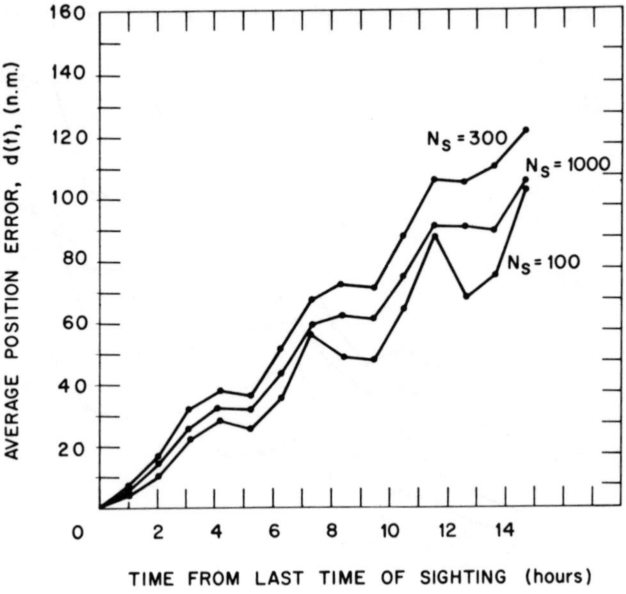


Fig. 7. Average Position Error as a Function of Time from Last Time of Sighting for (λ, p, q) = 1, 2, 1) ..... NOISE FREE.

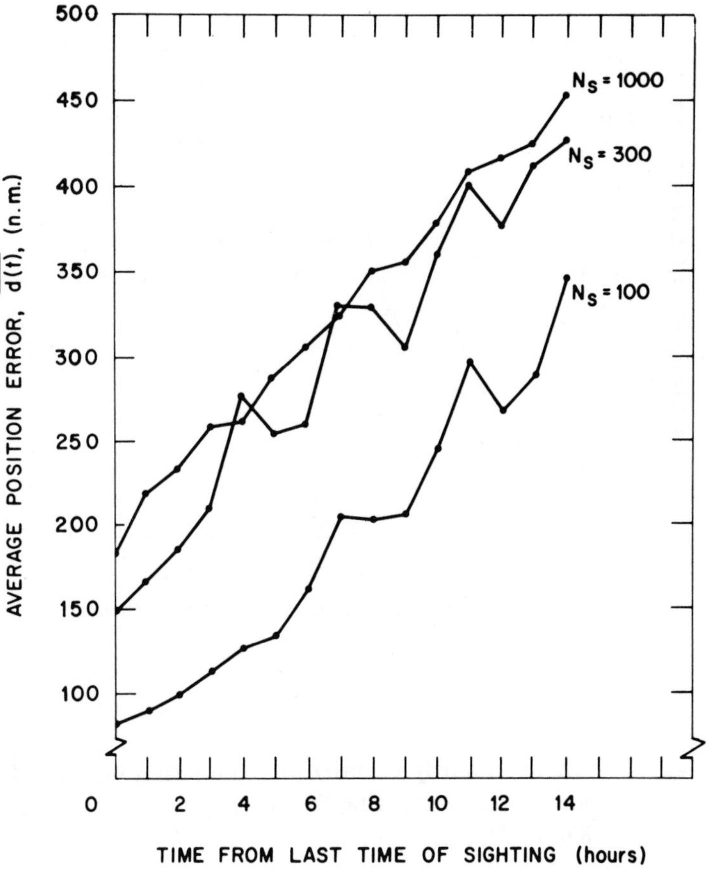


Fig. 8. Average Position Error as a Function of Time from Last Time of Sighting for $(\lambda, p, q) = (2, 2, 1)$ .... NOISE FREE.

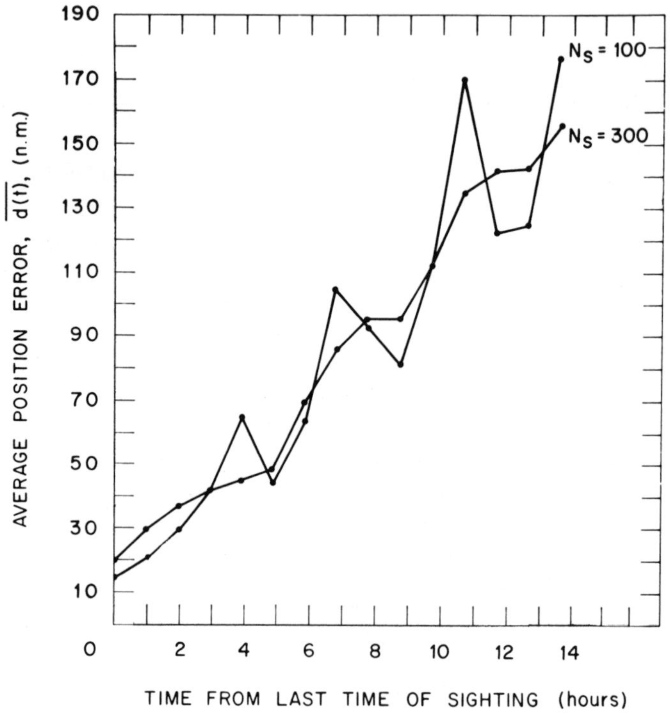


Fig. 9. Average Position Error as a Function of Time from Last Time of Sighting for (λ, p, q) = (1, 2, 2) .... NOISE FREE.

satellite in three simulated populations of size 100, 300 and 1000.

If the effects of round-off errors, etc., are discounted, one must look elsewhere for the factors which contribute to what seem to be significantly large values of $\overline{d(t)}$ in the noise-free case. The most obvious source may be the very low data rate of three returns per minute. It is possible that some of the approximations made, for example, in the estimation of $\dot{\alpha}$ and $\beta$ (Eq. 11) break down when the returns are separated by twenty seconds.

Results such as shown in these figures point up a number of trends. As might be expected, the size of the population has an appreciable effect upon the estimates of system performance. If, as mentioned previously, we wish to measure several system characteristics $\pi_1, \pi_2, \ldots, \pi_m$, we generate a random satellite population of size N, and assume that

$$\lim_{N \to \infty} \pi_i\{O_N\} = \pi_i\{O_\infty\} \qquad i = 1, 2, \ldots, m \quad (14)$$

As we do not know, a priori, the characteristics of the limiting population, $\{O_\infty\}$, we are forced to proceed by choosing an ordered sequence of population sizes, say $N_1 < N_2, \ldots, < N_k$.

We then select the largest value of N, say N*, in this sequence which yields a program running time which is practical for production purposes. A measure of how well we will estimate the true population characteristics can then be obtained by calculating the quantities

$$Q_i = \left| \pi_i\{O_{N*}\} - \pi_i\{O_{N_k}\} \right| \qquad i = 1, 2, \ldots, m \qquad (15)$$

on the assumption that

$$\lim_{N*, N_k \to \infty} Q_i = 0 \qquad (16)$$

A careful analysis will have to be made along these lines to determine appropriate population sizes for future production runs.

For a fixed number of raw data points, at any one of the processing parameters increases (say, the shift parameter q), the number of pairings decreases. In particular, for satellites represented by as few as four or five data points, estimation of the orbital elements may be dependent upon only one pairing This situation contributes large position errors to the population average position error, $\overline{d(t)}$, which is sensitive to extreme values.

Because of this apparent behavior, a tentative conclusion in the noise-free case might be that estimation of the Keplerian orbital elements is best when the number of pairings, $\eta$, is a maximum for a given average number of data points per satellite. This is equivalent to the condition that there be a minimum of smoothing. One might expect, however, that in the presence of noisy data such a conclusion would be reversed, and that more smoothing would be necessary. This would amount to choosing the parameters $\lambda$, p, q to lie in some intervals

$$1 \leq \lambda \leq L_1 \quad (17)$$

$$2 \leq p \leq L_2 \quad (18)$$

$$1 \leq q \leq L_3 \quad (19)$$

where the $L_i$, i = 1, 2, 3 are determined by the character of the noise, and by the condition that there be at least one pairing, viz.,

$$p\lambda \leq N \quad (20)$$

where N is the minimum number of data points for any satellite in a population.

In the noise-free case, all the position error curves obtained appear to have the form of an oscillation superimposed upon some nearly straight line. Further investigation will be required before general conclusions can be drawn relating the propagation of errors to the parameters of the system studied and the orbital characteristics of the satellite population used. Some type of oscillation should be reasonably expected, however, from a consideration of the assumptions made in this version of ARIES. As shown in Figure 10, the approximation of both the true and estimated orbits by ellipses demands that position error, as we are defining it, must go through successive stages of increasing and decreasing. The nature and extent of this variation will depend, among other things, upon the relative orientation of the two ellipses. In the non-Keplerian case, our two ellipses are changing with time, as a result of perturbation effects. As mentioned earlier, however, we are assuming that both orbits are affected to the same degree by these perturbations. With such an assumption, we would still expect oscillations in the position error to occur.

## Summary

An investigation of the general problem areas of satellite-orbit data-processing and prediction methods is being undertaken,

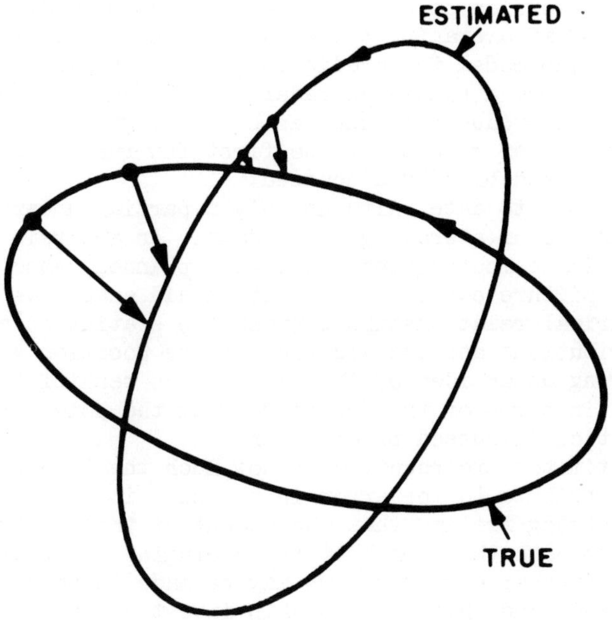


Fig. 10. Variation of d(t) Vector Along True and Estimated Orbits.

using a simulation system, composed of 709 computer programs, called ARIES. Each of the computer programs performs a separate function and may conveniently be replaced by a similarly coded program, if the function is to be modified or changed, without requiring significant changes in the remaining programs.

The first version of ARIES is being used to study the effectiveness of an averaging procedure in smoothing, and of a simple Keplerian model for predicting, on the basis of radar data obtained from a simulated radar model with a low data rate. A set of production runs has been designed for this study. Examples of results of the first few runs have been presented here and briefly discussed.

The results, to date, give us only a partial understanding of the technique of averaging radar data. An analysis of the remaining ARIES computer runs, currently planned, should clarify the picture considerably. It should enable us to formulate empirical relationships between the statistics of the noise distributions and the accuracy of the position estimates, thereby giving us an idea of the procedure's sensitivity to noisy data, in terms of the departure from the noise-free characteristics discussed briefly here.

Some estimates are required of how much the linear approximations contribute to the error in the position estimate. There is a strong feeling that the extent of this contribution is related to both the length of the averaging interval and the data rate. Further computer runs may be made in which the data rate is varied, and this relationship investigated.

Future plans call for the study and comparison of several other data-processing schemes, including a least-squares fitting of each radar measurement. The effect of first transforming the measurements to a cartesian coordinate system, before fitting the data, is being studied. It is hoped that ARIES will provide some useful results, which can be used to guide concurrent analytic investigations in the areas of orbit prediction and error propagation.

## References

1. Taussky, O. and J. Todd, "Generation and Testing of Pseudo-Random Numbers," Symposium on Monte Carlo Methods, John Wiley and Sons, Inc., 1956.

2. Cramer, H., Mathematical Methods of Statistics, Princeton University Press, 1957.

# INTERPLANETARY INJECTION GUIDANCE

C.G. Sauer, Jr.
Jet Propulsion Laboratory
California Institute of Technology
Pasadena, California

## Abstract

The injection criteria for an interplanetary trajectory may be satisfied by defining the direction and magnitude of the hyperbolic excess velocity vector of the escape conic near the Earth. If both the launch date and the desired date at encounter are specified, then the direction and magnitude of the hyperbolic excess velocity vector are uniquely determined. In the following paper the analytical derivation of guidance equations is described together with results as applied for example to a 1962 Mars mission.

## Introduction

The free flight trajectory of a space vehicle in which the entire velocity increment required for interplanetary transfer is achieved in a brief powered phase near the Earth is characterized by three principle phases; (1) an escape hyperbola near the Earth, (2) a heliocentric ellipse when in the influence of the Sun, and (3) an approach hyperbola to the target planet, each phase gradually merging with the next. A detailed description by K.A. Ehricke of interplanetary transfer trajectories may be found in (1). An injection analysis is primarily concerned with phase (1) where the defining parameters for the near Earth conic are the magnitude and direction of the hyperbolic excess velocity vector and the launch time. If the launch and encounter times are specified, then the magnitude and direction of the hyperbolic excess velocity vector are uniquely determined. The hyperbolic excess velocity vector is in the direction of the outgoing asymptote of the escape hyperbola.

The powered phase of the trajectory near the Earth lies in approximately the same plane as the escape hyperbola, this orbital plane being determined by a vector through the launch site at the instant of launch and a vector $\bar{S}$ in the direction of the outgoing asymptote of the hyperbola as shown in (Fig. 1), the projection of the trajectory on the orbital plane (Fig. 2).

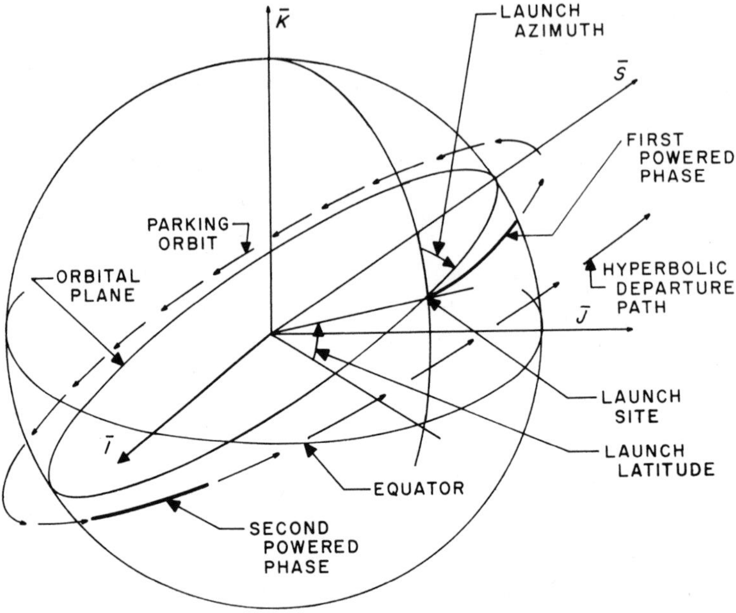


Fig. 1. Hyperbolic Departure Orbit

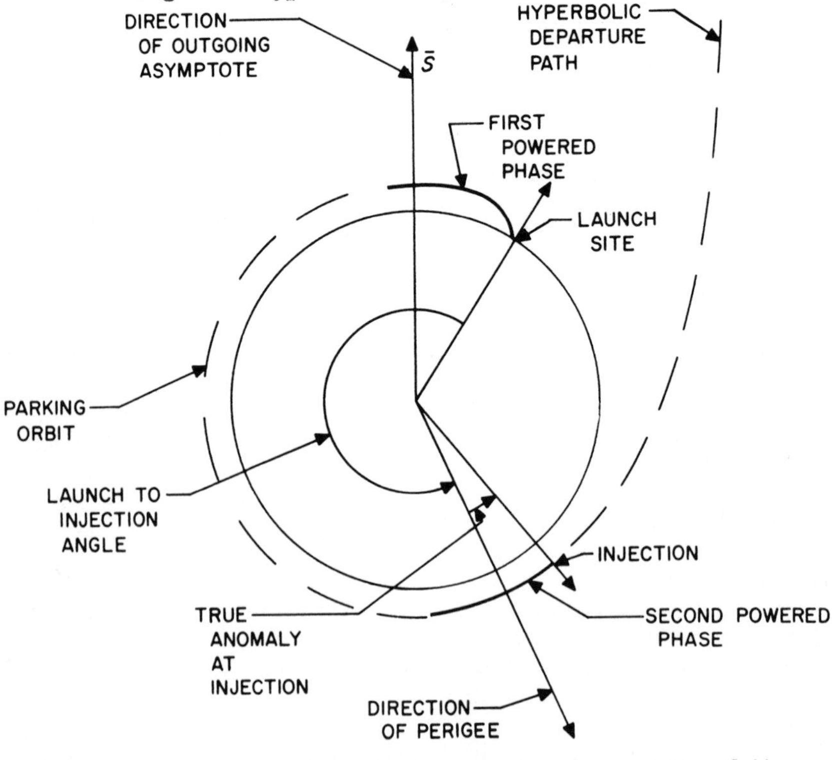


Fig. 2. Orbital Plane of Hyperbolic Departure Orbit

If it were not for various restrictions such as range safety, tracking and telemetry and the desire to fire as near to East as possible in order to use the rotational velocity of the Earth to advantage, the vehicle could be launched at any time of the day. For example, a graph of launch azimuth as a function of time of day for a Mars mission launched on October 28, 1962 is shown (Fig. 3). In this particular example it is not possible to have a satisfactory trajectory by a launching due east since the direction of the outgoing asymptote lies at a latitude greater than that of the assumed launch site at AMR ($28^{\circ}.5$). If the direction of the outgoing asymptote lies at a latitude less than that of the launch site such as for a Lunar or Venus mission in 1962, then launch azimuths due east from AMR are possible.

It has been shown by various authors[4] that maximum payload results when the vehicle follows a low flat trajectory during the powered portion of the flight. The resulting angle of the velocity vector of the vehicle above the local horizontal is in general several degrees at thrust termination, injection thus occurring around 5 to 10 degrees after perigee. If it is necessary to inject the vehicle farther from perigee than optimum, it is necessary that the vehicle fly a higher trajectory so as to have a greater path angle at shutoff. The payload falls off rapidly as larger values of path angle are demanded at shutoff. The angle between launch and perigee was calculated for the example used for (Fig. 3) and is shown as a function of launch time (Fig. 4). In this example a continuous powered phase does not result in a maximum payload since injection would occur relatively far from perigee and would require large values of path angle at injection. In order to achieve more payload an ascent into a coast or parking orbit is demanded as indicated (Fig. 2), followed by a brief powered phase near perigee so as to acquire the necessary escape velocity. Since the total powered portion of the trajectory may amount to about 30 degrees the coast angle will be about that amount less than the launch to perigee angle shown in (Fig. 4).

As illustrated (Fig. 3) two separate launch periods are possible corresponding to Northeast and Southeast launch azimuths. The times at which the rate of change of launch azimuth with respect to time becomes zero is generally preferred since these times correspond to the most easterly firing azimuths. For the example used (Fig. 3 and 4), coast angles of approximately 270 degrees and 170 degrees result for Northeast and Southeast launch azimuths at these optimum times. The Southeast launch period may be more desirable since the coasting angle is smaller and guidance may be more accurate.

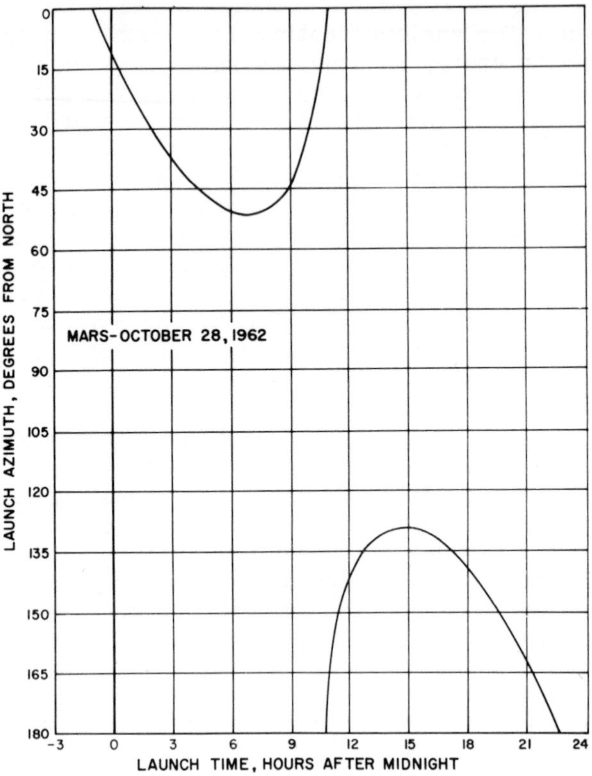


Fig. 3. Example of Launch Azimuth vs Time

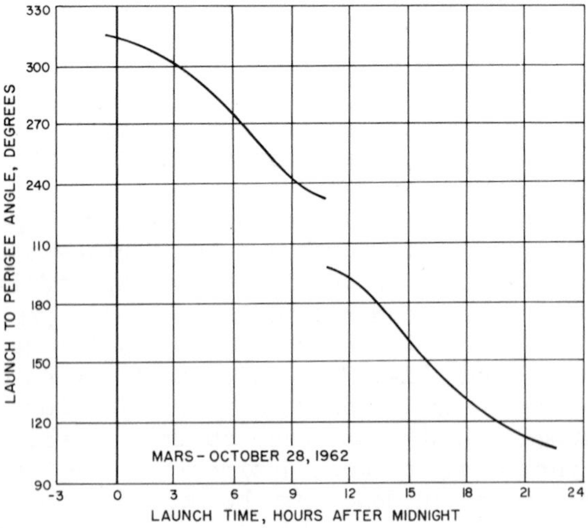


Fig. 4. Example of Launch to Perigee Angle vs Time

For a given position of the vehicle there exists a unique velocity vector which will insure an injection into a hyperbolic orbit with a given magnitude and direction of the hyperbolic excess velocity vector. In the analysis of an injection guidance system for interplanetary missions it is desirable to consider the required velocity vector $\bar{V}_C$ as the velocity vector which would be required by the vehicle at a specified position $\bar{R}$ along the powered phase of the trajectory such that if the thrust of the rocket engines were shutoff at that instant, the vehicle would be capable of performing its intended mission.

The guidance system for the vehicle would calculate the inertial position of the vehicle and compute as a function of this position, the required velocity vector $\bar{V}_C$. The path of the vehicle would then be controlled such that the difference between the required velocity vector and the actual inertial velocity vector of the vehicle was driven to zero. When these two velocity vectors became equal, a shutoff would be commanded of the rocket engines. Because of the additional requirement of a coasting phase between the powered phases of the trajectory, there is an additional injection necessary into the parking orbit. In the following analysis, only the final injection into the escape hyperbola is treated.

## Vector Orientation

Consider an inertial cartesian coordinate system with unit vectors $\bar{I}$, $\bar{J}$, $\bar{K}$ in the direction of the reference X, Y, Z axes respectively in which, for the purposes of illustration, the unit vector $\bar{I}$ lies in the equatorial plane and is directed toward the Vernal Equinox, the unit vector $\bar{K}$ is directed toward the North Pole of the Earth, and the unit vector $\bar{J}$ completes a right-handed rectangular coordinate system with $\bar{I}$ and $\bar{K}$.

Let $\bar{R}$ denote the unit position vector of the vehicle and $\bar{S}$ denote the unit vector in the desired direction of the hyperbolic excess velocity vector. The direction cosines of the unit vectors will be denoted by subscripts 1, 2, 3 such as $\bar{S}(S_1, S_2, S_3)$. A unit vector $\bar{W}$ is normal to the plane formed by $\bar{R}$ and $\bar{S}$,

$$\bar{W} = \frac{\bar{R} \times \bar{S}}{\sin \theta} \tag{1}$$

where $\theta$ is the angle between the unit vectors R and S. This angle may be calculated from:

$$\cos \theta = \bar{R} \cdot \bar{S} \tag{2}$$

and

$$\sin \theta = \left[ \bar{R} \times \bar{S} \right] \tag{3}$$

A unit vector $\bar{M}$ in the plane formed by $\bar{R}$ and $\bar{S}$ and 90 degrees ahead of R is given by

$$\bar{M} = \bar{W} \times \bar{R} = \frac{\bar{S} - \bar{R}\cos\theta}{\sin\theta} \tag{4}$$

The unit vectors $\bar{R}$, $\bar{M}$, and $\bar{W}$ form a right-handed set of unit vectors with $\bar{M}$ and $\bar{W}$ defining a local horizontal plane. A unit vector $\bar{V}$ in the direction of the desired velocity vector $\bar{V}_C$ of the vehicle lies in the plane formed by $\bar{R}$ and $\bar{S}$. If the angle $\gamma_C$ between $\bar{M}$ and $\bar{V}$ is defined as the desired path angle, then $\bar{V}$ is given by

$$\bar{V} = \bar{R}\sin\gamma_C + \bar{M}\cos\gamma_C \tag{5}$$

From Eqs. (4) and (5) $\bar{V}$ may be expressed as

$$\bar{V} = \frac{\bar{S}\cos\gamma_C - \bar{R}\cos(\gamma_C + \theta)}{\sin\theta} \tag{6}$$

If the magnitude of the velocity vector is denoted by $V_C$ then the required velocity vector $\bar{V}_C$ of the vehicle is

$$\bar{V}_C = V_C\,\bar{V} = \left[\frac{V_C\cos\gamma_C}{\sin\theta}\right]\bar{S} - \left[\frac{V_C\cos(\gamma_C + \theta)}{\sin\theta}\right]\bar{R} \tag{7}$$

The orientation of the above unit vectors is shown in figure (5).

## Derivation of the Required Speed and Required Path Angle

The required speed $V_C$ of the vehicle is dependent upon the distance r of the vehicle from the center of the Earth and the magnitude of the hyperbolic excess velocity vector which is specified. The required speed $V_C$ is from the vis-viva or energy integral

$$V_C^2 = GM\left[\frac{2}{r} - \frac{1}{a}\right] \tag{8}$$

where the convention is used of defining the semi-transverse axis, a, of the hyperbola to be negative. The quantity GM is the product of the constant of gravitation G and the mass of the Earth, M. The value of GM used in this analysis is

$GM = .3986\ 1350 \times 10^{15}$ (meters)$^3$/(second)$^2$.

In order that the direction of the hyperbolic excess

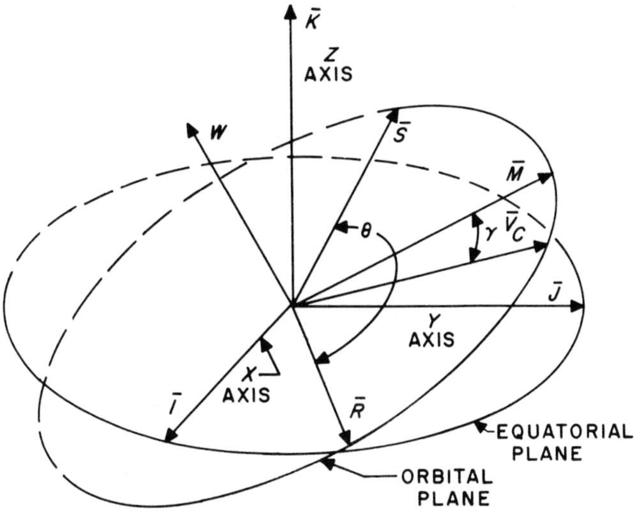


Fig. 5. Orientation of Unit Vectors

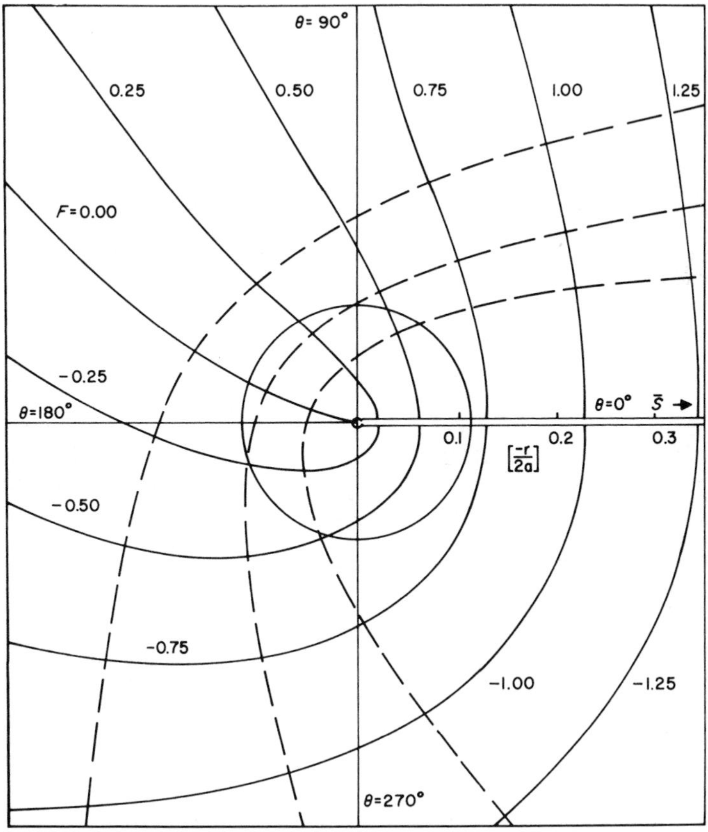


Fig. 6. Streamlines and Lines of Equipotential

velocity vector be directed along $\bar{S}$, it is necessary that the difference between the maximum true anomaly $\theta_H$ of the hyperbola and the true anomaly $\theta_0$ at injection be equal to the angle between $\bar{R}$ and $\bar{S}$

$$(\theta_H - \theta_0) = \theta \tag{9}$$

The maximum true anomaly is given by

$$\cos \theta_H = -\frac{1}{e} \tag{10}$$

and

$$\sin \theta_H = \frac{\sqrt{e^2 - 1}}{e} \tag{11}$$

where e is the eccentricity of the hyperbola. The eccentricity is given by

$$e^2 = 1 - q(2 - q) \cos^2 \gamma_C \tag{12}$$

where

$$q = \frac{r V_C^2}{GM} \tag{13}$$

The true anomaly $\theta_0$ at injection is found from

$$\cos \theta_0 = \frac{q \cos^2 \gamma_C - 1}{e} \tag{14}$$

and

$$\sin \theta_0 = \frac{q \sin \gamma_C \cos \gamma_C}{e} \tag{15}$$

By a little manipulation of the above equations the eccentricity may be eliminated and the required path angle found as a function of r and θ. The following expressions may be thus derived for the terms appearing in Eq. (7).

$$\frac{V_C \cos \gamma_C}{\sin \theta} = \frac{V_H}{2} \left[ 1 + \sqrt{1 + \left[\frac{2a}{-r}\right] \left[\frac{2}{(1 + \cos \theta)}\right]} \right] \tag{16}$$

$$\frac{V_C \cos (\gamma_C + \theta)}{\sin \theta} = \frac{V_H}{2} \left[ 1 - \sqrt{1 + \left[\frac{2a}{-r}\right] \left[\frac{2}{(1 + \cos \theta)}\right]} \right] \tag{17}$$

where $V_H$ is the magnitude of the hyperbolic excess velocity vector of the hyperbola and is the speed the vehicle would have at an infinite distance from the Earth. From Eq. 8 the hyperbolic excess velocity may be related to the semi-transverse axis, a, by setting r equal to infinity,

$$V_H^2 = V_C^2(r = \infty) = -\frac{1}{a} \tag{18}$$

## The Velocity Vector Field

The required velocity vector $\bar{V}_C$ may be considered as a vector velocity field with components $V_{CX}$, $V_{CY}$, $V_{CZ}$ along the reference X, Y, Z areas respectively. In order to determine the properties of this vector field, the curl and divergence are first examined. The derivatives of the components of the vector field taken with respect to the variables X, Y, Z are found to be

$$\frac{\partial V_{CX}}{\partial X} = \frac{V_A}{R}(R_1 + S_1)(R_1 + S_1) + \frac{V_B}{R}(1 - R_1^2) \tag{19-a}$$

$$\frac{\partial V_{CX}}{\partial Y} = \frac{V_A}{R}(R_1 + S_1)(R_2 + S_2) + \frac{V_B}{R}(-R_1R_2) \tag{19-b}$$

$$\frac{\partial V_{CX}}{\partial Z} = \frac{V_A}{R}(R_1 + S_1)(R_3 + S_3) + \frac{V_B}{R}(-R_1R_3) \tag{19-c}$$

$$\frac{\partial V_{CY}}{\partial X} = \frac{V_A}{R}(R_2 + S_2)(R_1 + S_1) + \frac{V_B}{R}(-R_2R_1) \tag{19-d}$$

$$\frac{\partial V_{CY}}{\partial Y} = \frac{V_A}{R}(R_2 + S_2)(R_2 + S_2) + \frac{V_B}{R}(1 - R_2^2) \tag{19-e}$$

$$\frac{\partial V_{CY}}{\partial Z} = \frac{V_A}{R}(R_2 + S_2)(R_3 + S_3) + \frac{V_B}{R}(-R_2R_3) \tag{19-f}$$

$$\frac{\partial V_{CZ}}{\partial X} = \frac{V_A}{R}(R_3 + S_3)(R_1 + S_1) + \frac{V_B}{R}(-R_3R_1) \tag{19-g}$$

$$\frac{\partial V_{CZ}}{\partial Y} = \frac{V_A}{R}(R_3 + S_3)(R_2 + S_2) + \frac{V_B}{R}(-R_3R_2) \tag{19-h}$$

$$\frac{\partial V_{CZ}}{\partial Z} = \frac{V_A}{R} (R_3 + S_3)(R_3 + S_3) + \frac{V_B}{R} (1 - R_3^2) \qquad (19\text{-i})$$

Where $R_1$, $R_2$, $R_3$ and $S_1$, $S_2$, $S_3$ are the direction cosines of the unit vectors $\bar{R}$ and $\bar{S}$. $V_A$ and $V_B$ are given by

$$V_A = -\frac{V_H}{2} \frac{\left[\frac{2a}{-r}\right] \left[\frac{1}{(1 + \cos\theta)^2}\right]}{\sqrt{1 + \left[\frac{2a}{-r}\right] \left[\frac{2}{(1 + \cos\theta)}\right]}} \qquad (20)$$

and

$$V_B = -\frac{V_H}{2} \left[ 1 - \sqrt{1 + \left[\frac{2a}{-r}\right] \left[\frac{2}{(1 + \cos\theta)}\right]} \right] \qquad (21)$$

The curl of the velocity vector field is given by

$$\text{curl } \bar{V}_C = \nabla \times \bar{V}_C$$

$$= \left[\frac{\partial V_{CZ}}{\partial Y} - \frac{\partial V_{CY}}{\partial Z}\right] \bar{I} + \left[\frac{\partial V_{CX}}{\partial Z} - \frac{\partial V_{CZ}}{\partial X}\right] \bar{J} + \left[\frac{\partial V_{CY}}{\partial X} - \frac{\partial V_{CX}}{\partial Y}\right] \bar{K} \qquad (22)$$

An observation of Eqs. (19) reveals the following identities,

$$\frac{\partial V_{CZ}}{\partial Y} = \frac{\partial V_{CY}}{\partial Z} \qquad (23\text{-a})$$

$$\frac{\partial V_{CX}}{\partial Z} = \frac{\partial V_{CZ}}{\partial X} \qquad (23\text{-b})$$

$$\frac{\partial V_{CY}}{\partial X} = \frac{\partial V_{CX}}{\partial Y} \qquad (23\text{-c})$$

such that

$$\text{curl } \bar{V}_C = \nabla \times \bar{V}_C = 0 \qquad (24)$$

Since the curl of the vector velocity field is zero, the field must be conservative, and furthermore may be represented, rather interestingly enough, as the gradient of a scaler potential function, F.

$$\bar{V}_C = \text{grad } F = \nabla F = \frac{\partial F}{\partial X}\bar{I} + \frac{\partial F}{\partial Y}\bar{J} + \frac{\partial F}{\partial Z}\bar{K} \tag{25}$$

The divergence of the velocity vector field is given by

$$\text{div } \bar{V}_C = \frac{V_H}{2r} \frac{\left[1 - \sqrt{1 + \left[\frac{2a}{-r}\right]\left[\frac{2}{(1+\cos\theta)}\right]}\right]^2}{\sqrt{1 + \left[\frac{2a}{-r}\right]\left[\frac{2}{(1+\cos\theta)}\right]}} \tag{26}$$

Since the potential function F satisfies Poisson's Equation, the velocity vector field may be likened to the velocity of flow of an ideal, incompressible, irrotational fluid with continuously distributed sources.

In order to determine the form of the scalar potential function F, it is simpler to visulize the velocity vector $\bar{V}_C$ in a system of orthogonal curvilinear coordinates such that the velocity vector depends upon only two of the coordinates and is independent of the third. Such a curvilinear coordinate system is a spherical polar system (r, θ, Ø) with the unit vector S aligned along the polar axis. Because of the orientation of the coordinate system, the vector velocity field is independent of Ø and has components $V_{CR}$ and $V_{CM}$, the third component $V_{CW}$ being zero, thus,

$$\bar{V}_C = V_{CR}\,\bar{R} - V_{CM}\,\bar{M} \tag{27}$$

where

$$V_{CR} = \frac{\partial F}{\partial R} = V_C \sin\gamma_C \tag{28}$$

$$= V_H \left\{ -1 + \frac{(1+\cos\theta)}{2} \left[1 + \sqrt{1 + \left[\frac{2a}{-r}\right]\left[\frac{2}{(1+\cos\theta)}\right]}\right]\right\}$$

and

$$V_{CM} = -\frac{1}{r}\frac{\partial F}{\partial \theta} = V_C \cos\gamma_C$$

$$V_H \left\{ \frac{\sin\theta}{2} \left[1 + \sqrt{1 + \left[\frac{2a}{-r}\right]\left[\frac{2}{(1+\cos\theta)}\right]}\right]\right\} \tag{29}$$

In order to determine the potential function F, first $(r\,V_{CM})$ is integrated with respect to θ holding r fixed. A potential $F_\theta$ is thus derived as a function of r and θ,

$$F_\theta = \int (-r\,V_{CM})\,d\theta$$

$$= r\,V_H \left\{ \left[\frac{(1+\cos\theta)}{2}\right]\left[1+\sqrt{1+\left[\frac{2a}{-r}\right]\left[\frac{2}{(1+\cos\theta)}\right]}\right] + \left[\frac{2a}{-r}\right] \log_e \left[\sqrt{\left[\frac{(1+\cos\theta)}{2}\right]} + \sqrt{\left[\frac{2a}{-r}\right] + \left[\frac{(1+\cos\theta)}{2}\right]}\right]\right\} \quad (30)$$

The potential function F may be considered as being equal to

$$F = F_\theta + F_r + F_c \quad (31)$$

where $F_r$ must be an arbitrary function of r only and $F_c$ is a constant chosen so that the potential will have a particular value at a specified point such as the origin. Since the potential function F must satisfy Eq. (28),

$$\frac{\partial F}{\partial r} = \frac{\partial F_\theta}{\partial r} + \frac{dF_r}{dr} \quad (32)$$

where the total derivative is taken of $F_r$ since it is a function of r only.

Differentiating $F_\theta$ with respect to r, holding $\theta$ fixed, and then subtracting from $\frac{\partial F}{\partial r}$ yields

$$\frac{dF_r}{dr} = - V_H \left(1 + \frac{a}{r}\right) \quad (33)$$

Integrating Eq. (33) with respect to r, the potential function $F_r$ is found,

$$F_r = r\,V_H \left[-1 + \left[\frac{2a}{-r}\right] \log_e \sqrt{r}\right] \quad (34)$$

If the potential function $F_c$ is chosen so that the potential assumes the value of zero at the origin, the scalar potential function F becomes

$$F = r\,V_H \left\{-1 + \left[\frac{(1+\cos\theta)}{2}\right]\left[1+\sqrt{1+\left[\frac{2a}{-r}\right]\left[\frac{2}{(1+\cos\theta)}\right]}\right] + \left[\frac{2a}{-r}\right] \log_e \left[\frac{1+\sqrt{1+\left[\frac{2a}{-r}\right]\left[\frac{2}{(1+\cos\theta)}\right]}}{\sqrt{\left[\frac{2a}{-r}\right]\left[\frac{2}{(1+\cos\theta)}\right]}}\right]\right\} \quad (35)$$

A graph of the equipotentials F = constant, are shown (Fig. 6) as a function of r and θ. By normalizing dimensions such that the equipotentials have a scalefactor of (-2a) $V_H$, and the radial unit is equal to $\left|\frac{-r}{2a}\right|$, a set of universal curves of equipotential may be generated. Several streamlines representing the path the vehicle would follow after thrust termination are also shown in (Fig. 6). The circle on the graph indicates the size of the Earth for the example used in this analysis.

## Application of the Guidance Theory

In order to verify the guidance theory discussed in the previous sections, a Martian trajectory with a flight time of 224 days was used as an example. This example was chosen since it represents a fairly critical test of the injection criteria, corresponding closely to the minimum energy case for Martian trajectories launched during 1962. Because of the three dimensional nature of the transfer trajectory from the Earth to Mars, this particular example does not quite correspond to the minimum energy Hohman transfer, the heliocentric central angle being 158 degrees.

The nominal values of position and velocity at injection are shown in Table 1 for this example together with the defining elements of the near Earth oscullating conic. Values of the partial derivatives of $\bar{V}_C$ derived previously are shown in Table 2.

Several Martian trajectories were run, in which each of the position coordinates was varied in turn by ± 100 kilometers, the corresponding value of the required velocity vector $V_C$ being used as the initial velocity. The difference between the required velocity and the nominal value is shown in Table 3 for each of six varied trajectories. These perturbations likely represent a larger volume of space than that in which injection is likely to occur. The resulting uncompensated miss components at Mars for this example are shown (Fig. 7), the only trajectories actually resulting in a miss are those representing variations in the Z component which lie along the polar axis of the Earth. The miss due to variations in Z is not unexpected since a distortion of the trajectory results due to the neglected effects of the oblateness of the Earth. When several perturbed trajectories were run in which the oblateness of the Earth was eliminated, the resulting miss at Mars was not more than about ± 400 kilometers. The miss at Mars due to variations in the Z component are thus largely due to the uncompensated effects of oblateness of the Earth.

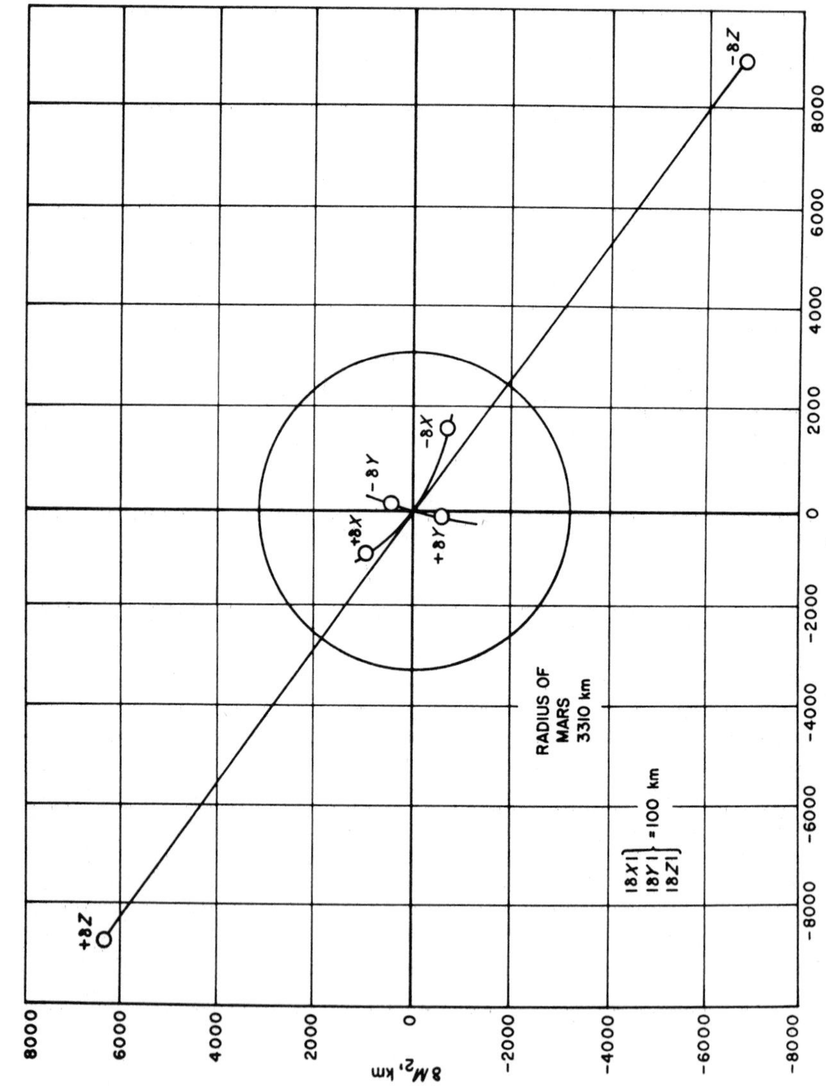


Fig. 7. Example of Uncompensated Miss Components at Mars Encounter

Table 1. Example of Injection Conditions

| | |
|---|---|
| **A. Time of Injection** | |
| Julian Date | 2,437,966.167831 |
| Calendar Date | October 28.6672, 1962 |
| **B. Space-Fixed, Cartesian Coordinates** | |
| X, meters | 5,593,048.6 |
| Y, meters | - 801,952.3 |
| Z, meters | - 3,351,551.6 |
| $\dot{X}$, meters/second | 5,388.6048 |
| $\dot{Y}$, meters/second | 8,702.8486 |
| $\dot{Z}$, meters/second | 5,637.2541 |
| **C. Earth-Fixed, Spherical Coordinates** | |
| R, meters | 6,569,491.3 |
| V, meters/second | 11,357.634 |
| $\phi$ (latitude), degrees | - 30.675 |
| $\theta$ (longitude), degrees | 74.903 |
| $\gamma$ (path angle), degrees | 3.278 |
| $\sigma$ (azimuth angle), degrees | 52.265 |
| **D. Defining Elements of near Earth Osculating Conic** | |
| $V_H$, meters/second | 3,899.0183 |
| $\bar{S}$ $S_1$ | - 0.3462 3581 |
| $S_2$ | 0.5992 8966 |
| $S_3$ | 0.7217 8437 |

Table 2. Examples of the Partial Derivatives

$$\frac{\partial V_C}{\partial R}$$

| $\bar{R}$ \ $\bar{V}_C$ | $V_{CX}$ | $V_{CY}$ | $V_{CZ}$ | dimensions |
|---|---|---|---|---|
| X | - .548336 | - .834894 | .418185 | $10^{-3}$ $sec^{-1}$ |
| Y | - .834894 | 1.012243 | -.564638 | $10^{-3}$ $sec^{-1}$ |
| Z | .418185 | - .564638 | 1.307817 | $10^{-3}$ $sec^{-1}$ |

TABLE 3

EXAMPLES OF VARIATIONS IN INJECTION CONDITIONS

| $\delta\bar{R}$ \ $\delta\bar{V}$ | $\delta\dot{X}$ | $\delta\dot{Y}$ | $\delta\dot{Z}$ | dimensions |
|---|---|---|---|---|
| δX = + 100 KM | -54.8467 | -82.2127 | 40.3034 | m/sec |
| δX = - 100 KM | 54.7843 | 84.8061 | -43.4008 | m/sec |
| δY = + 100 KM | -84.5169 | 99.1764 | -55.2950 | m/sec |
| δY = - 100 KM | 82.4034 | -103.2724 | 57.6365 | m/sec |
| δZ = + 100 KM | 40.0988 | - 57.0855 | 131.1385 | m/sec |
| δZ = - 100 KM | -43.5038 | 55.8181 | -130.3827 | m/sec |

## References

1. Seifert, H., Space Technology, Wiley, 1959.

2. Ehricke, K., Space Flight, Van Nostrand, 1960.

3. Herrick, S., Astrodynamics.

4. Clarke, V. C., Design of Lunar and Interplanetary Ascent Trajectories, JPL T.R. 32-30.

5. Mickelwait, A.B., Tompkins, E.H., Park, R.A., Three Dimensional Interplanetary Trajectories, Transactions of the I.R.E. MIL-3.

6. Moekel, W. E., Departure Trajectories for Interplanetary Vehicles, NASA TN D - 80, November 1959

# THE PROBLEM OF SATELLITE NAVIGATION BY USE OF A DOPPLER RECEIVER

Otto R. Spies
Burroughs Research Center
Paoli, Pennsylvania

## Abstract

A vehicle receives complete orbit data transmitted on a constant frequency by a "Transit"-type satellite, measures the Doppler shift of the transmitted frequency due to the satellite's motion relative to it, and uses this information to compute its own position.

This paper presents two methods of position determination which utilize fully the a priori knowledge of kinematic relations among the constituents of this navigational system. One method uses the cumulative Doppler shift, accurately measured by pulse-counting techniques, and requires relatively few computer operations. Its accuracy depends largely on that of the orbit data and of the process of computation.

## Introduction

The navigational problem of determining the geographic location of a vehicle by using currently acquired information regarding the motion of an artificial satellite has been successfully solved by the Transit system:

The satellite transmits on a known carrier frequency values of the parameters of its orbit from which its motion relative to Earth can be computed. The vehicle receives this information and, in addition, measures the Doppler shift of the transmitted frequency due to the satellite's motion relative to it. The frequency shift and the radial component of the satellite velocity relative to the vehicle are, with a negligibly small error, proportional to each other; specifically:

$$\dot{\rho}(t) = \lambda_o \left[ f_R(t) - f_o \right] \tag{1}$$

where:

| | | | |
|---|---|---|---|
| $\dot{\rho}(t)$ | – radial component of satellite velocity relative to vehicle | | |
| $f_R(t)$ | – received frequency | | |
| $f_o$ | – frequency | } | of radiation transmitted |
| $\lambda_o = c/f_o$ | – wave length | } | by satellite |
| $c$ | – speed of light | | |

Both, the received and the measured data are used to compute the vehicle's position relative to Earth by methods calling for highly redundant information and requiring a large number of computer operations.

The present study was undertaken in the belief that the effectiveness of this navigational system can be increased by the use of methods of position determination which fully utilize the a priori knowledge of kinematic relations among the constituents of that system.

Two such methods are presented in this paper: The first, "differential", method makes use of concepts of differential geometry. The second, "integral", method - utilizes the cumulative Doppler shift, which can be measured with a high accuracy by pulse-counting techniques.

Both methods require data relating to only four appropriately spaced satellite positions, the second calling for relatively few computer operations.

In conclusion the accuracy of these methods and its improvement by the use of repetitive techniques is discussed briefly.

## Part A: "Differential" Method

We consider, first, the ideal case in which $\bar{r}_o(t)$ and $\dot{\rho}\,(t)$ are precisely known continuous functions of time, $t$.

Given: Orbit of satellite, $\bar{r}_o(t)$, relative to Earth

Radial component, $\dot{\rho}\,(t)$, of satellite velocity, $\bar{v}(t)$, relative to position, $\bar{R}$, of Doppler receiver

Find: Position, $\bar{R}$, of Doppler receiver relative to Earth

Introduce a Cartesian frame fixed to Earth: origin, $O$, at Earth's center of mass; positive $z$-axis pointing towards its north pole, positive $x$-axis lying in the $0^o$ meridian plane, and the positive $y$-axis - in the $90^o$ meridian plane ($\equiv 90^o$ east longitude).

The known coordinates of the satellite in this frame are: $x_o \equiv x_o(t)$, $y_o \equiv y_o(t)$, $z_o \equiv z_o(t)$, so that

$$r_o \equiv |\bar{r}_o(t)| = \sqrt{x_o^2 + y_o^2 + z_o^2}\,, \tag{2}$$

the unknown coordinates of the Doppler receiver being:

$X$ = constant, $Y$ = constant, $Z$ = constant.

The unknown distance of the satellite from the Doppler receiver is then:

$$\rho \equiv |\bar{\rho}(t)| = \sqrt{(x_o - X)^2 + (y_o - Y)^2 + (z_o - Z)^2} \tag{3}$$

In addition, introduce a "local" Cartesian frame: origin, $o$, at the satellite's center of mass, positive $\xi$-axis being tangent to the satellite's orbit, positive $\eta$-axis lying in the direction of the principal normal to the orbit, and positive $\zeta$-axis - in the direction of its binormal (see Fig.1)

Since the orbit, $\bar{r}_0(t)$, is known, we know at any instant, $t$, the element of arc, $ds$, of the trajectory, the velocity, $\bar{v}(t) \equiv \dot{\bar{r}}_0(t)$, of the satellite, and its acceleration, $\bar{a}(t) \equiv \ddot{\bar{r}}(t)$. The satellite's speed is:

$$v \equiv |\bar{v}(t)| = \sqrt{\dot{x}_o^2 + \dot{y}_o^2 + \dot{z}_o^2} \tag{4}$$

and the direction of its displacement is defined by the tangent unit vector, $\bar{\xi} = d\bar{r}_0/ds$, whose components are the direction cosines:

$$\cos\alpha = \frac{dx}{ds}, \quad \cos\beta = \frac{dy}{ds}, \quad \cos\gamma = \frac{dz}{ds} \tag{5}$$

The direction of the principal normal, $\eta$, is defined by the normal unit vector, $\bar{\eta} = d\bar{\xi}/ds$, whose components are the direction cosines:

$$\cos l = \frac{1}{k}\frac{d^2x}{ds^2}, \quad \cos m = \frac{1}{k}\frac{d^2y}{ds^2}, \quad \cos n = \frac{1}{k}\frac{d^2z}{ds^2} \tag{6}$$

where:

$$k \equiv \sqrt{\left(\frac{d^2x}{ds^2}\right)^2 + \left(\frac{d^2y}{ds^2}\right)^2 + \left(\frac{d^2z}{ds^2}\right)^2} \tag{7}$$

is the orbit's curvature.

Last, the direction of the binormal, $\zeta$, is defined by the binormal unit vector, $\bar{\zeta} = \bar{\xi} \times \bar{\eta}$, whose components are the direction cosines:

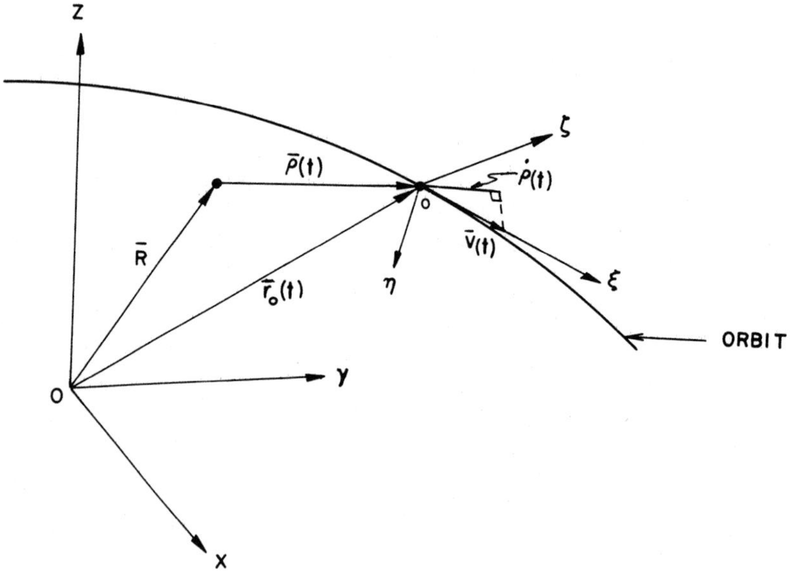


Fig. 1

$$\left.\begin{aligned} \cos\lambda &= \frac{1}{k}\left(\frac{dy}{ds}\frac{d^2z}{ds^2} - \frac{dz}{ds}\frac{d^2y}{ds^2}\right) \\ \cos\mu &= \frac{1}{k}\left(\frac{dz}{ds}\frac{d^2x}{ds^2} - \frac{dx}{ds}\frac{d^2z}{ds^2}\right) \\ \cos\nu &= \frac{1}{k}\left(\frac{dx}{ds}\frac{d^2y}{ds^2} - \frac{dy}{ds}\frac{d^2x}{ds^2}\right) \end{aligned}\right\} \tag{8}$$

Thus, at any instant, $t$, the position of the local frame relative to the fixed frame is specified by the coordinates, $x_o(t)$, $y_o(t)$, $z_o(t)$, of its origin, $o$, and by the matrix of direction cosines:

$$S \equiv \begin{Vmatrix} \cos\alpha & \cos\beta & \cos\gamma \\ \cos l & \cos m & \cos n \\ \cos\lambda & \cos\mu & \cos\nu \end{Vmatrix} \quad [S^{-1} \equiv S_t] \tag{9}$$

Any point, $P$, having coordinates, $\xi$, $\eta$, $\zeta$, in the local frame can then be specified in terms of the coordinates, $x$, $y$, $z$, of the fixed frame:

$$\begin{Vmatrix} \xi \\ \eta \\ \zeta \end{Vmatrix} = \begin{Vmatrix} \cos\alpha & \cos\beta & \cos\gamma \\ \cos l & \cos m & \cos n \\ \cos\lambda & \cos\mu & \cos\nu \end{Vmatrix} \cdot \begin{Vmatrix} x - x_o \\ y - y_o \\ z - z_o \end{Vmatrix} . \tag{10}$$

The Doppler receiver measures the radial component, $\dot{\rho}(t)$, of the satellite velocity, $\bar{v}(t)$. Denoting by $\bar{e}_\rho$ the unit vector in the direction of the unknown vector, $\bar{\rho}(t) = \bar{\rho}_o(t) - \bar{R}$, so that $\bar{\rho}(t) = \bar{e}_\rho(t) \cdot \rho(t)$, $\dot{\rho}(t)$ may be specified by the dot product

$$\dot{\rho}(t) = \bar{e}_\rho(t) \cdot \bar{v}(t) = v(t)\cos\delta(t), \tag{11}$$

where $\delta(t)$ is the angle between the known direction, $\bar{\xi}$, of $\bar{v}$ and the unknown direction, $\bar{e}_\rho$. Since $v(t)$ is known and $\dot{\rho}(t)$ is measured, we have at any instant $t$:

$$\cos\delta(t) = \frac{\dot{\rho}(t)}{v(t)} \tag{12}$$

Thus, a measured value of $\dot{\rho}(t)$ in conjunction with the known value of the satellite speed, $v(t)$, provides the information that the position of the Doppler receiver at the instant $t$ lies on a circular half-cone whose apex is at the known satellite position, $\overline{r}_o(t)$, whose axis is collinear with the orbit's tangent unit vector, $\overline{\xi}$ , and whose half-angle is $\delta(t)$. Evidently, the unknown vector $\overline{\rho}(t)$ is collinear with a generatrix of that half-cone.

The satellite speed, $v(t)$, is never negative, so that $\cos\,\delta(t)$ is positive, when $\dot{\rho}(t)$ is positive, that is, when the distance, $\rho \equiv |\overline{\rho}(t)|$, increases with time, and the range of $\delta$ is $[\pi/2 \geq \delta \geq 0]$ . For the same reason, $\cos\,\delta(t)$ is negative, when $\dot{\rho}(t)$ is negative, that is, when the distance, $\rho$, decreases with time and the range of $\delta$ is $[\pi \geq \delta > \pi/2]$. In the special case when $\dot{\rho} = 0$, $\cos\,\delta(t) = 0$, so that $\delta = \pi/2$, and the circular half-cone degenerates into a plane at right angles to the tangent unit vector $\overline{\xi}$. Evidently, in this special case the satellite velocity vector, $\overline{v}(t)$, is normal to the vector, $\overline{\rho}(t)$, so that the position, $\overline{R}$, of the Doppler receiver is contained in that plane.

Every circular half-cone is a member of a family and may be specified in terms of coordinates, $\xi$, $\eta$, $\zeta$, referring to the local frame by the equation:

$$\xi + \sqrt{\xi^2 + \eta^2 + \zeta^2} \cdot \cos\,\delta = 0 \qquad [\pi \geq \delta \geq 0] \tag{13}$$

or, using Eq. (12), by:

$$\xi + \sqrt{\xi^2 + \eta^2 + \zeta^2} \cdot \frac{\dot{\rho}}{v} = 0 \qquad [-v \leqq \dot{\rho} \leqq +v] \tag{14}$$

Eq. (14) shows that, when $\dot{\rho}$ is positive, the circular half-cone "flares-out" in the direction of the negative $\xi$-axis and when $\dot{\rho}$ is negative it "flares out" in the direction of the positive $\xi$-axis. In the special case when $\dot{\rho} = 0$, the second term vanishes and Eq. (14) reduces to:

$$\xi = 0\,, \qquad \left[\delta = \frac{\pi}{2}\,,\ \text{that is,}\ \dot{\rho} = 0\right] \tag{15}$$

representing the plane containing the (principal) normal unit vector, $\overline{\eta}$ and the binormal unit vector, $\overline{\zeta}$ .

Each circular half-cone is specified in terms of coordinates, $x$, $y$, $z$, referring to the fixed frame by an equation obtained from the above by the coordinate transformation given in Eq. (10):

$$\cos\alpha\,(x - x_o) + \cos\beta\,(y - y_o) + \cos\gamma\,(z - z_o) + \sqrt{(x - x_o)^2 + (y - y_o)^2 + (z - z_o)^2} \cdot \frac{\dot{\rho}}{v} = 0 \qquad [-v \leqq \dot{\rho} \leqq +v] \tag{16}$$

When $\dot{\rho} = 0$, this reduces to:

$$\cos \alpha_o (x - x_{oo}) + \cos \beta_o (y - y_{oo}) + \cos \gamma_o (z - z_{oo}) = 0, \qquad (17)$$

where the subscript, $o$, is used to indicate the specific values, $x_{oo}$, $y_{oo}$, $z_{oo}$ of the satellite's position coordinates, $x_o$, $y_o$, $z_o$ referring to the fixed frame and the specific values, $\cos \alpha_o$, $\cos \beta_o$, $\cos \gamma_o$, of the direction cosines specifying the direction of the $\xi$-axis of the local frame relative to the fixed frame at the instant, $t = t_o$, at which $\dot{\rho} = 0$.

Since the position, $\bar{R}$ of the Doppler receiver is contained in every one of the circular half-cones, including the plane passing through the satellite position, $\bar{r}_{oo}$, it lies at the common locus of intersection of all members of the family of circular half-cones. In the ideal case under consideration, this locus is defined precisely by the common intersection of any four members of this family. To simplify the algebraic expressions, it is convenient to include the above plane among these four.

The locus of intersection of any one of the circular half-cones with the above plane lies both on that half-cone and on that plane and, hence, satisfies the equations of both simultaneously. Thus, we have:

$$\left.\begin{aligned} &\cos \alpha (x - x_o) + \cos \beta (y - y_o) + \cos \gamma (z - z_o) + \\ &\qquad \sqrt{(x - x_o)^2 + (y - y_o)^2 + (z - z_o)^2} \cdot \frac{\dot{\rho}}{v} = 0 \\ &\cos \alpha_o (x - x_{oo}) + \cos \beta_o (y - y_{oo}) + \cos \gamma_o (z - z_{oo}) = 0 \end{aligned}\right\} \qquad (18)$$

We may eliminate any one of the three unknowns, $x$, $y$, $z$, obtaining a functional relationship between the remaining two. Since the symmetry of both equations is destroyed by such a procedure, the resulting expressions is quite awkward.

It is more advantageous to specify all circular half-cones in a frame of reference in which the equation of the plane intersected by these cones assumes its simplest form, namely, the special local frame at the satellite position, $\bar{r}_{oo}$. Using the subscript, $o$, to distinguish the coordinates, $\xi_o$ $\eta_o$ $\zeta_o$, referring to this local frame from those referring to any one of the other local frames whose origin, $o$, is at some satellite position $\bar{r}_o$, other than $\bar{r}_{oo}$, the equation of the special plane may be rewritten as

$$\xi_o = 0 \qquad (19)$$

The coordinates, $\xi$, $\eta$, $\zeta$, referring to a local frame whose origin,

$o$, is at the position, $\bar{r}_o$, relative to the fixed frame are related to the coordinates, $\xi_o$, $\eta_o$, $\zeta_o$, referring to the special local frame whose origin is at the position, $\bar{r}_{oo}$, relative to the fixed frame, as follows:

$$\begin{Vmatrix} \xi \\ \eta \\ \zeta \end{Vmatrix} = \begin{Vmatrix} \cos \widehat{\xi\xi_o} & \cos \widehat{\xi\eta_o} & \cos \widehat{\xi\zeta_o} \\ \cos \widehat{\eta\xi_o} & \cos \widehat{\eta\eta_o} & \cos \widehat{\eta\zeta_o} \\ \cos \widehat{\zeta\xi_o} & \cos \widehat{\zeta\eta_o} & \cos \widehat{\zeta\zeta_o} \end{Vmatrix} \cdot \begin{Vmatrix} \xi_{oo} - \xi_o \\ \eta_{oo} - \eta_o \\ \zeta_{oo} - \zeta_o \end{Vmatrix} \tag{20}$$

where:

$$\begin{Vmatrix} \xi_{oo} \\ \eta_{oo} \\ \zeta_{oo} \end{Vmatrix} = \begin{Vmatrix} \cos \alpha_o & \cos \beta_o & \cos \gamma_o \\ \cos l_o & \cos m_o & \cos n_o \\ \cos \lambda_o & \cos \mu_o & \cos \nu_o \end{Vmatrix} \cdot \begin{Vmatrix} x_o - x_{oo} \\ y_o - y_{oo} \\ z_o - z_{oo} \end{Vmatrix} \tag{21}$$

and where:

$$\begin{Vmatrix} \cos \widehat{\xi\xi_o} & \cos \widehat{\xi\eta_o} & \cos \widehat{\xi\zeta_o} \\ \cos \widehat{\eta\xi_o} & \cos \widehat{\eta\eta_o} & \cos \widehat{\eta\zeta_o} \\ \cos \widehat{\zeta\xi_o} & \cos \widehat{\zeta\eta_o} & \cos \widehat{\zeta\zeta_o} \end{Vmatrix} = \begin{Vmatrix} \cos \alpha & \cos \beta & \cos \gamma \\ \cos l & \cos m & \cos n \\ \cos \lambda & \cos \mu & \cos \nu \end{Vmatrix} \cdot \begin{Vmatrix} \cos \alpha_o & \cos l_o & \cos \lambda_o \\ \cos \beta_o & \cos m_o & \cos \mu_o \\ \cos \gamma_o & \cos n_o & \cos \nu_o \end{Vmatrix} \tag{22}$$

The mutual positions and orientations of the fixed frame, a local frame (origin at $\bar{r}_o$) and the special local frame (origin at $\bar{r}_{oo}$) are shown in Fig. 2.

Substituting for $\xi$, $\eta$, $\zeta$ in Eq. (14) their expressions in terms of the coordinates, $\xi_o$, $\eta_o$, $\zeta_o$, of the special local frame we obtain:

$$\left. \begin{aligned} &\cos \widehat{\xi\xi_o} (\xi_{oo} - \xi_o) + \cos \widehat{\xi\eta_o} (\eta_{oo} - \eta_o) + \cos \widehat{\xi\zeta_o} (\zeta_{oo} - \zeta_o) + \\ &\sqrt{(\xi_{oo} - \xi_o)^2 + (\eta_{oo} - \eta_o)^2 + (\zeta_{oo} - \zeta_o)^2} \cdot \frac{\dot{\rho}}{v} = 0 \end{aligned} \right\} \tag{23}$$

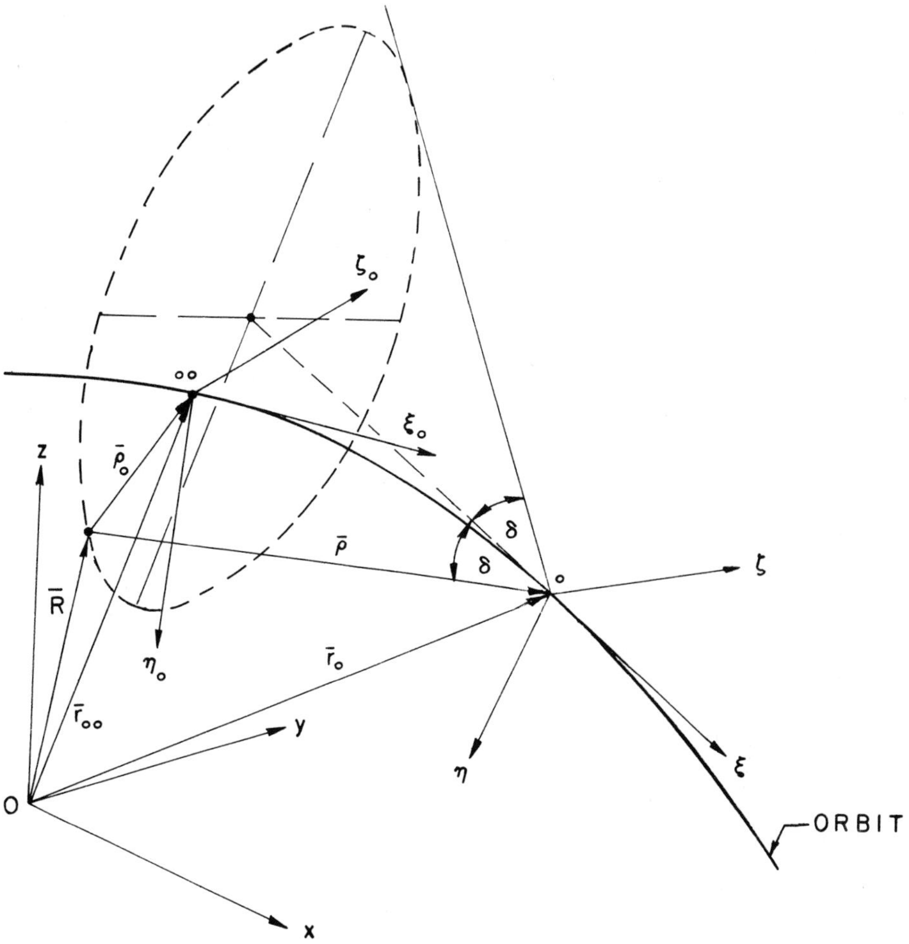


Fig. 2

It should be noted that, in order to obtain this equation in terms of the coordinates $\xi_o$ , $\eta_o$ , $\zeta_o$ referring to the special local frame, it is sufficient to determine merely the coordinates, $\xi_{oo}$ , $\eta_{oo}$, $\zeta_{oo}$, of the origin, $o$, of the local frame relative to the special local frame and the expression for the coordinate, $\xi$ , of the local frame in terms of the coordinates, $\xi_o$ , $\eta_o$ , $\xi_o$, of the special local frame. The corresponding expressions for the coordinates, $\eta$ and $\zeta$, of the local frame are not required.

This stems from the fact that in the second term of the equation of the half-cone a purely quadratic form of the coordinates is present, which is transformed into such a form in any orthogonal transformation.

This fact has the practical advantage that only three direction cosines need be computed, each of which is the sum of three products: a total of 9 multiplications, as against 27 multiplications in the general case.

The equation specifying the intersection of any circular half-cone with the special plane, $\xi_o = 0$, is now obtained simply by deleting, $\xi_o$ , in Eq. (23), giving:

$$\left.\begin{aligned} &\cos \widehat{\xi\xi_o}\, \xi_{oo} + \cos \widehat{\xi\eta_o}\, (\eta_{oo} - \eta_o) + \cos \widehat{\xi\xi_o}\, (\zeta_{oo} - \zeta_o) + \\ &\sqrt{\xi_{oo}^2 + (\eta_{oo} - \eta_o)^2 + (\zeta_{oo} - \zeta_o)^2} \cdot \frac{\dot{\rho}}{v} = 0 \end{aligned}\right\} \qquad (24)$$

Transferring the second term to the right side, squaring both sides and collecting terms we have:

$$\left.\begin{aligned} &\left(\cos^2 \widehat{\xi\xi_o} - \frac{\dot{\rho}^2}{v^2}\right)\xi_{oo}^2 + 2 \cos \widehat{\xi\xi_o} \cos \widehat{\xi\eta_o}\, \xi_{oo} (\eta_{oo} - \eta_o) + \\ &\left(\cos^2 \widehat{\xi\eta_o} - \frac{\dot{\rho}^2}{v^2}\right)(\eta_{oo} - \eta_o)^2 + 2 \cos \widehat{\xi\eta_o} \cos \widehat{\xi\zeta_o} (\eta_{oo} - \eta_o)(\zeta_{oo} - \zeta_o) + \\ &\left(\cos^2 \widehat{\xi\zeta_o} - \frac{\dot{\rho}^2}{v^2}\right)(\zeta_{oo} - \zeta_o)^2 + 2 \cos \widehat{\xi\zeta_o} \cos \widehat{\xi\xi_o}\, (\zeta_{oo} - \zeta_o)\, \xi_{oo} = 0 \end{aligned}\right\} \qquad (25)$$

Eq. (25), which can be simplified further by carrying out the squaring operations and collecting terms once more, represents an ellipse lying in the special plane, $\xi = 0$, whose center is displaced from the origin, $\eta_o = 0$ , $\zeta_o = 0$ , in that plane, and whose principal axes are rotated with respect to the $\eta_o$- and $\zeta_o$-axes.

The ellipse of intersection of any specific circular half-cone, corresponding to a specific position, $\bar{r}_o$, of the satellite is obtained from this equation by using the specific values of $\xi_{oo}$, $\eta_{oo}$, $\zeta_{oo}$, $\cos\widehat{\xi\xi_o}$, $\cos\widehat{\xi\eta_o}$, $\cos\widehat{\xi\zeta_o}$, $v$, and $\dot{\rho}$ corresponding to this satellite position.

Any two such specific ellipses will, in the general case, mutually intersect in two distinct points lying in the special plane. Any third specific elipse will, in the general case, intersect both of the former in one of these two points, but its second points of intersection with either of the former two ellipses will be distinct among themselves as well as from the second point of intersection of the former two ellipses.

To determine these points analytically, we must solve two sets of simultaneous quadratic equations, the first set representing the first and the second ellipse of intersection, the second set - the first and the third, or the second and the third, ellipse of intersection. Either set of equations has two solutions, both sets have one of these solutions in common. This triple point of intersection lying in the special plane, having the special local coordinates, $0$, $\eta_{oR}$, $\zeta_{oR}$, say, specifies the position, $\bar{R}_o$ of the Doppler receiver relative to the special local frame. Its position, $\bar{R}$, relative to the fixed frame is then obtained by expressing its coordinates, $X$, $Y$, $Z$, referring to that frame in terms of the coordinates, $\xi_o$, $\eta_o$, $\zeta_o$, of the special local. We have specifically:

$$\left\| \begin{matrix} X \\ Y \\ Z \end{matrix} \right\| = \left\| \begin{matrix} x_{oo} \\ y_{oo} \\ z_{oo} \end{matrix} \right\| + \left\| \begin{matrix} \cos\alpha_o & \cos l_o & \cos\lambda_o \\ \cos\beta_o & \cos m_o & \cos\mu_o \\ \cos\gamma_o & \cos n_o & \cos\nu_o \end{matrix} \right\| \cdot \left\| \begin{matrix} 0 \\ \eta_{oR} \\ \zeta_{oR} \end{matrix} \right\| \qquad (26)$$

Note that in this transformation only 6 rather than 9 multiplications are required since $\xi_{oR} = 0$.

Note also that in the above procedure the position of the Doppler receiver is determined relative to the known orbit of the satellite, so that it is unnecessary to assume that it is confined to a spheroidal, ellipsoidal, or pear-shaped Earth's surface. On the contrary, the position of the satellite's orbit relative to the fixed reference frame being known, this procedure can be employed to determine the actual shape of the Earth's surface by making measurements of $\dot{\rho}$ from a grid of suitably spaced "sampling positions" on that surface. Similarly, the actual shape of the oceans' surface as it varies with time (lunar tides, solar tides, etc.) can be determined by making simultaneous measurements of $\dot{\rho}$ from such a grid of water-borne sampling positions. Its primary purpose of serving as a navigational aid may readily be combined with the latter task, inasmuch as the instantaneous positions of all vessels using this navigational aid form such a grid, though not the most suitable one.

The task of expressing the Doppler receiver's position, $\bar{R}(t)$, relative to the fixed frame in terms of longitude and latitude involves a trivial, time-invariant coordinate transformation.

In the above derivation of the procedure required to solve the stated problem the satellite's orbit was assumed to be a space curve possessing double curvature which may be characterized at every satellite position by both its (principal) curvature and its torsion. Its smallest radius of curvature is larger than the shortest distance, $\rho_o \equiv |\bar{\rho}_o|$, between the Doppler receiver's position, $\bar{R}$, and the position, $\bar{r}_{oo}$, of the origin of the special local frame. Hence, in the present instance, the possibility of there being more than one satellite position at which $\dot{\rho} = 0$ is excluded.

Two special cases may be of more than academic interest: In the first, the satellite's orbit is confined to a single plane, in the second - it is a single straight line.

In the first case, the torsion of the orbit is equal to zero and the binormals of all local frames are mutually parallel. In consequence, the values of the $\zeta$-coordinates of all local frames are mutually equal and the direction-cosine matrix of the transformation of coordinates referring to any given local frame to those referring to any other local frame, e.g., the special one, reduces to that of a plane rotation. The axes of all circular half-cones ($\equiv$ the $\xi$-axes of the corresponding local frames) lie in the plane to which the trajectory is confined, so that all half-cones are symmetrical about this plane. As a result, the major axis of the ellipse of intersection of every one of the circular half-cones with the plane, $\xi_o = 0$, of the special local frame is collinear with the $\eta_o$-axis of that frame. The two points in which the ellipses of intersection of any two circular half-cones with the special plane mutually intersect are symmetrically placed about the plane to which the trajectory is confined. Evidently, in this, first, special case the position, $\bar{R}$, of the Doppler receiver is defined precisely, but ambivalently, by the common intersection of any three members of the family of circular half-cones, among which the special plane is conveniently included. (Fig.3). The ambivalent determination of the position, $\bar{R}$, of the Doppler receiver in this special, plane-symmetric, case is an inherent feature of the present procedure. This position can be determined uniquely only when $\bar{R}$ lies in the plane of symmetry to which the satellite's orbit is confined. In this event, the common locus of intersection of all circular half-cones with the special plane reduces to a common point of tangency lying on the $\eta_o$ -axis of the special local frame (Fig.4). In the second special case, the $\xi$-axes of all local frames are collinear and both the normal and the binormal of all local frames are mutually parallel (their direction in planes at right angles to the straight orbit is now arbitrary). The coordinate transformation from any one local frame to any other is now specified by the distance between their origins only. Thus, all circular half-cones are coaxial and their common locus of intersection with the special plane is a circle lying in that plane and passing through the position, $\bar{R}$, of the Doppler receiver. Hence, in this special case, this position is defined precisely, but multivalently, by the common intersection of any two members of the family of circular half-cones, one of which may be the special plane. Evidently, the position, $\bar{R}$, of the Doppler receiver relative to the special local frame is now known only to the extent that its distance, $\rho_o \equiv |\rho_o|$, from the origin, $\bar{r}_{oo}$, of this local frame is precisely specified by the radius of the circle of intersection of any circular half-cone with the special plane, the specific point of this circle at which, $\bar{R}$, is located remaining unknown. In this axi-symmetric case, the locus of possible positions $\bar{R}$, of the Doppler receiver is axi-symmetric and the multivalent determination of this position is an inherent feature of the present procedure.

Thus, in both special cases supplementary information regarding the position, $\bar{R}$, of the Doppler receiver is required to determine it uniquely. (E.g. use two satellites whose orbits do not lie in a single plane. An independent measurement of the distance of the satellite from the Doppler receiver provides merely redundant information, as this distance is determined by the present procedure in both special cases.)

The use of the local frame at the satellite position, $\bar{r}_{oo}$, at which $\dot{\rho} = 0$, as the special local frame resulting in a simplification of the analytic expressions specifying the locus of intersection of the circular half-cones is a matter of convenience only. Generally, any local frame may be used as the special local frame. In this case, the common locus of intersection of any three circular half-cones with the special half-cone fixed in that frame lies on that special half-cone.

Denoting the coordinates referring to this more general type of special local frame by $\xi_o'$ , $\eta_o'$ , $\zeta_o'$ , we can specify the special circular half-cone fixed in that frame by the equation:

$$\xi_o' + \sqrt{\xi_o'^2 + \eta_o'^2 + \zeta_o'^2} \cdot \frac{\dot{\rho}'}{v'} = 0 \qquad (27)$$

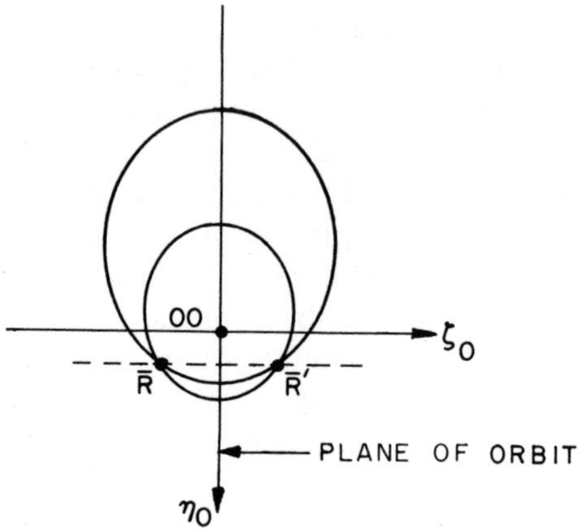
OO
$\zeta_0$
$\bar{R}$
$\bar{R}'$
PLANE OF ORBIT
$\eta_0$

Fig. 3

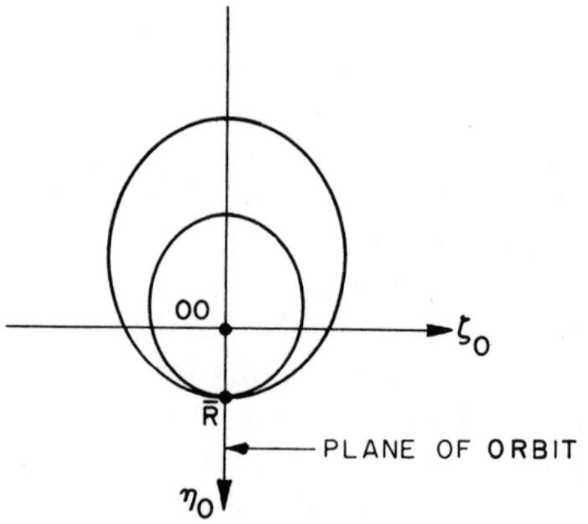
OO
$\zeta_0$
$\bar{R}$
PLANE OF ORBIT
$\eta_0$

Fig. 4

where: $\dot{\rho}'/v' \equiv \cos\delta'$ is a known constant, $\dot{\rho}'$ being the measured radial component of the known velocity, $\bar{v}'$, of the satellite at the position, $\bar{r}_o'$, at which the origin, $o'$, of the special local frame is located, and $v' \equiv |\bar{v}'|$ is the known speed of the satellite at that position.

The locus of intersection of any other circular half-cone with the special half-cone is specified by the set of two simultaneous quadratic equations

$$\left.\begin{aligned} &\xi_o' + \sqrt{\xi_o'^2 + \eta_o'^2 + \zeta_o'^2} \cdot \frac{\dot{\rho}'}{v'} = 0 \\ &\cos\widehat{\xi\xi_o'}(\xi_{oo}' - \xi_o') + \cos\widehat{\xi\eta_o'}(\eta_{oo}' - \eta_o') + \cos\widehat{\xi\zeta_o'}(\zeta_{oo}' - \zeta_o') + \\ &\qquad \sqrt{(\xi_{oo}' - \xi_o')^2 + (\eta_{oo}' - \eta_o')^2 + (\zeta_{oo}' - \zeta_o')^2} \cdot \frac{\dot{\rho}}{v} = 0 \end{aligned}\right\} \quad (28)$$

Here $\xi_{oo}'$, $\eta_{oo}'$, $\zeta_{oo}'$, are the coordinates, referring to the special local frame, of the origin, $o$, of the local frame at the satellite position, $\bar{r}_o$ and the direction-cosines, $\cos\widehat{\xi\xi_o'}$, $\cos\widehat{\xi\eta_o'}$, $\cos\widehat{\xi\zeta_o'}$, are those of the $\xi$-axis of that local frame relative to the $\xi_o'$-, $\eta_o'$-, and $\zeta_o'$-axis, respectively, of the special local frame. Evidently, the transformation of coordinates referring to any local frame to those referring to the more general type of special local frame is of the same form as that given in Eqs. (22) to (24).

Now, however, the locus of intersection of the two circular half-cones is a space-curve lying on the special half-cone.

Proceeding analogously as in the originally considered case, we obtain the two space-curves of intersection of any two other circular half-cones with the special half-cone which also lie on that special half-cone. Each such locus of intersection is specified by the set of two simultaneous quadratic equations of the form of Eq. (28), formed by the equation of the special half-cone and that of either of the other two circular half-cones. In all, we have four quadratic equations forming 3! = 6 pairs of simultaneous ones. Each such pair defines a space-curve of intersection of the respective pair of circular half-cones. Of these, only those three which lie on the special half-cone are of direct interest. Analogously as in the originally considered case, any pair of space-curves lying on the special half-cone mutually intersect in two distinct points lying on the special half-cone. All three space-curves have but one common point of intersection lying on the special half-cone, the remaining three points of intersection being distinct from the common one and among themselves.

This common point of intersection specifies the position, $\overline{R}_o$, of the Doppler receiver relative to the special local frame and its position, $\overline{R}$, relative to the fixed frame is obtained by expressing its coordinates, X, Y, Z, referring to that frame in terms of the coordinates, $\xi_o'$, $\eta_o'$, $\zeta_o'$, referring to the special local frame, by a transformation of the same form as Eq. (26). In contrast with the originally considered case, this transformation requires 9 rather than 6 multiplications, since in the present, more general, case, $\xi_o' \neq 0$.

The ambivalence and multivalence of determination of the position, $\overline{R}$, of the Doppler receiver in the special cases when the satellite's orbit is confined, respectively, to a single plane or to a single straight line, obviously exists also when the more general type of special local frame is used.

The problem of determining analytically, the common point of intersection of three ellipses in the special plane and of that of three space-curves lying on the special half-cone remains to be investigated in detail.

It appears off-hand that the second problem can be reduced to a problem involving but two, rather than three, unknowns by introducing, e.g., spherical coordinates in the special local frame, in terms of which the special half-cone is specified by the equation: $\delta = \delta' =$ const.

Similarly, the first problem may be simplified by using a simple strain of the coordinates $\eta_o$, $\zeta_o$, and a shift to a new origin, which reduces the equation of the first ellipse of intersection with the special plane, to that of a circle in terms of the strained coordinates referring to the new origin. This transformation transforms the second and third ellipses into ellipses specified in terms of the strained coordinates. A transformation to polar coordinates, referring to the new origin, reduces the equation of the circle to a constant radial coordinate. Thus, the points of intersection of the two ellipses with this circle are found by solving for the polar angle the equations of the two ellipses in terms of the polar coordinates in which the radial coordinate is replaced by that constant.

Since the circular half-cones at the successive satellite positions on its orbit form a continuous family of mutually intersecting surfaces, this family possesses an envelope. Its analytical description is obtained by differentiating the typical half-cone equation partially with respect to the arc-length parameter, $s$, measured along the satellite's orbit. The envelope is then represented by two parametric equations: the typical half-cone equation and the above equation derived from it.

The common point of intersection of all half-cones is a focal point of this envelope which may be determined from the equations representing it.

This may offer certain analytical advantages, which remain to be studied in detail.

## Part B: "Integral" Method

We consider the same problem and use the same notation as in Part A.

The function, $\dot{\rho}(t)$, specifying the radial component of the satellite velocity, $\bar{v}(t) \equiv \dot{\bar{r}}_o(t)$, relative to the position, $\bar{R}$, of the Doppler receiver is related to the function, $\bar{r}_o(t)$, specifying the satellite's orbit relative to the frame fixed to Earth as follows (Fig.5):

We have:

$$\bar{\rho}(t) = \bar{r}_o(t) - \bar{R}, \tag{29}$$

so that:

$$\rho(t) \equiv |\bar{\rho}(t)| = |\bar{r}_o(t) - \bar{R}| = + \sqrt{[x_o(t) - X]^2 + [y_o(t) - Y]^2 + [z_o(t) - Z]^2}, \tag{30}$$

whence:

$$\left.\begin{aligned} \dot{\rho}(t) &= \frac{d}{dt} \sqrt{[x_o(t) - X]^2 + [y_o(t) - Y]^2 + [z_o(t) - Z]^2} \\ &= \frac{[x_o(t) - X]\,\dot{x}_o(t) + [y_o(t) - Y]\,\dot{y}_o(t) + [z_o(t) - \dot{Z}]\,\dot{z}_o(t)}{\sqrt{[x_o(t) - X]^2 + [y_o(t) - Y]^2 + [z_o(t) - Z]^2}} \end{aligned}\right\} \tag{31}$$

Instead of using the measured values of $\dot{\rho}(t)$ directly in the determination of the unknown position, $\bar{R}$, of the Doppler receiver, as described in Part A, we can use the following alternative procedure:

We integrate the (ideally, continuous) sequence of measured values of $\dot{\rho}(t)$ with respect to $t$, beginning at some arbitrary position, $\bar{r}_s(t_s)$, of the satellite at the instant, $t = t_s$, and sample the values of this integral at a sequence of later instants, $t_i$ $[i = 1, 2 \ldots n]$, where $n$ is arbitrary. Thus, we have:

$$\left.\begin{aligned} \rho_i(t_i) &= \int_{t=t_s}^{t_i} \dot{\rho}(t)\,dt = \rho(t_i) - \rho_s(t_s) = \\ &\sqrt{(x_i(t_i) - X)^2 + (y_i(t_i) - Y)^2 + (z_i(t_i) - Z)^2} - \rho_s(t_s) \end{aligned}\right\} \tag{32}$$

so that:

$$\sqrt{(x_i - X)^2 + (y_i - Y)^2 + (z_i - Z)^2} = \rho_i + \rho_s \quad [i = 1, 2 \ldots n], \tag{33}$$

the unknown value of $\rho_s \equiv \rho_s(t_s)$ at the initial instant $t = t_s$ being given by:

$$\sqrt{(x_s - X)^2 + (y_s - Y)^2 + (z_s - Z)^2} = \rho_s \tag{34}$$

Since $\bar{r}_o(t) \equiv [x_o(t), y_o(t), z_o(t)]$ is known, the values of the satellite's position coordinates, $x_s, y_s, z_s$ and $x_i, y_i, z_i$ at the instants, $t_s$ and $t_i$ $[i = 1, 2, ., n]$, respectively, are known. The unknown quantities are: the initial distance, $\rho_s$, of the satellite from the unknown position, $\bar{R}$, of the Doppler receiver, and the latter's position coordinates, $X, Y, Z$.

Thus, to determine the four unknowns, $\rho_s$, $X, Y, Z$, we must know the values, $\rho_i$, of the above integral and the satellite's positions, $(x_i, y_i, z_i)$, at three instants, $t_i$, of time, in addition to its position, $(x_s, y_s, z_s)$, at the initial instant, $t_s$.. In all, then, we must know these quantities at four instants of time.

We use the four equations:

$$\left.\begin{aligned}
\sqrt{(x_s - X)^2 + (y_s - Y)^2 + (z_s - Z)^2} &= \rho_s \\
\sqrt{(x_1 - X)^2 + (y_1 - Y)^2 + (z_1 - Z)^2} &= \rho_1 + \rho_s \\
\sqrt{(x_2 - X)^2 + (y_2 - Y)^2 + (z_2 - Z)^2} &= \rho_2 + \rho_s \\
\sqrt{(x_3 - X)^2 + (y_3 - Y)^2 + (z_3 - Z)^2} &= \rho_3 + \rho_s
\end{aligned}\right\} \tag{35}$$

Each of Eqs. (35) represents a sphere, whose center lies at a point, $\bar{r}_s \equiv [x_s, y_s, z_s]$, or $\bar{r}_i \equiv [x_i, y_i, z_i]$ $[i = 1, 2, 3]$ of the satellite's orbit and whose radius is specified by that equation's right side.

In solving these four equations simultaneously, we may proceed as follows:

Introduce new position coordinates, $X'$, $Y'$, $Z'$, referring to a Cartesian frame whose origin lies at the known position, $\bar{r}_s$, of the satellite and whose axes are parallel to the axes of the fixed frame: Thus, we have

$$\left.\begin{aligned} X' &= X - x_s \\ Y' &= Y - y_s \\ Z' &= Z - z_s \end{aligned}\right\} \quad \therefore \quad \left\{\begin{aligned} X &= x_s + X' \\ Y &= y_s + Y' \\ Z &= z_s + Z' \end{aligned}\right. \tag{36}$$

and Eqs. (35) assume the form:

$$\left.\begin{aligned} \sqrt{X'^2 + Y'^2 + Z'^2} &= \rho_s \\ \sqrt{(x_1' - X')^2 + (y_1' - Y')^2 + (z_1' - Z')^2} &= \rho_1 + \rho_s \\ \sqrt{(x_2' - X')^2 + (y_2' - Y')^2 + (z_2' - Z')^2} &= \rho_2 + \rho_s \\ \sqrt{(x_3' - X')^2 + (y_3' - Y')^2 + (z_3' - Z')^2} &= \rho_3 + \rho_s \end{aligned}\right\} \tag{37}$$

where

$$\left.\begin{aligned} x_1' &= x_1 - x_s \qquad & x_2' &= x_2 - x_s \qquad & x_3' &= x_3 - x_s \\ y_1' &= y_1 - y_s \qquad & y_2' &= y_2 - y_s \qquad & y_3' &= y_3 - y_s \\ z_1' &= z_1 - z_s \qquad & z_2' &= z_2 - z_s \qquad & z_3' &= z_3 - z_s \end{aligned}\right\} \tag{38}$$

Squaring both sides of each Eqs. (37) and expanding the binomial terms, we have:

$$\left.\begin{aligned} X'^2 + Y'^2 + Z'^2 &= \rho_s^2 \\ x_1'^2 - 2x_1'X' + X'^2 + y_1'^2 - 2y_1'Y' + Y'^2 + z_1'^2 - 2z_1'Z' + Z'^2 &= \rho_1^2 + 2\rho_1\rho_s + \rho_s^2 \\ x_2'^2 - 2x_2'X' + X'^2 + y_2'^2 - 2y_2'Y' + Y'^2 + z_2'^2 - 2z_2'Z' + Z'^2 &= \rho_2^2 + 2\rho_2\rho_s + \rho_s^2 \\ x_3'^2 - 2x_3'X' + X'^2 + y_3'^2 - 2y_3'Y' + Y'^2 + z_3'^2 - 2z_3'Z' + Z'^2 &= \rho_3^2 + 2\rho_3\rho_s + \rho_s^2 \end{aligned}\right\} \tag{39}$$

or, upon collecting terms quadratic and linear in the unknowns, $X'$, $Y'$, $Z'$, $\rho_s$:

$$X'^2 + Y'^2 + Z'^2 - \rho_s^2 = 0$$

$$\left.\begin{aligned} (X'^2 + Y'^2 + Z'^2 - \rho_s^2) - 2(x_1'X' + y_1'Y' + z_1'Z' + \rho_1\rho_s) + (x_1'^2 + y_1'^2 + z_1'^2 - \rho_1^2) &= 0 \\ (X'^2 + Y'^2 + Z'^2 - \rho_s^2) - 2(x_2'X' + y_2'Y' + x_2'Z' + \rho_2\rho_s) + (x_2'^2 + y_2'^2 + z_2'^2 - \rho_2^2) &= 0 \\ (X'^2 + Y'^2 + Z'^2 - \rho_s^2) - 2(x_3'X' + y_3'Y' + z_3'Z' + \rho_3\rho_s) + (x_3'^2 + y_3'^2 + z_3'^2 - \rho_3^2) &= 0 \end{aligned}\right\} \tag{40}$$

According to the first of Eqs. (40), the first term of each of the other three is equal to zero and, thus, may be omitted. Hence, introducing the abbreviations:

$$\left.\begin{aligned} x_1'^2 + y_1'^2 + z_1'^2 &= r_1'^2 \\ x_2'^2 + y_2'^2 + z_2'^2 &= r_2'^2 \\ x_3'^2 + y_3'^2 + z_3'^2 &= r_3'^2 \end{aligned}\right\} \quad (41)$$

we can rewrite Eqs. (40) in the form:

$$\left.\begin{aligned} X'^2 + Y'^2 + Z'^2 &= \rho_s^2 \\ x_1' X' + y_1' Y' + z_1' Z' &= -\rho_s \rho_1 + \frac{1}{2}(r_1'^2 - \rho_1^2) \\ x_2' X' + y_2' Y' + z_2' Z' &= -\rho_s \rho_2 + \frac{1}{2}(r_2'^2 - \rho_2^2) \\ x_3' X' + y_3' Y' + z_3' Z' &= -\rho_s \rho_3 + \frac{1}{2}(r_3'^2 - \rho_3^2) \end{aligned}\right\} \quad (42)$$

The last three of Eqs. (42) form a system of linear equations in the three unknowns, $X'$, $Y'$, $Z'$, in which the fourth unknown, $\rho_s$, plays the role of a linear parameter. The solution of this system in explicit form is, by Cramer's rule:

$$\left.\begin{aligned} X'(\rho_s) &= -\frac{\rho_s P_x - \frac{1}{2} Q_x}{\Delta} \\ Y'(\rho_s) &= -\frac{\rho_s P_y - \frac{1}{2} Q_y}{\Delta} \\ Z'(\rho_s) &= -\frac{\rho_s P_z - \frac{1}{2} Q_z}{\Delta} \end{aligned}\right\} \quad (43)$$

where:

$$\left.\begin{aligned}
\Delta &\equiv \begin{vmatrix} x_1' & y_1' & z_1' \\ x_2' & y_2' & z_2' \\ x_3' & y_3' & z_3' \end{vmatrix} \\
P_x &\equiv \begin{vmatrix} \rho_1 & y_1' & z_1' \\ \rho_2 & y_2' & z_2' \\ \rho_3 & y_3' & z_3' \end{vmatrix} \qquad
Q_x \equiv \begin{vmatrix} (r_1'^2 - \rho_1^2) & y_1' & z_1' \\ (r_2'^2 - \rho_2^2) & y_2' & z_2' \\ (r_3'^2 - \rho_3^2) & y_3' & z_3' \end{vmatrix} \\
P_y &\equiv \begin{vmatrix} x_1' & \rho_1 & z_1' \\ x_2' & \rho_2 & z_2' \\ x_3' & \rho_3 & z_3' \end{vmatrix} \qquad
Q_y \equiv \begin{vmatrix} x_1' & (r_1'^2 - \rho_1^2) & z_1' \\ x_2' & (r_2'^2 - \rho_2^2) & z_2' \\ x_3' & (r_3'^2 - \rho_3^2) & z_3' \end{vmatrix} \\
P_z &\equiv \begin{vmatrix} x_1' & y_1' & \rho_1 \\ x_2' & y_2' & \rho_2 \\ x_3' & y_3' & \rho_3 \end{vmatrix} \qquad
Q_z \equiv \begin{vmatrix} x_1' & y_1' & (r_1'^2 - \rho_1^2) \\ x_2' & y_2' & (r_2'^2 - \rho_2^2) \\ x_3' & y_3' & (r_3'^2 - \rho_3^2) \end{vmatrix}
\end{aligned}\right\} \quad (44)$$

Substituting Eqs. (43) in the first of Eqs. (42), we, then, have :

$$\left.\begin{aligned}
&\Big[\rho_s^2 P_x^2 - \rho_s P_x Q_x + \frac{1}{4} Q_x^2 + \rho_s^2 P_y^2 - \rho_s P_y Q_y + \frac{1}{4} Q_y^2 + \\
&\qquad \rho_s^2 P_z^2 - \rho_s P_z Q_z + \frac{1}{4} Q_z^2\Big] \cdot \frac{1}{\Delta^2} = \rho_s^2
\end{aligned}\right\} \quad (45)$$

$$\left.\begin{aligned}
&\rho_s^2 (P_x^2 + P_y^2 + P_z^2 - \Delta^2) - \rho_s (P_x Q_x + P_y Q_y + P_z Q_z) + \\
&\qquad \frac{1}{4} (Q_x^2 + Q_y^2 + Q_z^2) = 0
\end{aligned}\right\} \quad (46)$$

The solutions of this quadratic equation in $\rho_s$ are:

$$\left.\begin{aligned}
\rho_s &= \frac{1}{2 (P_x^2 + P_y^2 + P_z^2 - \Delta^2)} \cdot \Big[(P_x Q_x + P_y Q_y + P_z Q_z) \pm \\
&\sqrt{(P_x Q_x + P_y Q_y + P_z Q_z)^2 - (Q_x^2 + Q_y^2 + Q_z^2)(P_x^2 + P_y^2 + P_z^2 - \Delta^2)}\Big]
\end{aligned}\right\} \quad (47)$$

Since $\rho_s$ is a distance, both solutions will be real and at-least-one of these must be positive. The question whether the case when both solutions are positive is possible within the limitations of the present problem has not, as yet, been investigated in detail. Off hand, it appears that even in that event the choice of the pertinent solution can be made on the basis of other criteria.

The value of $\rho_s$ being expressed in terms of known quantities only, we substitute it in Eqs. (43) and substitute these, in turn, in Eqs. (36) to obtain the values of the coordinates, $X$, $Y$, $Z$, of the position of the Doppler receiver referring to the frame, Oxyz, fixed to Earth.

$$\left.\begin{aligned} X &= x_s - \frac{\rho_s P_x - \frac{1}{2} Q_x}{\Delta} \\ Y &= y_s - \frac{\rho_s P_y - \frac{1}{2} Q_y}{\Delta} \\ Z &= z_s - \frac{\rho_s P_z - \frac{1}{2} Q_z}{\Delta} \end{aligned}\right\} \tag{48}$$

where $\rho_s$ is given by Eq. (47), $\Delta$, $P_x$, $P_y$, $P_z$, $Q_x$, $Q_y$ and $Q_z$ - by Eq. (44), $r_1'^2$, $r_2'^2$, $r_3'^2$ being defined in Eq. (41) and $x_1'$, $x_2'$, $x_3'$, $y_1'$, $y_2'$, $y_3'$, $z_1'$, $z_2'$, $z_3'$ - in Eq. (38).

The above solution of the set of four simultaneous quadratic equations represents the common point of intersection of all four spheres of radii $\rho_s$, $\rho_1 + \rho_s$, $\rho_2 + \rho_s$, $\rho_3 + \rho_s$, whose centers are at some four positions, $\bar{r}_o(t_s) \equiv \bar{r}_s$, $\bar{r}_o(t_1) \equiv \bar{r}_1$, $\bar{r}_o(t_2) \equiv \bar{r}_2$, $\bar{r}_o(t_3) \equiv \bar{r}_3$, of the satellite on its orbit at the instants $t_s$, $t_1$, $t_2$, $t_3$, respectively.

This can readily be seen from the following geometrical considerations paralleling those of Part A. Using the first sphere of radius $\rho_s$, whose center is at the position, $\bar{r}_s \equiv [x_s, y_s, z_s]$, on the satellite's orbit at the instant $t_s$, as the "special" sphere on which, as we know, the position, $\bar{R} \equiv [X, Y, Z]$, of the Doppler receiver lies, we consider the loci of intersection of the other three spheres with this special sphere. Evidently each of these three loci of intersection is a circle lying on the special sphere and defining a plane at right angles to the straight on which this circle's center lies and which passes through the centers of the respective pair of mutually intersecting spheres. The radius, $a_{si}$ $[i = 1, 2, 3]$, of this circle is related to the radii, $\rho_s$ and $\rho_i + \rho_s$ $[i = 1, 2, 3]$, of these spheres and to the distance, $r_i' \equiv |\bar{r}_i - \bar{r}_s|$ $[i = 1, 2, 3]$, between their centers by the equality:

$$\frac{1}{2} r_i' a_{si} = m_i (m_i - \rho_s) [m_i - (\rho_i + \rho_s)](m_i - r_i') \qquad (49)$$

where $m_i \equiv \frac{1}{2} [\rho_s + (\rho_i + \rho_s) + r_i'] \; [i = 1, 2, 3]$, both sides of which are equal to the area of the triangle shown in Fig. 6.

In the general case, when the satellite's orbit relative to the frame fixed to Earth possesses both curvature and torsion (see Part A), the four positions, $\bar{r}_s$, $\bar{r}_1$, $\bar{r}_2$, $\bar{r}_3$, on this orbit at which the centers of our four spheres lie are not coplanar, so that the three straights from the center of the special sphere to the centers of the other three spheres are, likewise, not coplanar. Consequently, also the three planes defined by the circles of intersection of these three spheres with the special sphere mutually intersect in straights having different directions.

The circles of intersection of the second and the third sphere with the special sphere mutually intersect in two distinct points lying on the special sphere as well as on the straight of intersection of the pair of planes defined by these two circles of intersection. Also the circles of intersection of the second and the fourth sphere with the special sphere as well as those of the third and the fourth sphere with the special sphere, respectively, mutually intersect in two distinct points lying on the special sphere as well as on the straights of intersection of the respective pairs of planes defined by these two pairs of circles of intersection.

Thus, in all, the four spheres mutually intersect in three pairs of points which lie on the special sphere. (We don't need to consider the points in which the second, third, and fourth sphere mutually intersect which do not lie on the special sphere.) One point of each of the three pairs of points of intersection lying on the special sphere is at the position, $\bar{R}$, of the Doppler receiver, so that this position is the common point of intersection of all four spheres. The second points of each of the three pairs of points of intersection are distinct both among themselves and from the common point of intersection, since each lies on one of three straights passing through the common point of intersection, $\bar{R}$, and having different directions. This is shown schematically in Fig. 7.

In the special case, when the satellite's orbit is confined to a single plane (see Part A), the positions, $\bar{r}_s$, $\bar{r}_1$, $\bar{r}_2$, $\bar{r}_3$, of the centers of the four spheres lie in that plane, so that the three straights from the center of the special sphere to the centers of the other three spheres are coplanar. Consequently, all three planes defined by the circles of intersection of these three spheres with the special sphere are normal to the plane to which the satellite's orbit is confined and

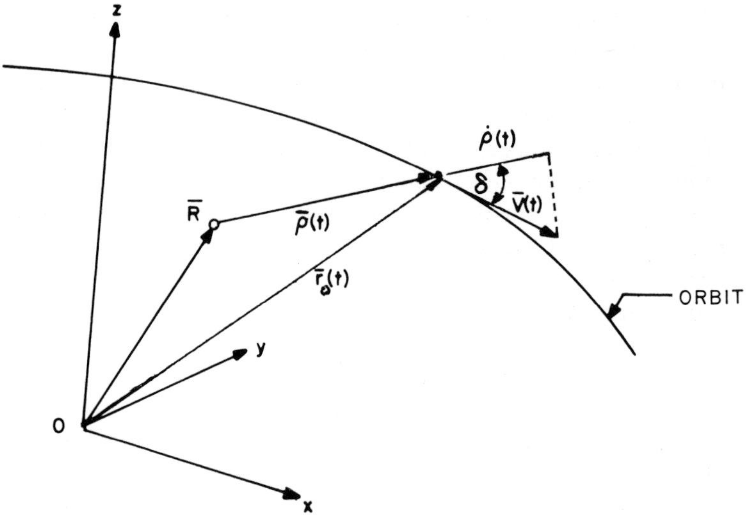


Fig. 5

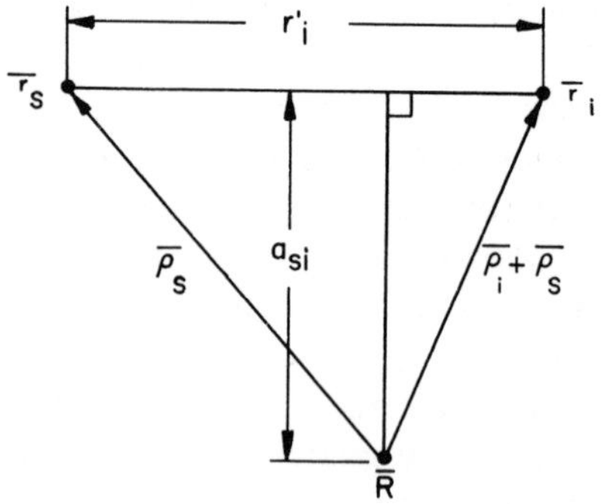


Fig. 6

mutually intersect in three mutually parallel straights. Since all three straights pass through the common point of intersection, $\overline{R}$ , of all four spheres, all three are collinear. Hence, the three second points of each of the three pairs of points of intersection of the circles of intersection with the special sphere of, respectively, the second and third, the second and fourth, and the third and fourth spheres are mutually coincident in a second common point of intersection. The position of this second common point of intersection, $\overline{R}'$, of all four spheres is symmetric to that of the first, lying at the position, $\overline{R}$, of the Doppler receiver, about the plane to which the satellite's orbit is confined.

Evidently, in this plane-symmetric case the ambivalence of determination of the position, $\overline{R}$ , of the Doppler receiver can be removed (as pointed out in Part A) only by using information contained by methods extraneous to the present one. Moreover, the position, $\overline{R}$ , can be found (ambivalently) in this case as the common point intersection of only three spheres whose centers lie at three positions, $\overline{r}_s$ , $\overline{r}_1$ , $\overline{r}_2$ , on the satellite's orbit. This is shown schematically in Fig. 8.

In the second special case, considered in Part A, when the satellite's orbit is a single straight, the three straights from the center of the special sphere to the centers of the other three spheres are collinear with the orbit. In consequence, the three planes defined by the three circles of intersection of these three spheres with the special sphere are mutually parallel. Since all three planes pass through the common point of intersection, $\overline{R}$, of all four spheres, all three are coplanar. Hence, the three circles of intersection are mutually coincident, so that the determination of the position, $\overline{R}$ , of the Doppler receiver by the present method is multivalent. Evidently, in this axi-symmetric case the position, $\overline{R}$ , can be found (multivalently) as the circle of intersection of only two spheres whose centers lie at two positions, $\overline{r}_s$ , $\overline{r}_1$ , on the satellite's orbit.

As in the case of the circular half-cones considered in Part A, the spheres whose centers lie at all satellite positions form a continuous family of mutually intersecting surfaces. This family possesses an envelope whose analytical description may be obtained from the typical sphere equation in the manner indicated in Part A. The common point of intersection of all spheres is a focal point of this envelope which may be determined directly from the equations representing it. As in the previous case, this task has not yet been undertaken, however.

## Part C: Accuracy Considerations

In the ideal case considered in Parts A and B in which the satellite's orbit, $\bar{r}_o(t)$, and the measured value of $\dot{\rho}(t)$ or that of the integral, $\rho_i(t_i) = \rho_i(t_i) - \rho_s(t_s)$, respectively, were viewed as being precisely known at every instant, $t$, the specific choice of the four positions of the satellite used for determination of the position, $\bar{R}$, of the Doppler receiver by either method is a matter of indifference.

The indeterminacy of our knowledge of these four positions and the measured values in the "real" case raises the question as to the effect of any specific choice of these positions on the accuracy with which the position, $\bar{R}$, of the Doppler receiver can be determined by these methods.

It appears possible to formulate a variational problem whose solution would specify the optimal choice of these four positions within the practically possible domain of variation of these positions on the satellite's orbit. This analytical approach to the above question has, as yet, not been undertaken.

However, a general answer to this question can be given in geometrical terms as follows:

It is well known that the excursion from its true position of the point of intersection of two straights whose directions are fixed, but which may be displaced, from their true positions by a small distance in any direction in their respective normal planes, assumes its smallest value when these straights are mutually orthogonal. As the angle of intersection decreases from its largest possible value, $|\pi/2|$, the excursion of the point of intersection from its true position increases as the cotangent of that angle, becoming indefinitely large as this angle approaches zero.

Thus, for the most accurate determination of the common point of intersection by the "differential" method (Part A), the positions of the apices of the four half-cones (one of which may be the special plane) on the satellite's orbit must be such that the angles between the tangents to the orbit at these positions are as large as possible within the limitations set by the shape of the orbit and the working range of the Doppler receiver.

As for the "integral" method (Part B), the positions, $\bar{r}_s$, $\bar{r}_1$, $\bar{r}_2$, $\bar{r}_3$, of the centers of the four spheres on the satellite's orbit must be such that the angles of intersection of the tangent cones at the circle of intersection of every pair of spheres be as large as possible, within these limitations. This is shown schematically in Fig. 9.

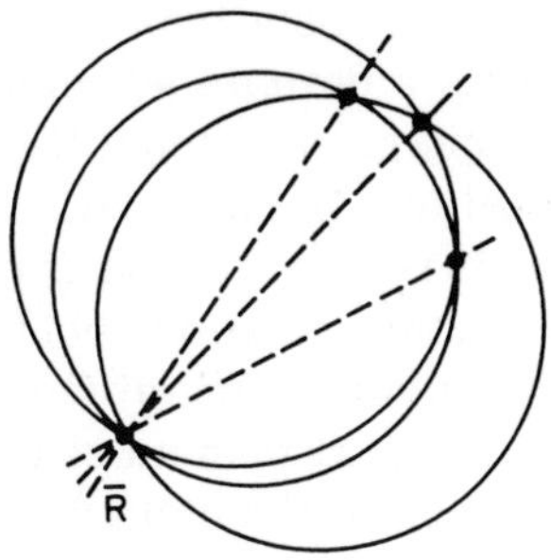


Fig. 7

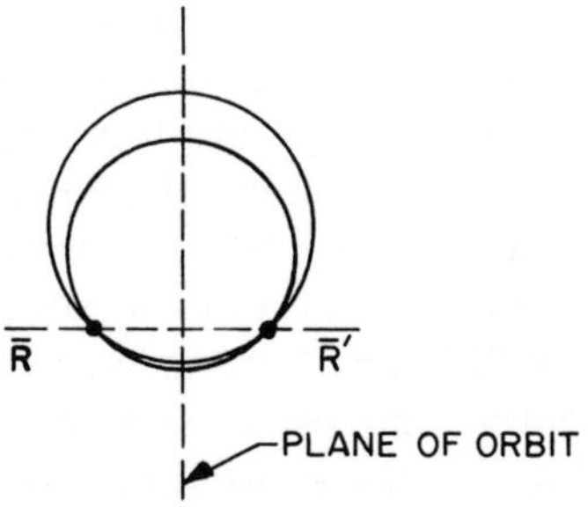


Fig. 8

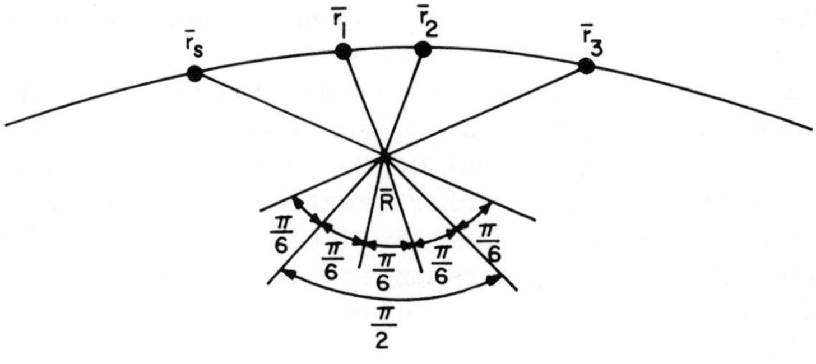


Fig. 9

Note that the distance between the two outer positions, $\bar{r}_s$ and $\bar{r}_3$, may very well be smaller than the distance between the two extreme points of the orbit which can be utilized by the Doppler receiver located at a specific position, $\bar{R}$, relative to it.

In this connection, it is a definite advantage that the satellite moves in the axi-symmetric gravitational field of an oblate spheroid and, hence, is not confined to a plane fixed in an inertial frame, so that the torsion of its orbit relative to the frame, Oxyz, fixed to Earth is not solely due to the Earth's rotation about its axis. Of course, this is true only if the orbit data transmitted by the satellite refer to an orbit of a shape more general than an ellipse, and if the accuracy of the process of computation of the orbit from the received data is sufficiently high for the more exacting task.

In addition to the accuracy with which the satellite's positions on its orbit can be computed, the accuracy with which the position, $\bar{R}$, of the Doppler receiver can be determined depends largely on the accuracy of the measured values of the "instantaneous" or the "cumulative" Doppler shift, and on that of the process of computation of this position from these pre-computed and measured values.

Both methods presented in this paper require pre-computed and measured values referring to only four, appropriately spaced, positions of the satellite in its orbit. Hence, the number of computing operations required by either is considerably smaller than that employed by largely statistical methods relying on highly redundant data. In this respect, the "integral" method is superior to the "differential" one, in that it requires merely the values of the position coordinates at the four satellite positions, whereas the latter calls, in addition, for those of the first and second derivatives of the orbit function at these positions.

Both methods can, of course, be used with redundant data by taking any practicable number of "interlaced" sets of four satellite positions each and by determining the weighted average of the position coordinates of $\bar{R}$ computed from each set.

Since both the "instantaneous" and the cumulative Doppler shift are determined by pulse-counting techniques, the measured values of the former represent, essentially, the sliding average of a monotonically increasing function, rather than this function itself. By contrast, the relative error in the cumulative Doppler shift decreases with the duration of the counting operation, so that the accuracy of the measured value of the cumulative Doppler shift at the second satellite position, is already high.

Thus, the "integral" method possesses the double advantage of high accuracy of the measured data and of a small number of preliminary computing operations on the received data.

A preliminary investigation of the errors associated with the process of computation of the position, $\bar{R}$, of the Doppler receiver by the "integral" method, has shown that, while the explicit form of the solution given by Cramer's rule is not suited for numerical computation, because of the presence of "ill-conditioned" determinants, a good accuracy can be attained by the use of more efficient numerical methods.

## Conclusions

The use of orbit data of a transit-type satellite in conjunction with measured values of the cumulative Doppler shift according to the "integral" method presented in this paper may provide an accurate and inexpensive navigational system. A preliminary study of the accuracy of this system indicates that the major errors will occur in computation rather than in measurement. As a result, errors can be held to relatively small values.

# THE EFFECT OF OUTAGE ON MISSILE PERFORMANCE

D. G. Stechert
The Martin Company
Denver, Colorado

## Abstract

The role that outage, or residual propellant due to the early exhaustion of one of the propellants of a bipropellant system, plays in determining missile performance is examined. The probability density function for the non-normal outage distribution is derived. The mean and standard deviation of this distribution are obtained. The central limit theorem then permits the combining of outage variations with other variations to allow the determination of missile performance variation. Using the outage probability density function, an expression for optimum fuel bias is obtained based on the concept of minimizing the variance of outage about the zero value.

## Introduction

Missile performance can be expressed quantitatively in terms of such quantities as range or burnout velocity (magnitude and direction). There are certain principal variables which are independent and which have a definite influence on performance. Some of these principal variables may be combined in expressions of intermediate variables, which together with other primary or intermediate variables affect performance. The situation may be illustrated as in Fig. 1.

In a tolerance study we are interested in the effect of random variations or errors in the primary or intermediate variables about their nominal values, on range or velocity. The assumption that the resultant range or velocity variation is normally distributed is not one of expediency, but rather is forced on us in the absence of precise information about the individual contributions (1). Even with detailed knowledge of the individual errors one is quite safe in concluding

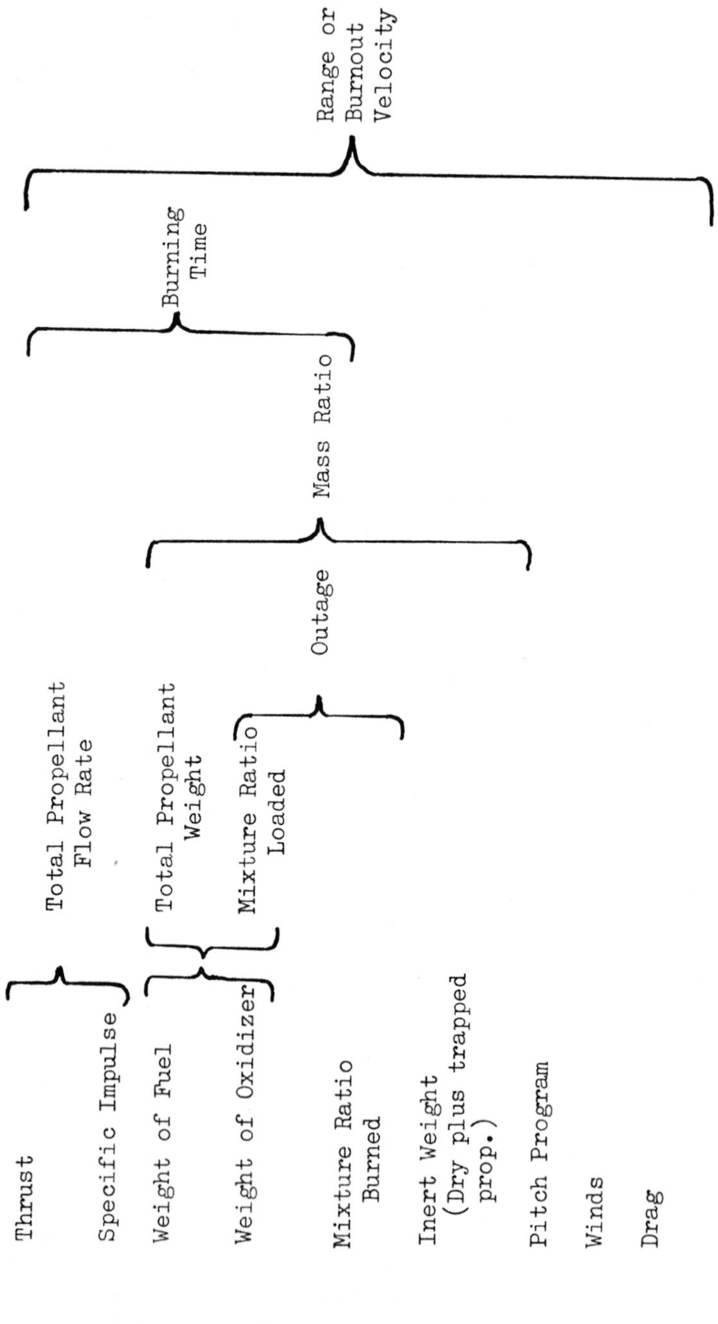


Fig. 1. Performance as Function of Primary and/or Intermediate Variables

that the resulting distribution is nearly normal, due to the central limit theorem of statistics. This theorem states that the function of a large number of independent variables is approximately normally distributed regardless of the particular distributions of the individual components of the function.

Now in a missile performance study we know that outage is non-normally distributed. The exact distribution will be derived below. But when the effect of outage is compounded statistically with the effects due to all other variables, which for lack of better information are in most cases assumed to be distributed normally (though this is not required), the resulting range or velocity variation has a very near normal distribution.

In this paper the probability density function for outage is derived. The mean and standard deviation of this non-normal distribution are obtained. The central limit theorem then permits the combining of outage variations with other variations to determine the variation in such quantities as burning time, velocity, or range. Using the outage probability density function, an expression for determining optimum fuel bias is obtained based on the concept of minimizing the variance of outage about the zero value.

## Definition

Outage is the result of a difference in two types of mixture ratio of a given stage of a liquid bipropellant rocket. The mixture ratio is the ratio by weight of oxidizer to fuel. The two types referred to are the ratio in which the propellants are loaded, and the ratio in which the propellants are actually consumed by the rocket engine. For maximum performance the ratio loaded and the ratio burned should obviously be equal. If there is some difference in these ratios, due perhaps to statistical uncertainties, a certain amount of one of the propellants will remain unconsumed at the time that the other propellant has been used to exhaustion. Even though there no doubt are fluctuations in the mixture ratio burned during flight, we shall assume that these variations are small; and we shall use the mean value in this paper.

The relationships between total weight of usable propellant loaded, $W_P$, and mixture ratio loaded, $r_L$, on the one hand, and weight of oxidizer and fuel loaded, $W_O$ and $W_F$, are:

$$\left.\begin{aligned} W_P &= W_O + W_F \\ r_L &= W_O / W_F \end{aligned}\right\} \quad \text{OR} \quad \left\{\begin{aligned} W_O &= \frac{W_P}{1+1/r_L} \\ W_F &= \frac{W_P}{1+r_L} \end{aligned}\right. \tag{1}$$

Similar relationships apply for the actually consumed or burned quantities:

$$\left.\begin{aligned} W_P' &= W_O' + W_F' \\ r_B &= W_O'/W_F' \end{aligned}\right\} \quad \text{OR} \quad \left\{\begin{aligned} W_O' &= \frac{W_P'}{1+1/r_B} \\ W_F' &= \frac{W_P'}{1+r_B} \end{aligned}\right. \tag{2}$$

Eqs. (2) may also be written in terms of burning rates:

$$\left.\begin{aligned} \dot{W}_P &= \dot{W}_O + \dot{W}_F \\ r_B &= \dot{W}_O/\dot{W}_F \end{aligned}\right\} \quad \text{OR} \quad \left\{\begin{aligned} \dot{W}_O &= \frac{\dot{W}_P}{1+1/r_B} \\ \dot{W}_F &= \frac{\dot{W}_P}{1+r_B} \end{aligned}\right. \tag{3}$$

There are two possibilities for an outage condition: one where the burned equals the loaded oxidizer, implying a fuel outage and a value of $\lambda = r_L/r_B \leq 1$ ; and the other where the burned equals the loaded fuel, implying an oxidizer outage and $\lambda = r_L/r_B \geq 1$ .

$$\lambda = r_L/r_B \leq 1$$

$$W_O = W_O'$$

$$W_F = W_F' + \Delta W_F$$

$$Z_F = \Delta W_F/W_P$$

$$\lambda = \frac{r_L}{r_B} = \frac{W_O/W_F}{W_O'/W_F'}$$

$$= \frac{W_F - \Delta W_F}{W_F} \leq 1$$

$$= 1 - \frac{\Delta W_F}{W_P}\frac{W_P}{W_F}$$

$$= 1 - Z_F(1+r_L)$$

$$Z_F = \frac{1-\frac{r_L}{r_B}}{1+r_L}$$

$$Z_F = \frac{1-\lambda}{1+r_L} \tag{4a}$$

$$\lambda = r_L/r_B \geq 1$$

$$W_F = W_F'$$

$$W_O = W_O' + \Delta W_O$$

$$Z_O = \Delta W_O/W_P$$

$$\lambda = \frac{r_L}{r_B} = \frac{W_O/W_F}{W_O'/W_F'}$$

$$= \frac{W_O}{W_O - \Delta W_O} \geq 1$$

$$= \frac{1}{1 - \frac{\Delta W_O}{W_P}\frac{W_P}{W_O}}$$

$$= \frac{1}{1 - Z_O(1 + 1/r_L)}$$

$$Z_O = \frac{1-\frac{r_B}{r_L}}{1+1/r_L}$$

$$Z_O = \frac{1-1/\lambda}{1+1/r_L} \tag{4b}$$

Thus it will be seen that outage can be considered as a function of $\lambda = r_L/r_B$ and $r_L$ .

## Small Variations

We are interested in the effect of small variations in $\lambda$ and $r_L$ on $Z$. We, therefore, expand Eqs. (4) in a Taylor's series about the nominal point $(\bar{\lambda}, \bar{r}_L)$, writing only the linear terms:

$$z(\lambda, r_L) - z(\bar{\lambda}, \bar{r}_L) = \frac{\partial z}{\partial \lambda}(\lambda - \bar{\lambda}) + \frac{\partial z}{\partial r_L}(r_L - \bar{r}_L)$$

Getting the partial derivatives from Eqs. (4),

$$z_F(\lambda, r_L) - z_F(\bar{\lambda}, \bar{r}_L) = -\frac{1}{1+r_L}(\lambda - \bar{\lambda}) - \frac{1-\lambda}{(1+r_L)^2}(r_L - \bar{r}_L)$$

$$z_o(\lambda, r_L) - z_o(\bar{\lambda}, \bar{r}_L) = \frac{\frac{1}{\lambda^2}}{1+\frac{1}{r_L}}(\lambda - \bar{\lambda}) + \frac{1-\frac{1}{\lambda}}{r_L^2(1+\frac{1}{r_L})^2}(r_L - \bar{r}_L)$$

Now at the nominal condition $\lambda = \bar{\lambda} = \frac{\bar{r}_L}{r_B} = 1$, and the outage is zero, so that these equations become

$$z_F = -\frac{1}{1+\bar{r}_B}(\lambda - 1) \quad (5a) \qquad z_o = \frac{\bar{r}_B}{1+\bar{r}_B}(\lambda - 1) \quad (5b)$$

A graphical presentation of Eqs. (5) is helpful. For the case $\bar{r}_B = 2$ it would appear as in Fig. 2.

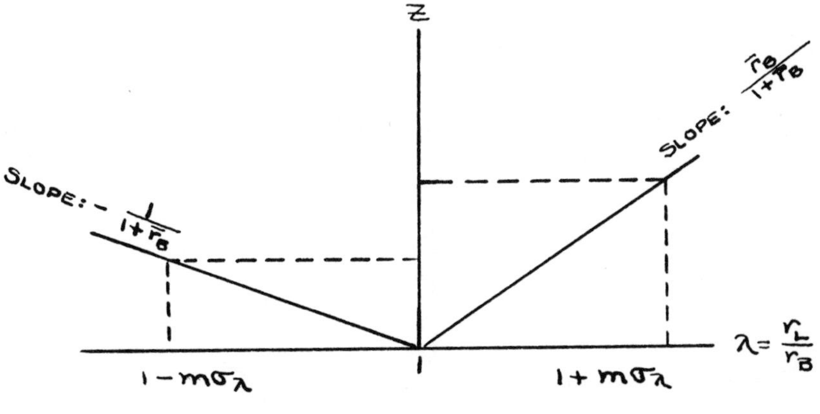


Fig. 2. Outage as a Function of Ratio of Mixture Ratios

Let us now consider random errors or uncertainties in $\lambda$. By definition we have

$$\lambda = r_L / r_B = \frac{W_o}{W_F \, r_B}$$

Then $\quad LN\,\lambda = LN\,W_0 - LN\,W_F - LN\,r_B$

Differentiating,

$$\frac{d\lambda}{\lambda} = \frac{dW_0}{W_0} - \frac{dW_F}{W_F} - \frac{dr_B}{r_B}$$

Now the quantities $W_0$, $W_F$, and $r_B$ are independent (Fig. 1). Therefore, the standard deviation of $\lambda$, $\sigma_\lambda$, can be written

$$\left(\frac{\sigma_\lambda}{\bar{\lambda}}\right)^2 = \sigma_\lambda^2 = \left(\frac{\sigma_{W_0}}{\bar{W}_0}\right)^2 + \left(\frac{\sigma_{W_F}}{\bar{W}_F}\right)^2 + \left(\frac{\sigma_{r_B}}{\bar{r}_B}\right)^2 \qquad (6)$$

$W_0$, $W_F$, and $r_B$ need not be distributed normally.

Fuel Bias

If we can now expect a certain plus and minus deviation in $\lambda$ about $\lambda = 1$, say $\pm m\sigma_\lambda$ (where $m$ is related to the desired probability level), it will be seen from Fig. 2 that the corresponding values of outage will not be equal due to the difference in slopes, generally, of the two branches of the curve. This situation can be remedied by introducing a bias in $\lambda$, namely,

$$\beta = \Delta\lambda = \frac{\Delta r_L}{\bar{r}_B} \qquad (7)$$

Graphically this is portrayed in Fig. 3.

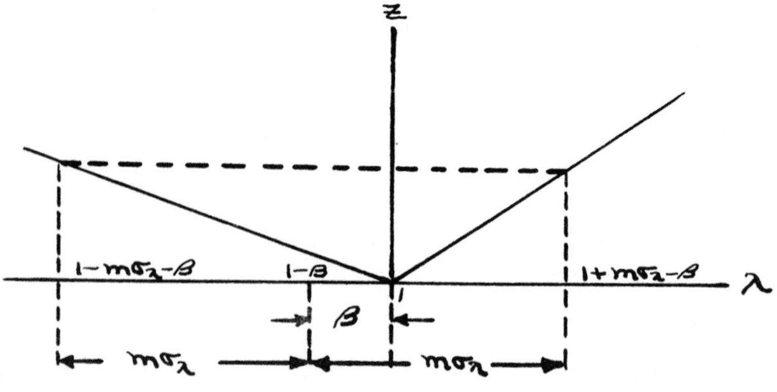


Fig. 3. Extreme Outages Equalized

$\beta$ is determined from Eqs. (5) as follows:

$$z_F(\bar{r}_B, 1-m\sigma_\lambda-\beta) = z_o(\bar{r}_B, 1+m\sigma_\lambda-\beta)$$

or $$-\frac{1}{1+\bar{r}_B}(-m\sigma_\lambda-\beta) = \frac{\bar{r}_B}{1+\bar{r}_B}(m\sigma_\lambda-\beta) \qquad (8)$$

Solving, $$\beta = \frac{\bar{r}_B-1}{\bar{r}_B+1} m\sigma_\lambda$$

Notice that for $\bar{r}_B > 1$ a positive $\beta$ implies a slight increase in fuel at the expense of oxidizer, so that Eqs. (1) are modified to

$$\left.\begin{aligned} W_P'' &= W_P = (\bar{W}_o - W_B) + (\bar{W}_F + W_B) \\ &= \bar{W}_o + \bar{W}_F \\ r_L'' &= \bar{r}_L - \Delta r_L = \frac{\bar{W}_o - W_B}{\bar{W}_F + W_B} \\ &= \frac{\bar{W}_o}{\bar{W}_F}\left(\frac{1-W_B/\bar{W}_o}{1+W_B/\bar{W}_F}\right) \end{aligned}\right\} \qquad (9a)$$

$$r_L'' \cong \frac{\bar{W}_o}{\bar{W}_F}\left(1-\frac{W_B}{\bar{W}_o}\right)\left(1-\frac{W_B}{\bar{W}_F}\right)$$ if $W_B$ is small compared to $\bar{W}_o$ and $\bar{W}_F$,

$$\cong \bar{r}_L\left(1-\frac{W_B}{\bar{W}_o}-\frac{W_B}{\bar{W}_F}\right)$$

Then $$\Delta r_L = \frac{W_B}{W_P}(\bar{r}_L+1)^2$$

and $$W_B = \frac{W_P\,\Delta r_L}{(\bar{r}_L+1)^2} = \frac{\bar{W}_F\,\Delta r_L}{\bar{r}_L+1}$$

or $$W_B = \frac{\Delta r_L}{\bar{r}_B+1}\bar{W}_F = \frac{\bar{r}_B}{\bar{r}_B+1}\beta\,\bar{W}_F \qquad (10a)$$

Here the total weight of propellant was maintained constant before and after applying the fuel bias.

If, however, it is desired to maintain the weight of oxidizer unchanged, then fuel must be added in the amount $W_B$.

$$\left.\begin{aligned} W_P'' &= \overline{W}_o + \overline{W}_F + W_B \\ r_L'' &= \bar{r}_L - \Delta r_L = \frac{\overline{W}_o}{\overline{W}_F + W_B} \\ &\cong \frac{\overline{W}_o}{\overline{W}_F}\left(1 - \frac{W_B}{\overline{W}_F}\right) \\ &\cong r_L\left(1 - \frac{W_B}{\overline{W}_F}\right) \end{aligned}\right\} \qquad (9b)$$

Then $$\Delta r_L = \bar{r}_L \frac{W_B}{\overline{W}_F}$$

and $$W_B = \frac{\overline{W}_F \Delta r_L}{\bar{r}_L}$$

or $$W_B = \frac{\Delta r_L}{\bar{r}_B} \overline{W}_F = \beta \overline{W}_F \qquad (10b)$$

If, on the other hand, the weight of fuel is to be kept constant, then oxidizer must be removed in the amount $W_B$.

$$W_B = \Delta r_L \overline{W}_F = \beta \bar{r}_B \overline{W}_F \qquad (10c)$$

Eqs. (6), (7), (8), (10) are used as follows in determining the required fuel bias. Knowing deviations in oxidizer and fuel loading and $\bar{r}_B$, $\sigma_\lambda$ is computed from Eq. (6). Based on the desired probability level at which oxidizer and fuel outage are to be equalized, $\beta$ is computed from Eq. (8). Then $W_B$ can be computed from Eq. (10).

## Outage Distribution

Let us next consider the determination of the probability density function for the outage $Z$. Even though the contributing factors in Eq. (6) may not be normally distributed, the resulting distribution for $\lambda$ is nearly normal. This follows from the central limit theorem. Let us then assume that $\lambda$ is normally distributed about the mean at $\lambda = 1-\beta$, with standard deviation $\sigma_\lambda$. The problem is demonstrated graphically in Fig. 4.

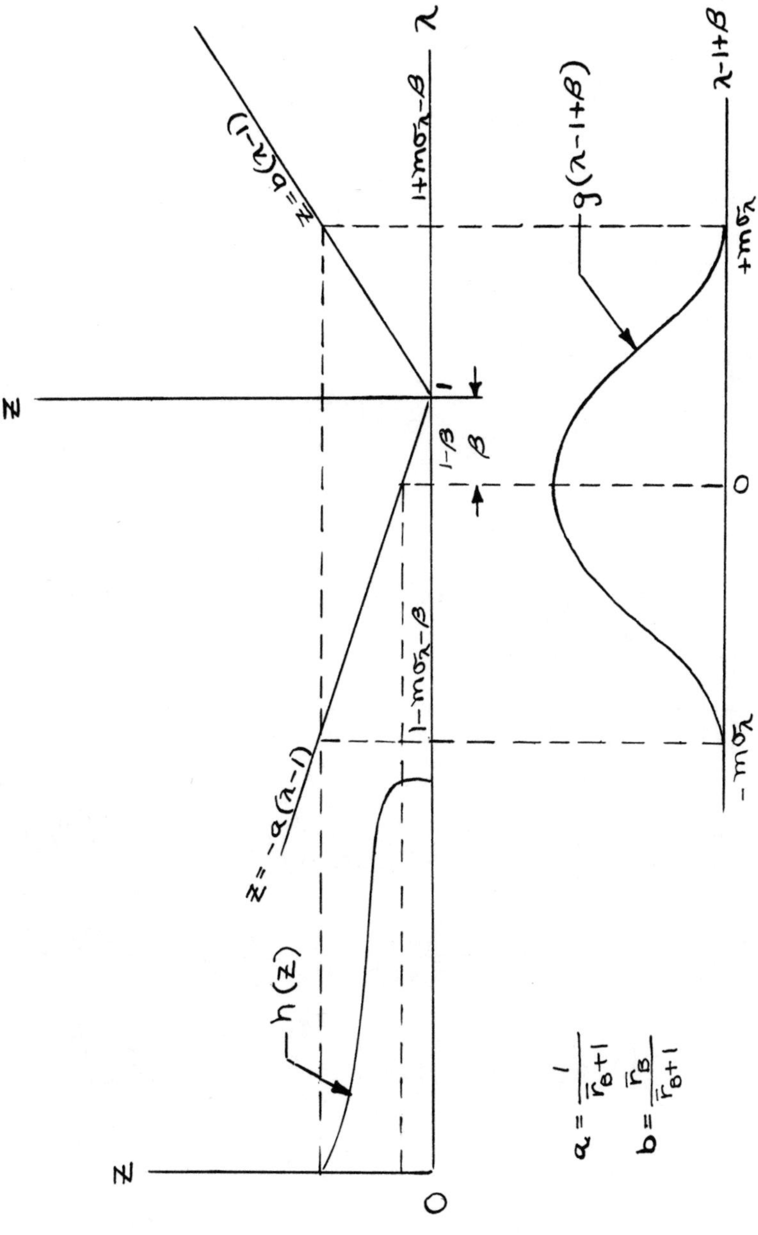


Fig. 4. Probability Density Function for Outage

The problem is that of reflecting $g(\lambda-1+\beta)$ in the two branches $Z=-a(\lambda-1)$ and $Z=b(\lambda-1)$ to obtain $h(Z)$. For non-monotonic functions such that more than one value, namely $n$ values, of the abscissa $X$ correspond to a given value of the ordinate $Y$, it can be shown (2, 3) that

$$h(Y)=\sum_i^n \frac{g(x_i)}{\left|\frac{dY}{dX}\right|_{x_i}} \; ; \; i=1,2,\cdots n \tag{11}$$

Corresponding to a given value of $Z$, there are two values of $\lambda$, namely, $\frac{Z}{-a}+1$ and $\frac{Z}{b}+1$. Therefore, using Eq. (11),

$$h(Z)=\frac{1}{a}g\left(\lambda=\frac{Z}{-a}+1\right)+\frac{1}{b}g\left(\lambda=\frac{Z}{b}+1\right) \tag{12}$$

$g(\lambda-1+\beta)$ is assumed normal,

$$g(\lambda-1+\beta)=\frac{1}{\sigma_\lambda\sqrt{2\pi}}\, e^{-\frac{1}{2}\left(\frac{\lambda-1+\beta}{\sigma_\lambda}\right)^2} \tag{13}$$

Then Eq. (12) becomes

$$h(Z)=\frac{1}{\sigma_\lambda\sqrt{2\pi}}\left[\frac{1}{a}e^{-\frac{1}{2\sigma_\lambda^2}\left(-\frac{Z}{a}+\beta\right)^2}+\frac{1}{b}e^{-\frac{1}{2\sigma_\lambda^2}\left(\frac{Z}{b}+\beta\right)^2}\right] \tag{14}$$

The mean and variance of this non-normal distribution were obtained (See Appendix) and are given below:

$$\frac{\bar{Z}}{\sigma_\lambda}=\frac{1}{\sqrt{2\pi}}\,e^{-\frac{1}{2}(\beta/\sigma_\lambda)^2}-\frac{1}{2}\frac{\beta}{\sigma_\lambda}\left(\frac{\bar{r}_B-1}{\bar{r}_B+1}\right)+\frac{\beta}{\sigma_\lambda}\frac{1}{\sqrt{2\pi}}\int_0^{\beta/\sigma_\lambda} e^{-u^2/2}du \tag{15}$$

$$\left(\frac{\sigma_Z}{\sigma_\lambda}\right)^2=\frac{1}{2}\left(1+\frac{\beta^2}{\sigma_\lambda^2}\right)\frac{\bar{r}_B^2+1}{(\bar{r}_B+1)^2}-\frac{1}{\sqrt{2\pi}}\frac{\beta}{\sigma_\lambda}\left(\frac{\bar{r}_B-1}{\bar{r}_B+1}\right)e^{-\frac{1}{2}(\beta/\sigma_\lambda)^2}$$
$$-\left(1+\frac{\beta}{\sigma_\lambda^2}\right)\left(\frac{\bar{r}_B-1}{\bar{r}_B+1}\right)\frac{1}{\sqrt{2\pi}}\int_0^{\beta/\sigma_\lambda} e^{-u^2/2}du-\left(\frac{\bar{Z}}{\sigma_\lambda}\right)^2 \tag{16}$$

Values of $\bar{Z}/\sigma_\lambda$ and $\sigma_Z/\sigma_\lambda$ were computed for various values of $\bar{r}_B$ and $\beta/\sigma_\lambda$. These are shown in Table 1.

Table 1. Outage Mean and Standard Deviation

| | $\beta/\sigma_{\bar{\lambda}}$ | $\bar{r}_B$ 1.5 | 2.0 | 2.5 | 3.0 |
|---|---|---|---|---|---|
| $\bar{Z}/\sigma_{\bar{\lambda}}$ | .25 | .386 | .369 | .358 | .349 |
| | .50 | .392 | .359 | .335 | .317 |
| | .75 | .431 | .381 | .346 | .319 |
| | 1.00 | .483 | .416 | .368 | .333 |
| | 1.25 | .551 | .468 | .408 | .363 |
| | 1.50 | .629 | .529 | .458 | .404 |
| $\sigma_t/\sigma_{\bar{\lambda}}$ | .25 | .294 | .303 | .315 | .331 |
| | .50 | .297 | .283 | .283 | .287 |
| | .75 | .299 | .266 | .250 | .241 |
| | 1.00 | .319 | .274 | .244 | .226 |
| | 1.25 | .338 | .283 | .244 | .215 |
| | 1.50 | .360 | .300 | .255 | .223 |

## Performance Deviation

On the basis of the central limit theorem this mean and standard deviation can now be used, along with the standard deviations of the remaining variables, to arrive at the standard deviation of range.

Range can be considered a function as follows:

$$R = R(T, I_{sp}, Z, W_p, W_o, \cdots)$$

There should be a set of such variables for each stage.

Then $$dR = \left(\frac{\partial R}{\partial T}\right) dT + \left(\frac{\partial R}{\partial I_{sp}}\right) dI_{sp} + \left(\frac{\partial R}{\partial Z}\right) dZ + \left(\frac{\partial R}{\partial W_p}\right) dW_p + \left(\frac{\partial R}{\partial W_o}\right) dW_o + \cdots$$

Since the contributing variables are independent, as explained in the introduction, it follows that

$$\sigma_R^2 = \left(\frac{\partial R}{\partial T}\right)^2 \sigma_T^2 + \left(\frac{\partial R}{\partial I_{sp}}\right)^2 \sigma_{I_{sp}}^2 + \left(\frac{\partial R}{\partial Z}\right)^2 \sigma_Z^2 + \left(\frac{\partial R}{\partial W_p}\right)^2 \sigma_{W_p}^2 + \left(\frac{\partial R}{\partial W_o}\right)^2 \sigma_{W_o}^2 + \cdots \qquad (17)$$

and

$$\bar{R} = R(\bar{T}, \bar{I}_{sp}, \bar{Z}, \bar{W}_p, \bar{W}_o, \cdots) \qquad (18)$$

where the values of $\sigma_Z^2$ and $\bar{Z}$ in Eqs. (17) and (18) come from Eqs. (15) and (16). Eq. (18) and the partial derivatives in Eq. (17) are usually evaluated through the solution of the differential equations of motion using a high speed digital computer.

For purpose of demonstration, let us look at the effect of outage, thrust, specific impulse, and total propellant weight on burning time, for which there can be written a simple closed analytical expression:

$$t_B = \frac{W_p - Z W_p}{\dot{W}_p} = \frac{I_{sp} W_p (1 - Z)}{T} \qquad (19)$$

Then

$$\ln t_B = \ln I_{sp} + \ln W_p - \ln T + \ln(1 - Z)$$

Differentiating,

$$\frac{dt_B}{t_B} = \frac{dI_{sp}}{I_{sp}} + \frac{dW_P}{W_P} - \frac{dT}{T} - \frac{dZ}{1-Z}$$

The quantities on the right are independent. Therefore,

$$\left(\frac{\sigma_{t_B}}{\bar{t}_B}\right)^2 = \left(\frac{\sigma_{I_{sP}}}{\bar{I}_{sP}}\right)^2 + \left(\frac{\sigma_{W_P}}{\bar{W}_P}\right)^2 + \left(\frac{\sigma_T}{\bar{T}}\right)^2 + \left(\frac{\sigma_Z}{1-\bar{Z}}\right)^2 \quad (20)$$

and the mean is

$$\bar{t}_B = \frac{\bar{I}_{sp}\,\bar{W}_P\,(1-\bar{Z})}{\bar{T}} \quad (21)$$

## Bias Optimization

Rather than determine bias on the basis of equalizing outages at an arbitrarily chosen probability level as was done above, another basis may be used which takes into consideration the entire range of probability levels. This method is based on determining $\beta$ from a minimization of the variance of $Z$ about $Z = 0$. This variance was determined above as the second moment ( see Eq. A-4, in Appendix, and Eq. 16):

$$M = \int_0^\infty Z^2 h(Z)\,dZ = \sigma_Z^2 + \bar{Z}^2$$

$$= \frac{\beta^2 + \sigma_\lambda^2}{2}\,\frac{\bar{r}_B^{\,2}+1}{(\bar{r}_B+1)^2} - \frac{\beta\sigma_\lambda}{\sqrt{2\pi}}\left(\frac{\bar{r}_B-1}{\bar{r}_B+1}\right)e^{-\frac{1}{2}(\beta/\sigma_\lambda)^2}$$

$$- (\beta^2+\sigma_\lambda^2)\left(\frac{\bar{r}_B-1}{\bar{r}_B+1}\right)\frac{1}{\sqrt{2\pi}}\int_0^{\beta/\sigma_\lambda} e^{-u^2/2}\,du$$

The optimum value for $\beta$ is now found by equating the partial derivative of $M$ with respect to $\beta$ to zero, and solving the resulting expression for $\beta$,

$$\frac{\partial M}{\partial \beta} = \beta\,\frac{\bar{r}_B^{\,2}+1}{(\bar{r}_B+1)^2} - \frac{\sigma_\lambda}{\sqrt{2\pi}}\left(\frac{\bar{r}_B-1}{\bar{r}_B+1}\right)\left[-\frac{\beta^2}{\sigma_\lambda^2}+1\right]e^{-\frac{1}{2}(\beta/\sigma_\lambda)^2}$$

$$-\left(\frac{\bar{r}_B-1}{\bar{r}_B+1}\right)\left[(\beta^2+\sigma_\lambda^2)\frac{1}{\sqrt{2\pi}}\,\frac{1}{\sigma_\lambda}\,e^{-\frac{1}{2}(\beta/\sigma_\lambda)^2} + 2\beta\frac{1}{\sqrt{2\pi}}\int_0^{\beta/\sigma_\lambda} e^{-u^2/2}\,du\right]$$

Simplifying and equating to zero,

$$F\left(\frac{\beta}{\sigma_\lambda}\right)=\frac{1}{2}\frac{\beta}{\sigma_\lambda}\left(\frac{\bar{r}_B^2+1}{\bar{r}_B^2-1}\right)-\frac{1}{\sqrt{2\pi}}e^{-\frac{1}{2}(\beta/\sigma_\lambda)^2} - \frac{\beta}{\sigma_\lambda}\frac{1}{\sqrt{2\pi}}\int_0^{\beta/\sigma_\lambda} e^{-u^2/2}\,du=0 \tag{22}$$

It will be seen that the optimum bias $\beta/\sigma_\lambda$ is a function only of $\bar{r}_B$ . Values $(\beta/\sigma_\lambda)_{OPT}$ were computed for several values of $\bar{r}_B$ , and corresponding values of $\bar{z}/\sigma_\lambda$ , $\sigma_z/\sigma_\lambda$ , and $z_\beta/\sigma_\lambda$ were also found using Eqs. (15) and (16). Here $z_\beta=\frac{\beta}{\bar{r}_B+1}$ is the outage corresponding to the bias.

Table 2. Optimum Bias and Corresponding Outage Mean and Standard Deviation

| | $\bar{r}_B$ | | | |
|---|---|---|---|---|
| | 1.5 | 2.0 | 2.5 | 3.0 |
| $(\beta/\sigma_\lambda)_{OPT}$ | .32 | .55 | .72 | .86 |
| $\bar{z}/\sigma_\lambda$ | .388 | .366 | .344 | .323 |
| $\sigma_z/\sigma_\lambda$ | .291 | .273 | .253 | .237 |
| $z_\beta/\sigma_\lambda$ | .128 | .183 | .206 | .215 |

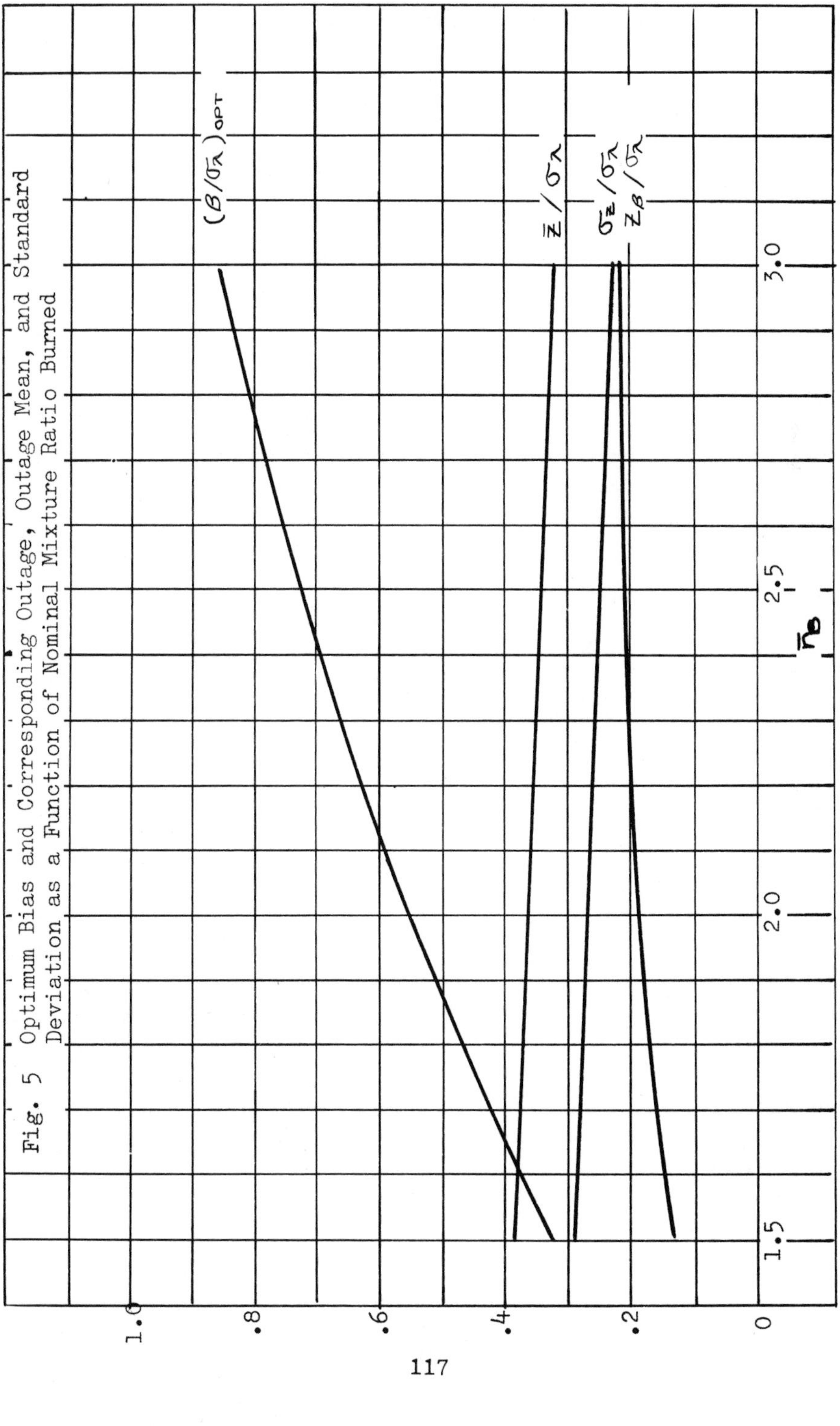


Fig. 5 Optimum Bias and Corresponding Outage, Outage Mean, and Standard Deviation as a Function of Nominal Mixture Ratio Burned

## Numerical Example

Given:

| | | | |
|---|---|---|---|
| $\bar{T} =$ | 80,000 lb | $\sigma_T/\bar{T} =$ | .01 |
| $\bar{I}_{SP} =$ | 310 sec | $\sigma_{I_{SP}}/\bar{I}_{SP} =$ | .005 |
| $\bar{r}_B =$ | 2 | $\sigma_{r_B}/\bar{r}_B =$ | .0075 |
| $\bar{W}_P =$ | 60,000 lb | $\sigma_{W_0}/\bar{W}_0 =$ | .0017 |
| | | $\sigma_{W_F}/\bar{W}_F =$ | .0017 |

Let us proceed with the calculations in two different ways:

Using Eqs. (8) for $m = 3$ which represents a .9973 probability level:

$$\beta/\sigma_\lambda = \frac{\bar{r}_B - 1}{\bar{r}_B + 1}\, m$$

$$= \frac{2-1}{2+1}\, 3$$

$$= 1$$

Using Table 1:

$$\bar{Z}/\sigma_\lambda = 0.416$$

$$\sigma_Z/\sigma_\lambda = 0.274$$

Using Table 2 to determine optimum bias:

$$(\beta/\sigma_\lambda)_{OPT} = 0.55$$

Notice that this is equivalent to using, according to Eqs. (8):

$$m = \frac{\bar{r}_B + 1}{\bar{r}_B - 1}\left(\frac{\beta}{\sigma_\lambda}\right)$$

$$= \frac{2+1}{2-1}\, 0.55$$

$$= 1.65$$

Note that $\pm\, 1.65\sigma_\lambda$ represents a .90 probability level.

Also from Table 2:

$$\bar{Z}/\sigma_\lambda = 0.366$$

$$\sigma_Z/\sigma_\lambda = 0.273$$

Using Eq. (6):

$$\sigma_\lambda^2 = \left(\frac{\sigma_{W_0}}{\overline{W}_0}\right)^2 + \left(\frac{\sigma_{W_F}}{\overline{W}_F}\right)^2 + \left(\frac{\sigma_{r_B}}{\overline{r}_B}\right)^2$$

$$= (.0017)^2 + (.0017)^2 + (.0075)^2$$

$$\sigma_\lambda = .0079$$

| | |
|---|---|
| Then $\overline{Z} = (.416)(.0079)$ <br> $= .0033$ <br> $\sigma_Z = (.274)(.0079)$ <br> $= .0022$ <br> $\beta = (1)(.0079)$ <br> $= .0079$ <br> Thus $\overline{Z} = .0033$ and $Z + 3\sigma_Z = .0099$ | Then $\overline{Z} = (.366)(.0079)$ <br> $= .0029$ <br> $\sigma_Z = (.273)(.0079)$ <br> $= .0022$ <br> $\beta = (.55)(.0079)$ <br> $= .0044$ <br> Thus $\overline{Z} = .0029$ and $Z + 1.65\sigma_Z = .0065$ |

For purposes of comparison, the outage corresponding to the bias is:

| | |
|---|---|
| $\frac{\beta}{\overline{r}_B + 1} = \frac{.0079}{3} = .0026$ | $\frac{\beta}{\overline{r}_B + 1} = \frac{.0044}{3} = .0015$ |

And the $m$ value of outage is:

| | |
|---|---|
| $\frac{m\sigma_\lambda + \beta}{\overline{r}_B + 1} = \frac{3(.0079) + (.0079)}{3}$ <br> $= .0105$ | $\frac{m\sigma_\lambda + \beta}{\overline{r}_B + 1} = \frac{1.65(.0079) + .0044}{3}$ <br> $= .0058$ |

Next, using Eq. (21):

$$\overline{t}_B = \frac{\overline{I}_{SP}\,\overline{W}_P(1 - \overline{Z})}{\overline{T}}$$

$$= \frac{(310)(60{,}000)(1 - .0029)}{80{,}000}$$

$$= 232 \text{ sec}$$

Now it will be necessary to find $\sigma_{W_P}/\overline{W}_P$
From $W_P = W_O + W_F$ it follows that

$$\sigma_{W_P}^2 = \sigma_{W_O}^2 + \sigma_{W_F}^2$$

Then
$$\left(\frac{\sigma_{W_P}}{\overline{W}_P}\right)^2 = \left(\frac{\sigma_{W_O}}{\overline{W}_O}\right)^2\left(\frac{\overline{W}_O}{\overline{W}_P}\right)^2 + \left(\frac{\sigma_{W_F}}{\overline{W}_F}\right)^2\left(\frac{\overline{W}_F}{\overline{W}_P}\right)^2$$

$$= \left(\frac{\sigma_{W_O}}{\overline{W}_O}\right)^2\left(\frac{1}{1+1/\overline{r}_L}\right)^2 + \left(\frac{\sigma_{W_F}}{\overline{W}_F}\right)^2\left(\frac{1}{1+\overline{r}_L}\right)^2$$

$$= (.0017)^2\left(\frac{1}{1.5}\right)^2 + (.0017)^2\left(\frac{1}{3}\right)^2$$

$$\frac{\sigma_{W_P}}{\overline{W}_P} = .0013$$

Using Eq. (20):

$$\left(\frac{\sigma_{t_B}}{\overline{t}_B}\right)^2 = \left(\frac{\sigma_{I_{SP}}}{\overline{I}_{SP}}\right)^2 + \left(\frac{\sigma_{W_P}}{\overline{W}_P}\right)^2 + \left(\frac{\sigma_T}{\overline{T}}\right)^2 + \left(\frac{\sigma_Z}{1-\overline{Z}}\right)^2$$

$$= (.005)^2 + (.0013)^2 + (.01)^2 + \left(\frac{.0022}{.9971}\right)^2$$

$$\frac{\sigma_{t_B}}{\overline{t}_B} = .0115$$

$$\sigma_{t_B} = (.0115)\ (232)$$

$$= 2.7 \text{ sec}$$

## Appendix

### Determination of Outage Mean and Standard Deviation

The probability density function for outage is given in Eq. (14):

$$h(z)=\frac{1}{\sigma_\lambda\sqrt{2\pi}}\left[\frac{1}{a}e^{-\frac{1}{2\sigma_\lambda^2}\left(-\frac{z}{a}+\beta\right)^2}+\frac{1}{b}e^{-\frac{1}{2\sigma_\lambda^2}\left(\frac{z}{b}+\beta\right)^2}\right] \qquad \text{(A-1)}$$

where $a=\dfrac{1}{\bar{r}_B+1}$, $b=\dfrac{\bar{r}_B}{\bar{r}_B+1}$

Our objective here is to verify that

$$\int_0^\infty h(z)\,dz=1 \qquad \text{(A-2)}$$

and to determine expressions for

$$\bar{Z}=\int_0^\infty z\,h(z)\,dz \qquad \text{(A-3)}$$

$$\sigma_z^2=\int_0^\infty z^2 h(z)\,dz-\bar{z}^2 \qquad \text{(A-4)}$$

Since $h(z)$ consists of two terms, we shall be dealing with two terms in each of these integrals. We shall make a change of variable for these terms as follows:

**First Term**

Let $u=\dfrac{\frac{z}{a}-\beta}{\sigma_\lambda}$

Then $du=\dfrac{dz}{a\sigma_\lambda}$

when $u=\beta/\sigma_\lambda,\ z=0$

$u=\infty,\ z=\infty$

**Second Term**

Let $V=\dfrac{\frac{z}{b}+\beta}{\sigma_\lambda}$

Then $dV=\dfrac{dz}{b\sigma_\lambda}$

when $V=\beta/\sigma_\lambda,\ z=0$

$V=\infty,\ z=\infty$

We also need several integrals:

$\int e^{-t^2/2}dt$ : available in tables

$$\int t e^{-t^2/2}dt=-e^{-t^2/2}$$

$$\int t^2 e^{-t^2/2}dt=-te^{-t^2/2}+\int e^{-t^2/2}dt$$

Eq. (A-2) can then be readily verified.

Eq. (A-3) can be solved to result in

$$\frac{\bar{z}}{\sigma_\lambda} = \frac{1}{\sqrt{2\pi}} e^{-\frac{1}{2}(\beta/\sigma_\lambda)^2} - \frac{1}{2}\frac{\beta}{\sigma_\lambda}\left(\frac{\bar{r}_B - 1}{\bar{r}_B + 1}\right) + \frac{\beta}{\sigma_\lambda}\frac{1}{\sqrt{2\pi}}\int_0^{\beta/\sigma_\lambda} e^{-u^2/2}\,du \tag{A-5}$$

Eq. (A-4) can be solved to yield

$$\left(\frac{\sigma_z}{\sigma_\lambda}\right)^2 = \frac{\left(1 + \frac{\beta^2}{\sigma_\lambda^2}\right)}{2}\;\frac{\bar{r}_B^2 + 1}{(\bar{r}_B + 1)^2} - \frac{1}{\sqrt{2\pi}}\;\frac{\beta}{\sigma_\lambda}\left(\frac{\bar{r}_B - 1}{\bar{r}_B + 1}\right) e^{-\frac{1}{2}(\beta/\sigma_\lambda)^2} - \left(1 + \frac{\beta^2}{\sigma_\lambda^2}\right)\left(\frac{\bar{r}_B - 1}{\bar{r}_B + 1}\right)\frac{1}{\sqrt{2\pi}}\int_0^{\beta/\sigma_\lambda} e^{-u^2/2}\,du - \left(\frac{\bar{z}}{\sigma_\lambda}\right)^2 \tag{A-6}$$

## Symbols

- $a$ : $1/\bar{r}_B + 1$
- $b$ : $\bar{r}_B/\bar{r}_B + 1$
- $g$ : probability density function for $\lambda$
- $h$ : probability density function for $z$
- $I_{sp}$ : specific impulse, sec
- $m$ : coefficient of $\sigma_\lambda$ , chosen for the desired probability level at which oxidizer and fuel outages are to be equalized
- $M$ : statistical second moment
- $r_B$ : mixture ratio (oxidizer to fuel by weight) burned
- $r_L$ : mixture ratio (oxidizer to fuel by weight) loaded
- $R$ : range from launch to target, n mi
- $t_B$ : burning time of a given stage, sec
- $T$ : thrust, lb
- $W_B$ : weight of bias propellant, lb

$W_D$ : inert weight (dry plus trapped or unusable propellant), lb
$W_F$ : weight of usable fuel loaded, lb
$W_o$ : weight of usable oxidizer loaded, lb
$\Delta W_F$ : weight of unconsumed fuel, lb
$\Delta W_o$ : weight of unconsumed oxidizer, lb
$W_P$ : total weight of usable propellant loaded, lb
$Z$ : outage
$Z_F$ : fuel outage : $\Delta W_F / W_P$
$Z_o$ : oxidizer outage : $\Delta W_o / W_P$
$\beta$ : bias in $\lambda$
$\lambda$ : ratio of mixture ratio loaded to mixture ratio burned
$\sigma$ : standard deviation

Superscripts:

$'$ : quantity actually consumed
$''$ : quantities altered for propellant bias
$\cdot$ : time rate of change
$-$ : nominal or mean

## Acknowledgment

The writer wishes to express his gratitude for the assistance he has obtained from various members of the Systems Engineering Department, The Martin Company, Denver, Colorado, in the preparation of this paper.

## References

1. Christensen, R.R., "Error Budgets and Component Acceptable Criteria," GM-TM-0165-00315, Space Technology Laboratories, Los Angeles, California, 16 October 1958.

2. Mood, A.M., Introduction to the Theory of Statistics, McGraw-Hill, New York, 1950, Chapter 10.

3. Stechert, D.G., "Tolerance Analysis", Inter-Department Communication, The Martin Company, Denver, Colorado, 11 June 1957.

# TRACKING

# RADAR VELOCITY TRACKING SYSTEMS ANALYSIS

G.O. Young
Hughes Research Laboratories
and
University of Southern California

## Statement Of The Problem

A problem common to all guided missiles is the determination of various target coordinates and their time derivatives relative to the missile frame of reference. Often the coordinate-information-bearing signal in question need only be "tracked," i.e., selected in such a way as to separate it from other extraneous signals and noise. Pulse-Doppler and cw-Doppler radar-type target seekers are inherently capable of measuring the velocity of a target relative to the missile. The purpose of this paper is to discuss and analyze various ways of tracking a Doppler shifted signal in the presence of noise and other disturbances.

## Introduction

Specifically, the type of radar to be assumed is a cw-Doppler radar, although most of the analysis applies to other types of Doppler systems as well. Clearly, one way of partially separating the desired target signal from noise and undesired signals is to track the desired signal in velocity. Because of the Doppler effect, the received signal from a target which has a finite velocity relative to the missile will in general have a different frequency from that transmitted. The carrier frequency of the received signal differs from the carrier frequency of the transmitted signal by an amount dependent in part upon the missile-target relative velocity. If the carrier is represented by a term of the form B sin $[\phi(t)]$, the received "angle" $\theta(t)$ has been changed, i.e., modulated, compared with the transmitted "angle" $\phi(t)$. This "angle" modulation carries the desired velocity information. Information about $\phi(t)$ is not necessary to track $\theta(t)$, although this knowledge is necessary if an absolute measurement of velocity (or range and its time derivatives) is to be made. Thus, if the input to a servo is $\theta(t)$ and the servo output is also $\theta(t)$, perfect "angle" tracking has been achieved. In order to avoid confusion with the spatial angles of the target relative to the missile, the angles $\phi(t)$ and $\theta(t)$ will henceforth be called "phase angles."

Thus, a servo which will track the phase angle $\theta(t)$ is defined as a "phase-locked" servo or phase-locked loop. "Frequency" will be herein defined as the time rate of change of phase, i.e.,

$$f(t) = \frac{1}{2\pi} \frac{d}{dt} \left[\theta(t)\right] \tag{1}$$

A servo which will track $\omega(t) = \dot{\theta}(t)$ is defined as a "frequency-locked" loop. Clearly, servos which track higher derivatives of $\theta(t)$ could also be defined. The phase- and frequency-locked loops turn out to be the most important servos to be considered from a practical design viewpoint and consequently the principal effort will be concerned with them.

Certain general requirements can be imposed on velocity tracking loops which are to be used in missile applications. Perfect tracking requires that the difference between servo input and output, or "error," be zero. This requires infinite open loop servo gain. Because of system time lags, stability requirements limit the gain. Receiver noise also tends to limit the allowable gain. Since high loop gains will tend to cause the servo to follow the noise, the useful output of the velocity gate will be very noisy. Since the principal purpose of the velocity tracking loop is usually to reduce the noise and interfering signals associated with the target signal, it might appear that at low S/N ratios, as low a loop gain as possible is desirable. Of course the loop gain must always be sufficient to follow the expected accelerations of the target signal in the absence of noise. To discriminate successfully against undesired signals and noise, the servo must be selective. This selectivity depends upon the "width" of the velocity gate in the servo loop, i.e., the range of velocities the gate will pass. The word "gate" here is not to be construed as a pulse or switching arrangement in the time domain, but rather as a frequency filter, since differences in velocity are represented by Doppler frequency shifts. Suppose the loop gain is low so that the servo will not follow the noise well at low S/N ratios. The servo error voltage which represents the target signal-plus-noise velocity at the velocity gate input will then be very nearly as noisy as it would be without any feedback. If any noise fluctuation causes the composite signal to exceed the equivalent maximum (or minimum) velocity that the gate can handle, the target is said to be "lost." Actually, the target may fluctuate back into the gate, so that it may not be lost permanently. However, since the target loss prevents the missile from tracking the target, it is highly desirable that the probability of loss be as small as possible. One way to insure this is to make the gate wide enough so that at low S/N ratios the number of noise fluctuations which can exceed the gatewidth is very small. Widening the gate, however, reduces the servo selectivity and tends to defeat the purpose of the system. If the gate is narrowed, the loop gain must be increased so that the error fluctuations are reduced, thereby keeping the probability of loss low. But increasing the gain conflicts with the other basic servo requirement; namely, keeping the velocity gate output S/N ratio high. Consequently, some sort of compromise must be made. One of the main purposes of this paper is to determine what that compromise must be.

## Block Diagram Analysis in the Absence of Noise

The basic design requirement for the velocity tracking system is that a narrow velocity gate be placed about a target Doppler signal so that this gated signal can be used in the missile (space) angle tracking system. Since the signal frequency as defined in Eq. (1) is proportional to the target velocity, the velocity gate is logically a filter whose "velocity width" is proportional to its frequency bandwidth. One way of tracking the Doppler signal is to vary the filter center frequency in accordance with the input frequency while maintaining a constant bandwidth. Such a procedure is quite hard to instrument. A scheme, which is much easier to instrument and which accomplishes the same purpose, uses a fixed center frequency gate and heterodynes the desired input signal frequency into the gate by means of a local oscillator whose frequency is controlled by a servo. A generalized block diagram of a "phase angle" tracking servo based on this principle appears in Fig. 1.

The input is $A(t) \sin \theta(t)$. The loop is to operate the phase angle $\theta(t)$, so the comparator yields $\epsilon(t)$ which is a function of the difference between the input and feedback phase angles, $\theta(t) - \theta_f(t)$. After gating, the useful output to the (space) angle tracking system is $C(t) \sin \theta_o(t)$ which is similar to the input signal with much of the undesired interference and noise gated out. It will be assumed that the gate is appreciably narrower than the PRF so that in the absence of noise and interference, the gate output is an amplitude-modulated sine wave where the a-m carries the space angle information. In general, there is gain and gain control associated with the filtering action of the gate. The demodulator developes a voltage which is proportional to the difference between $\theta_o(t)$ and a reference phase, or to the difference between $\dot{\theta}_o(t)$ and a reference frequency, depending on the demodulator used.

Voltages proportional to higher derivates of the difference between $\theta_o(t)$ and a reference could also be used. The demodulator output voltage is operated upon by a transfer function Y(s) which contains a frequency invariant gain term. The form of Y(s) is dictated by tracking requirements, especially the servo "memory" desired and stability considerations. The voltage output of Y(s) controls a modulator which develops a phase, $\theta_f(t)$, whose frequency is such as to heterodyne the input target signal frequency into the gate. Some of the auxiliary functions, such as the rear reference scheme, limiting and/or AGC, search and lockon, have not been shown in the basic velocity tracking system in Fig. 1.

Some of the basic design decisions include where to perform the comparison (i.e., mixing), what center frequency and bandwidth the velocity gate should have, etc. Most of these design parameter determinations require analysis, but some can be set by qualitative reasoning. For example, one can argue that comparison should occur in the r-f followed immediately by the narrow gate. Since the r-f input signal is very small, considerable i-f amplification is necessary for the signal to be usable for angle track and for the demodulator to operate properly. Before the i-f gain is sufficient to cause noise, main bang, etc., to saturate the system, the signal is gated. The amplified gated signal is much less noisy and more free from undesired signals than if the i-f amplification were performed before gating; as a consequence, the space angle tracking loop design may be simplified. The i-f gate center frequency should be high enough to give good image rejection and Q, and yet not so high that the required bandwidth and skirt attenuation cannot be attained.

Two types of tracking servos will be considered; phase-locked and frequency-locked. In both, the comparator will be assumed to be an ideal mixer whose output is the low frequency portion of the product of the two inputs and the modulator an ideal voltage controlled oscillator (VCO) whose output frequency is proportional to the input control voltage. The demodulator in the phase-locked case is an ideal phase detector whose output is proportional to the phase shift of the input relative to the phase reference. In the frequency-locked case the demodulator is a frequency discriminator whose output is proportional to the difference between input frequency and crossover. Crossover is defined as the frequency at which the discriminator output is zero. The crossover is set at the velocity gate center frequency. For the initial analysis, it will be assumed that the system is tracking well and that the velocity gate is sufficiently wide so that the effect of the gate on the servo transfer function can be neglected. With these modifications, Fig. 1 for the phase-locked case becomes Fig. 2.

Although the input is actually pulsed, only the cw Doppler component is important for tracking. It will therefore be assumed that the input is a cw sine wave at the Doppler shifted carrier frequency. The input amplitude is assumed constant to simplify the analysis. The servo equations are therefore

$$e_i(t) = A \cos \theta(t) = A\cos\left[(\omega_c + \omega_d)\, t + \phi_d\right] \tag{2}$$

The mixer output frequency must be at the center frequency of the velocity gate for perfect tracking. Let this center frequency be $f_o$. The VCO output for closed loop operation will be assumed to be a constant amplitude cosine wave whose frequency in the absence of a control voltage is $\omega_o$ below the input. Hence

$$e_f(t) = A_f \cos \theta_f(t) \tag{3}$$

where

$$\dot{\theta}_f = \omega_f - k_2 V_2(t) \tag{4}$$

$$\theta_f = \omega_f t - k_2 \int_o^t V_2(t)\, dt \tag{5}$$

$$\omega_f = \omega_c - \omega_o \tag{6}$$

where $\omega_c$ is the signal carrier frequency and $\omega_f$ is the VCO frequency. In the absence of a control voltage, assuming the mixer to be a multiplier,

$$\epsilon(t) = e_i(t)\, e_f(t) = A \cos \theta\,(t)\, A_f \cos \theta_f(t) \tag{7}$$

The gate passes only the difference frequency, so that

$$e_o\,(t) = C\,(t) \cos\,(\theta - \theta_f) \tag{8}$$

where C(t) is proportional to $AA_f$. The input to the phase detector is assumed to have constant amplitude. Since C(t) must carry the angle information, some sort of limiting or equivalent preceding the phase detector is necessary to satisfy this assumption. Define $\epsilon_\theta$ as the phase on the phase detector input. Thus

$$\epsilon_\theta = \theta - \theta_f \tag{9}$$

Both the gate and the phase detector are aligned at the cross-over frequency, $\omega_o$. The phase detector output is therefore

$$V_1(t) = k_1(\epsilon_\theta - \omega_o t) \tag{10}$$

Also

$$V_2(t) = \int_0^t V_1(a)\, g_\phi(t - a)\, da \tag{11}$$

where

$$g_\phi(t) = \mathcal{L}^{-1}\left[Y_\phi(s)\right] \tag{12}$$

Taking Laplace transforms of Eqs. (9), (10), (11), and (5) yields the loop equations:

$$\epsilon_\theta(s) = \theta(s) - \theta_f(s) \tag{13}$$

$$V_1(s) = k_1\left[\epsilon_\theta(s) - \frac{\omega_o}{s^2}\right] \tag{14}$$

$$V_2(s) = Y_\phi(s)\, V_1(s) \tag{15}$$

$$\theta_f(s) = \frac{\omega_f}{s^2} + \frac{k_2}{s} V_2(s) \tag{16}$$

Eqs. (13) through (16) may be combined to give

$$\theta_f(s) = \frac{\omega_f}{s^2} + \frac{k_1 k_2}{s} Y_\phi(s) \left[ \epsilon_\theta(s) - \frac{\omega_o}{s^2} \right]$$

$$= \frac{\omega_f}{s^2} + Y_1(s) \left[ \theta(s) - \theta_f(s) - \frac{\omega_o}{s^2} \right] \qquad (17)$$

where

$$Y_1(s) = \frac{k_1 k_2 Y_\phi(s)}{s} \qquad (18)$$

$$\theta_f(s) = \frac{\frac{\omega_f}{s^2} + Y_1(s) \left[ \theta(s) - \frac{\omega_o}{s^2} \right]}{1 + Y_1(s)} \qquad (19)$$

$$\epsilon_\theta(s) = \frac{\theta(s) - \frac{\omega_f}{s^2} + Y_1(s) \frac{\omega_o}{s^2}}{1 + Y_1(s)} \qquad (20)$$

Making use of Eq. (6) and the fact that from Eq. (2)

$$\theta(s) = \frac{\omega_c + \omega_d}{s^2} + \frac{\phi_d}{s} \qquad (21)$$

allows Eqs. (19) and (20) to be written as

$$\theta_f(s) = \frac{\frac{\omega_c - \omega_o}{s^2} + Y_1(s) \left[ \frac{\omega_c + \omega_d}{s^2} + \frac{\phi_d}{s} - \frac{\omega_o}{s^2} \right]}{1 + Y_1(s)}$$

$$= \frac{\omega_c - \omega_o}{s^2} + \frac{Y_1(s)}{1 + Y_1(s)} \left( \frac{\omega_d}{s^2} + \frac{\phi_d}{s} \right) \qquad (22)$$

$$\epsilon_\theta(s) = \frac{\dfrac{\omega_c + \omega_d}{s^2} + \dfrac{\phi_d}{s} - \dfrac{\omega_c}{s^2} + \dfrac{\omega_o}{s^2}\left[1 + Y_1(s)\right]}{1 + Y_1(s)}$$

$$= \frac{\omega_o}{s^2} + \frac{\dfrac{\omega_d}{s^2} + \dfrac{\phi_d}{s}}{1 + Y_1(s)} \qquad (23)$$

In the frequency-locked case, similar equations may be derived. In this case Fig. 1 becomes Fig. 3. The phase-locked loop discussion up to Eq. (9) also applies in the frequency-locked case ($V_2$ is replaced by $v_2$). The frequency discriminator is, however, sensitive only to rates of change of phase. Define the frequency on the discriminator input as

$$\epsilon_{\dot{\theta}} = \dot{\theta} - \dot{\theta}_f \qquad (24)$$

The discriminator crossover frequency is $\omega_o$ and its output is

$$v_1 = K_1 \left(\epsilon_{\dot{\theta}} - \omega_o\right) \qquad (25)$$

Also

$$v_2(t) = \int_o^t v_1(a)\, g_f\,(t - a)\, da \qquad (26)$$

where

$$g_f(t) = \mathcal{L}^{-1}\left[Y_f(s)\right] \qquad (27)$$

The transformed equations are therefore

$$\epsilon_{\dot{\theta}}(s) = \dot{\theta}(s) - \dot{\theta}_f(s) = s\left[\theta(s) - \theta_f(s)\right] = s\,\epsilon_\theta(s) \qquad (28)$$

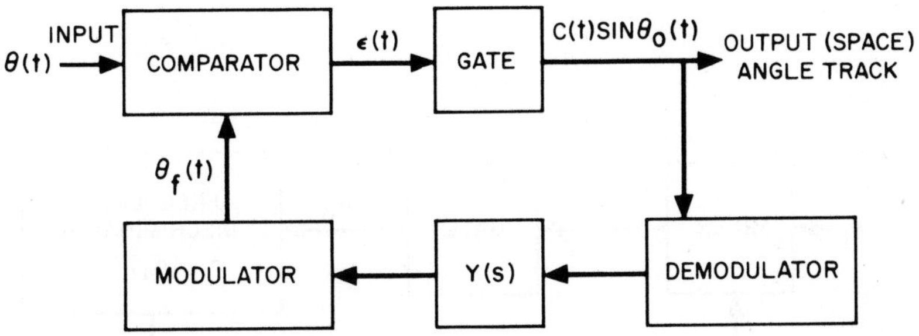


Fig. 1. Block Diagram of a Phase Angle Tracking Servo

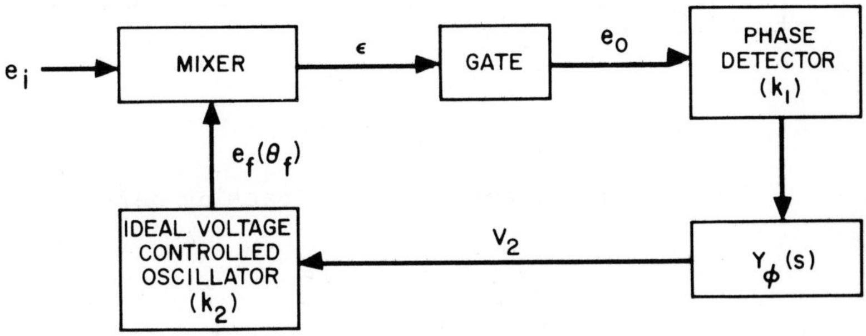


Fig. 2. Phase-locked Tracking Servo

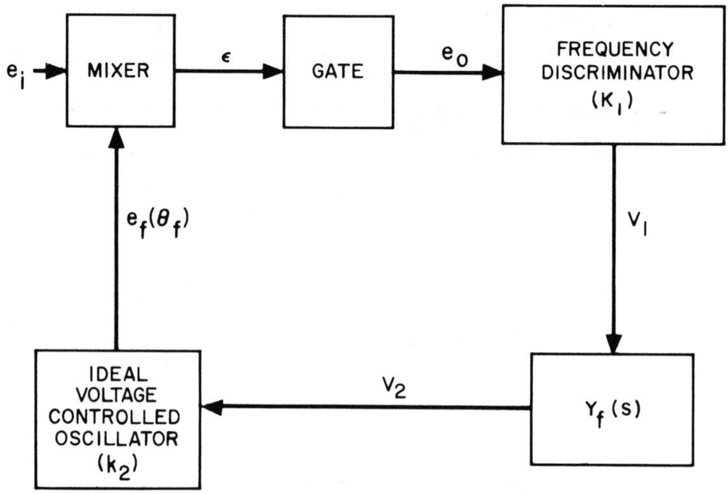


Fig. 3. Frequency-locked Tracking Servo

$$v_1(s) = K_1 \left[ \epsilon_{\dot{\theta}}(s) - \frac{\omega_o}{s} \right] = K_1 \; s \left[ \epsilon_{\theta}(s) - \frac{\omega_o}{s^2} \right] \tag{29}$$

$$v_2(s) = Y_f(s) v_1(s) \tag{30}$$

$$\dot{\theta}_f(s) = s\theta_f(s) = \frac{\omega_f}{s} + k_2 v_2(s) \tag{31}$$

Eqs. (28) through (31) combine to give

$$\dot{\theta}_f(s) = \frac{\omega_f}{s} + k_2 K_1 Y_f(s) \left[ \epsilon_{\dot{\theta}}(s) - \frac{\omega_o}{s} \right]$$

$$= \frac{\omega_f}{s} + Y_2(s) \left[ \dot{\theta}(s) - \dot{\theta}_f(s) - \frac{\omega_o}{s} \right] \tag{32}$$

where

$$Y_2(s) = k_2 K_1 Y_f(s) \tag{33}$$

Thus

$$\omega_F = \dot{\theta}_f(s) = \frac{\frac{\omega_f}{s} + Y_2(s) \left[ \dot{\theta}(s) - \frac{\omega_o}{s} \right]}{1 + Y_2(s)} \tag{34}$$

$$\epsilon_{\dot{\theta}}(s) \; \frac{\theta(s) - \frac{\omega_f}{s} + Y_2(s) \frac{\omega_o}{s}}{1 + Y_2(s)} \tag{35}$$

Making use of Eq. (16) and the fact that

$$\dot{\theta}(t) = \omega_c + \omega_d \tag{36}$$

or

$$\dot{\theta}(s) = \frac{\omega_c + \omega_d}{s} \tag{37}$$

$$\omega_F(s) = \frac{\frac{\omega_c - \omega_o}{s} + Y_2(s)\,\frac{\omega_c + \omega_d - \omega_o}{s}}{1 + Y_2(s)}$$

$$= \frac{\omega_c - \omega_o}{s} + \frac{Y_2(s)}{1 + Y_2(s)}\left(\frac{\omega_d}{s}\right) \tag{38}$$

$$\epsilon_{\dot{\theta}}(s) = \frac{\frac{\omega_c + \omega_d}{s} - \frac{\omega_c}{s} + \frac{\omega_o}{s}\,(1 + Y_2(s))}{1 + Y_2(s)}$$

$$= \frac{\omega_o}{s} + \frac{\frac{\omega_d}{s}}{1 + Y_2(s)} \tag{39}$$

## Servo Analysis in the Absence of Noise

The velocity tracking servo design must be based on several conflicting requirements. It must be capable of tracking a given acceleration and still have small steady-state error in response to accelerations on the input. It must track at long ranges and yet have a low probability of loss due to noise. It must provide adequate velocity discrimination and yet be easily locked on. These and other requirements necessitate a compromise design.

Several factors affect the servo design. The system must be capable of following a given acceleration which lasts for a given duration. This requires a reasonably high gain servo, capable of following rates of change on the input. A step in acceleration corresponds to a ramp input in frequency and a parabolic input in phase. In order that a servo follow a ramp input with zero steady-state error, two integrators must be employed in the loop. In order that a parabolic input be followed with zero error, three integrators must be employed. The general effect of adding integrations in the loop is to increase the tendency toward instability. For the same gain a three-integrator loop will have a greater overshoot and longer settling time than the corresponding two-integrator servo. With the aid of simple lead networks, a two-integrator servo can be made stable at all gains. On the other hand, a three-integrator servo is always unstable for some range of gains. This conclusion is evident from an explanation of the following root locus plots (see Fig. 4).

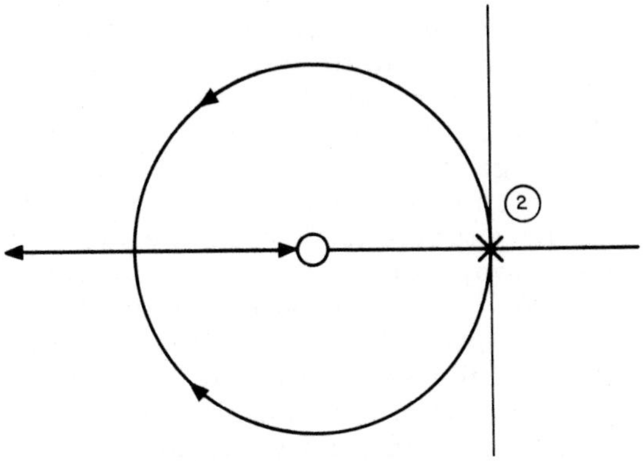


a. Two-integration servo

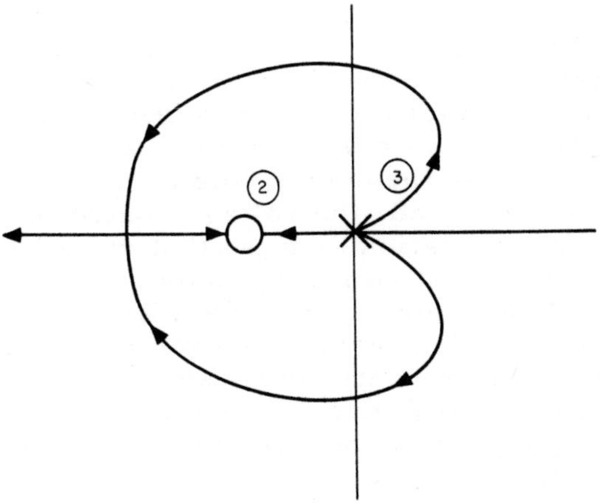


b. Three-integration servo

Fig. 4. Root Locus Plots

It will be observed that the two-integrator servo locus never enters the right hand plane; while, the three-integrator servo is unstable for all values of gain which cause the closed loop poles to lie in the right hand plane. It is also interesting to note that in the three integrator servo the range of unstable gains runs from zero to some value $K_c$. It therefore follows that the three integrator servo is stable for values of gain larger than $K_c$. On this basis, then, when the loop gain falls below the critical gain $K_c$, the servo becomes unstable. These decreases in gain can be expected due to scintillation. This effect will also be experienced when the servo is turned on. Of course, if the loop gain is made independent of the signal level, then a three-integrator servo may be employed with a gain setting sufficiently high to maintain the stability at all times, except when the set is turned on. Because of the danger of loop gain variation with amplitude, (unless a counter or hard limiting is employed), a two-integrator servo is recommended. If phase tracking is employed, the acceleration will be followed with a constant error in the steady state. Actually, the concern is not so much with steady-state error as it is with the ability to track the acceleration over the period during which it exists. In any case, the steady-state error can be made small by making the loop gain sufficiently high. If a two-integrator frequency locked loop is employed, the steady-state error to a step acceleration is zero and no problem is encountered. The frequency-locked loop requires two external active integrators to obtain the double pole at the origin. If a phase-locked loop is employed, the voltage controlled oscillator will supply its own integration term so that only one additional external integrator must be incorporated.

The two-integrator servo is very simply stabilized by means of a single zero term as shown in Fig. 4. A passive lead equalizer cannot contribute a single zero but must add an additional pole. In order to approximate the situation shown in Fig. 4, the separation between the zero and pole must be as great as possible.

## Comparison of Frequency- and Phase-Locked Loops in the Presence of Noise

A detailed noise analysis of one- and two-integrator frequency-locked loops appears in the next section. A brief semiquantitative comparison of frequency- and phase-locked loops is possible at this point, however.

The input to both servos is assumed to be a Doppler-shifted signal plus band limited noise where the Doppler signal does not necessarily lie in the center of the noise spectrum. Thus

$$e_i(t) = x(t) \cos \omega_i t + y(t) \sin \omega_i t + A \cos (\omega_d t + \phi_d)$$

$$= B_i \cos (\omega_i t - \psi) \tag{40}$$

where

$$B_i = \left\{ \left[ A \cos (\delta t + \phi_d) + x \right]^2 + \left[ y - A \sin (\delta t + \phi_d \right]^2 \right\}^{1/2} \tag{41}$$

$$= \tan^{-1} \frac{y - A \sin (\delta t + \phi_d)}{x + A \cos (\delta t + \phi_d)} \tag{42}$$

$$\delta = \omega_d - \omega_i \tag{43}$$

It can be shown that the standard frequency discriminators (Foster-Seely, slope, etc.) involve an incoherent process in that the input is filtered and then serves as a reference, while in the standard phase discriminator, the reference is independent of the input. However, in the phase-tracking case, it can be shown that the noisy output of the VCO is equivalent to the reference for the phase detector so that the phase-tracking loop is not purely phase-coherent. Figure 5a shows the actual servo connection, (no velocity gate) and Fig. 5b shows its functional equivalent. That these are equivalent follows since, if for case (a),

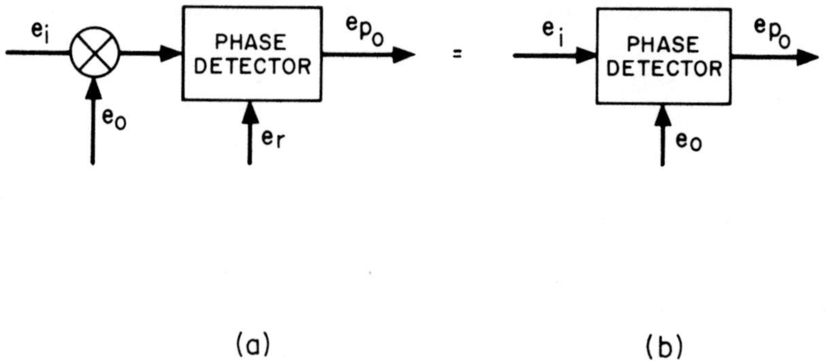


Fig. 5. Servo Phase Detector Connection

$$\left.\begin{aligned} e_i &= \cos(\omega t + \phi_i) \\ e_o &= \cos(\omega t + \phi_o) \\ e_r &= \sin(\omega t + \phi_r) \end{aligned}\right\} \tag{44}$$

then,

$$\epsilon = e_i e_o = \frac{1}{2} \cos(\phi_i - \phi_o) \tag{45}$$

$$e_{po} = e_r \epsilon = \frac{1}{4} \sin(\phi_r - \phi_i + \phi_o) \tag{46}$$

For case (b)

$$\left.\begin{aligned} e_i &= \cos(\omega t + \phi_i) \\ e_o &= \sin(\omega t + \phi_o) \\ e_{po} &= e_i e_o = \frac{1}{2} \sin(\phi_o - \phi_i) \end{aligned}\right\} \tag{47}$$

When the servo is tracking with zero error the phase detector output $e_{po}$ must be zero. In case (a), the servo adjusts its output phase to make $\phi_o - \phi_i = \phi_r$. Since $\phi_r$ is completely arbitrary, it may be set equal to zero. But this is the condition for zero output in case (b).

Note that the servo output, $e_o$, in the actual case is noisy, i. e., it is not a clean reference. Therefore, the phase-tracking servo is not truly phase-coherent since it derives its reference from its input. Again, if the filtering between the input and the reference makes the reference spectrum narrow compared with the input spectrum, the incoherent effect is small. Even though the phase-locked loop is not truly phase coherent, nor is the frequency-locked loop truly frequency-conerent, the two loops still differ by a constant of integration which is the phase-constant. It will be shown that this suggests a 3-db signal-to-noise ratio difference between the two loops. In order that absolutely no additional incoherence be introduced by the frequency detector itself, it appears necessary to employ a phase coherent detector followed by a differentiator. This type of discriminator truly satisfies the assumption that the discriminator output is proportional to the time rate of change on the input. However, there is no point in the additional differentiator in this case—the phase-locked loop might as well be used directly. Phase-coherence is defined as the case where the phase reference has a perfectly correlated phase with the input phase. Frequency coherence is defined as the case where the reference frequency is coherent with the input frequency, but the phases are not coherent. Incoherence is defined as the case where there is neither perfect phase nor perfect frequency correlation, i. e., noise-noise products exist. By careful design of standard frequency discriminators (i. e., by making the reference as uncorrelated as possible with the input noise), the incoherent effects can be made negligible. The differentiation of $\psi(t)$ and subsequent integration to $\theta(t)$ in the frequency-locked case results in loss of the known constant of integration (this constant is $\phi_d$ in the noiseless case) and replaces it with a constant which is not coherent with the incoming signal phase. The phase coherency is maintained in the phase-locked case.

Figure 6a represents a phase detector in which the phase of the reference voltage $e_r$ is coherent with (in this case, the same as) the input signal phase. Figure 6b represents a phase detector in which the frequency is coherent with the input signal frequency but the reference phase is not. While the output of the low pass filter in Fig. 6a is independent of the input phase $\phi_d$, the respective outputs of the low pass filters in Fig. 6b are not.

The quadrature reference voltage arrangement in Fig. 6b is necessary to make the output $V_o$ independent of $\phi_d$. An ideal phase detector measures the difference between the input and reference phases. If these two phases are coherent, the difference is a constant (or at least there is a linear relationship between them). If they are incoherent, the difference is unknown a priori, and can, in fact, be treated as a random variable. In any case, the output of the detector should be independent of the input phase, i. e., a function of the difference between reference and input phases only.

The following mathematical comparison of these idealized detectors will show a 3-db S/N ratio advantage of the phase-coherent detector over the frequency coherent detector. Since coherence with the phase constant $\phi_d$ is lost in a frequency discriminator, the implication is that an idealized frequency detector has a poorer output S/N ratio than an idealized phase detector for the same input S/N ratio. A rigorous quantitative comparison is difficult, since the frequency discriminator

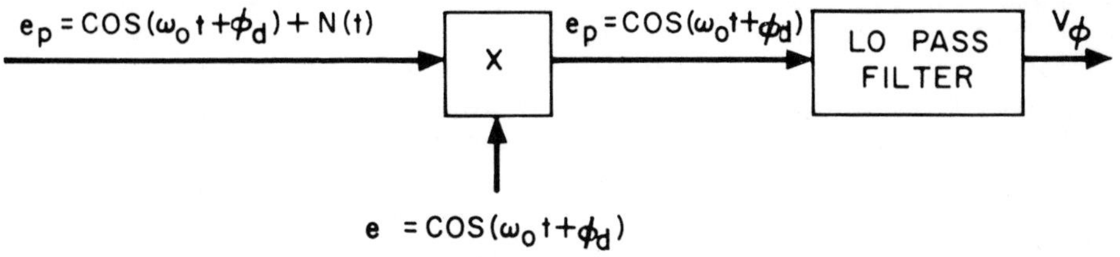


Fig. 6(a). Block Diagram of Phase-Coherent Phase Detector

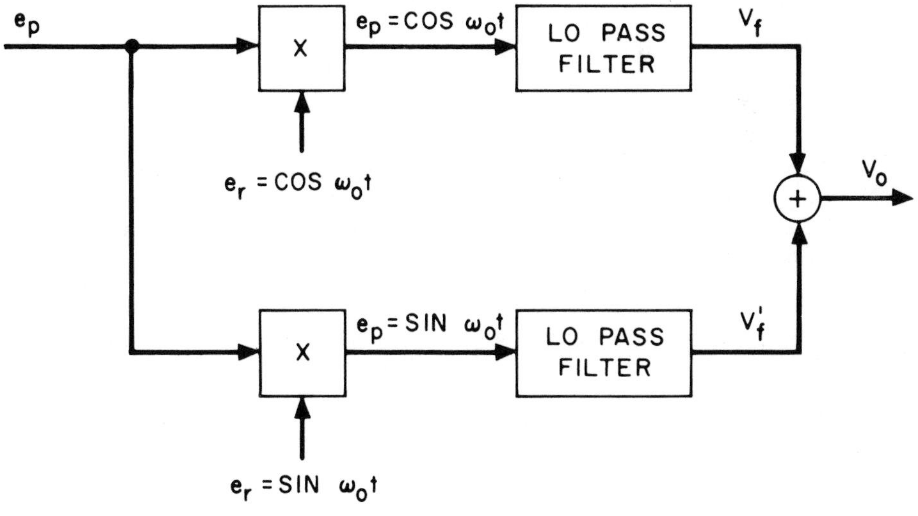


Fig. 6(b). Block Diagram of Frequency-Coherent Phase Detector

output is proportional to input frequency and the phase detector output is proportional to input phase. The effect of the loss of phase coherence in a frequency-locked loop can best be shown by comparing the voltage S/N ratio at the output of the velocity gate with the corresponding S/N ratio in the phase-locked loop. This would require a careful noise analysis of the phase-locked loop similar to that made for the frequency-locked loop in the latter part of this paper. In any case, the constant of integration $\phi_d$ is lost in the frequency-locked loop, but not in the idealized phase-locked loop.

The effect of the loss of this constant of integration can be illustrated. Suppose the filter $Y_f(s)$ is such that the VCO output consists of the desired output phase plus narrow-band noise in the phase-locked case and the desired output frequency (incoherent phase) plus narrow-band noise in the frequency-locked case. Thus, in the phase-coherent case, let the input to the phase detector in Fig. 6a be

$$e_p = \cos(\omega_o t + \phi_d) + N(t) \tag{48}$$

and the VCO output be

$$e_f = \cos\left[(\omega_f t + \phi_d) + N'(t)\right] \tag{49}$$

where $\omega_d - \omega_f = \omega_o$. The signal-noise intermodulation in the VCO output has been neglected in Eq. (49) and the spectrum of N' is much narrower than that of N. If the servo is tracking well, as it has been assumed, the phase detector output is given approximately by

$$V_\phi = e_p \cos(\omega_o t + \phi_d) = \frac{1}{2} + N(t)\cos(\omega_o t + \phi_d) \tag{50}$$

The average power $\overset{\simeq}{V}{}_\phi^2$ is

$$\overset{\simeq}{V}{}_\phi^2 = \frac{1}{4} + \frac{\overline{N^2}}{2} \tag{51}$$

where the signal components $\omega_o$ and $\omega_f$ are assumed to be essentially uncorrelated with the noise.

In the frequency-coherent case, for the same input to the detector in Fig. 6b, the outputs are

$$V_f = e_p \cos\omega_o t = \frac{1}{2} \cos \phi_d + N(t) \cos\omega_o t \tag{52}$$

$$V_f' = e_f \sin\omega_o t = \frac{1}{2} \sin \phi_d + N(t) \sin \omega_o t \tag{53}$$

Note the loss of the phase constant. Thus

$$\tilde{V}_f^2 = \frac{1}{4} \cos^2 \phi_d + \frac{\overline{N^2}}{2} \tag{54}$$

$$\tilde{V}_f'^2 = \frac{1}{4} \sin^2 \phi_d + \frac{\overline{N^2}}{2} \tag{55}$$

$$\tilde{V}_o^2 = \tilde{V}_f^2 + \tilde{V}_f'^2 = \frac{1}{4} + \overline{N^2} \tag{56}$$

The power signal-to-noise ratio in Eq. (51) is

$$\frac{S}{N} = \frac{\frac{1}{4}}{\frac{\overline{N^2}}{2}} = \frac{1}{2\overline{N^2}} \tag{57}$$

while in Eq. (56) it is

$$\frac{S}{N} = \frac{\frac{1}{4}}{\overline{N^2}} = \frac{1}{4\overline{N^2}} \tag{58}$$

Note that the signal-to-noise ratio in the phase-coherent case is always 3-db higher than in the frequency-coherent case. Note that this same result is obtained if the expression in Eq. (54) is averaged over $\phi_d$, where $\phi_d$ is a random variable uniformly distributed between $-\pi$ and $\pi$ in the phase-incoherent case. The greatest degradation in signal-to-noise ratio occurs when there is no coherence whatever, i.e., when the noise as well as the signal multiplies itself. For example, if the signal plus noise,

$$e = \cos(\omega_o t + \phi_d) + N(t) \tag{59}$$

were multiplied by itself,

$$\overline{e^2} = \frac{1}{2} + 2\overline{N}\cos(\omega_o t + \phi_d) + \overline{N^2} \tag{60}$$

the corresponding average power is

$$\tilde{\tilde{e}}^4 = \frac{1}{4} + 2\overline{N^2} + 3\overline{N^2}^2 \tag{61}$$

If the signal and noise are uncorrelated and N is Gaussian with mean 0, $\overline{N} = \overline{N^3} = 0$. The signal-to-noise ratio is

$$\frac{S}{N} = \frac{1}{4\left(2\overline{N^2} + 3\overline{N^2}\right)^2} \tag{62}$$

which is clearly considerably worse than in either the phase or frequency coherent cases.

## Noise Analysis of a Frequency-Locked Loop

### General Analysis

The problem is to keep the probability of loss during the flight time less than some prescribed minimum and still optimize system parameters so that the S/N ratio out of the velocity gate is a maximum. Since minimizing the probability of loss is a very difficult analysis problem, the "loss rate" will be minimized instead. The loss rate is defined as the reciprocal of the mean time to loss. The procedure will be to minimize the loss rate with respect to the servo parameters, particularly the "closed loop bandwidth," and then set a certain maximum allowable loss rate to determine the parameter values. At the same time the S/N ratio out of the gate for this optimum system will be found. The minimum receivable power will then be determined so as to find the maximum range of the missile.

The following simplifying assumptions have been made:

1. The system is initially locked on such that the signal is near the center of the gate.

2. The system is linear to the frequency variable.

3. For mathematical convenience (no loss in generality), the reference carrier frequency, velocity gate center frequency, and discriminator crossover will all be assumed to be at zero frequency. The servo will first be analyzed with one integrator in the open loop, then with two integrators and a lead term.

4. The S/N ratio is low so that signal-noise intermodulation products are neglected.

5. The mixer input is a single frequency Doppler signal in broadband thermal noise.

6. The velocity gate passband is square with a half bandwidth (equivalent audio bandwidth) of $\beta = 1000$ cps. Its effect on the servo transfer function will be neglected since the signal is assumed to be well within the gate.

7. The discriminator is linear in the region of interest and the slope of the discriminator characteristic is proportional to the signal level (i. e., no limiter).

8. In determining the spectrum from the discriminator, fluctuations in amplitude on the input will be neglected.

9. The frequency of the VCO is linearly proportional to the control voltage in the region of interest. The VCO output amplitude is constant.

10. The noise bandwidth on the VCO output is sufficiently narrow compared with the mixer input noise bandwidth so that the noise at the mixer input appears essentially unchanged at the mixer output. A corollary to this assumption is that, in other words, the input and VCO frequency noise are almost uncorrelated.

11. The mixer input noise is normally distributed about the Doppler signal as a mean. From assumption 10, the implication is that, consequently, the error noise

frequencies (i.e., mixer output) are normally distributed about the signal error frequency as a mean.

The servo block diagram and notation to be used for the analysis appears in Fig. 7. The input voltage contains signal and noise which can be represented as a sine wave with a time-varying argument such that the time rate of change of this argument is proportional to

$$f_i = f_d + f_N \tag{63}$$

where

$f_i$ = input frequency

$f_d$ = Doppler frequency (i.e., the desired signal)

$f_N$ = noise "frequency"

$f_N$ can be thought of as the resultant, or sum, of a large number of random noise frequencies. $f_N$ is therefore a normally distributed stochastic process which is stationary in the steady state and is normally distributed by the central limit theorem. $f_d$ is a nonrandom "signal" which is in general time-varying (and hence nonstationary) even in the steady state. $f_f$ is the frequency of the constant amplitude VCO output voltage. $f_f$ is noisy, but because of filtering in the velocity gate and $Y_f(s)$, or, more properly, because of filtering by the servo closed loop passband, the noise bandwidth of $f_f$ is narrow compared with that of $f_N$. Furthermore, $f_f$ and $f_N$ are almost uncorrelated. The mixer output, or "error," is then

$$\epsilon = f_i - f_f = (f_d - f_f) + f_N = \epsilon_s + \epsilon_N \tag{64}$$

where

$$\epsilon_s = f_d - f_f \tag{65}$$

$$\epsilon_N = f_N \tag{66}$$

Note that $\epsilon_s$, the "signal" error, is noisy since $f_f$ is noisy. The noise bandwidth of $\epsilon_s$ is assumed less than the noise

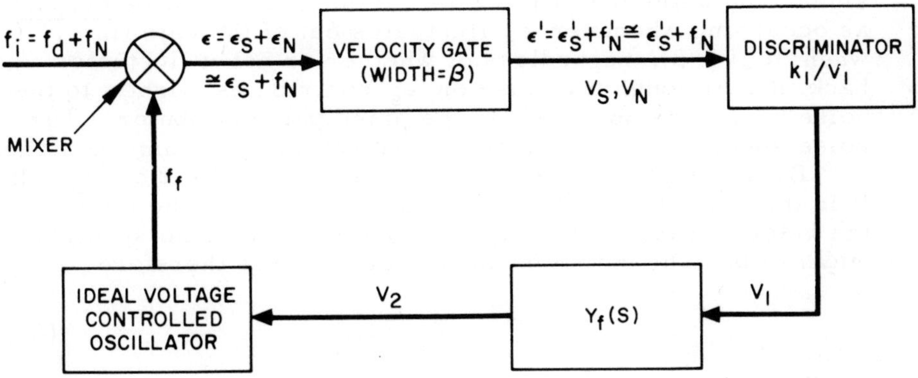


Fig. 7. Functional Block Diagram

bandwidth of $\epsilon_N$, and $\epsilon_s$ and $\epsilon_N$ are almost uncorrelated. It is important to observe that the fluctuations of $\epsilon_s$ cause loss, not the fluctuations of $\epsilon_N$. With the assumptions made in this paper, the spectrum of $f_f$ will contain a delta function corresponding to $f_d$ after being operated upon the loop. If the difference between the frequency of this line and $f_d$ lies in the velocity gate, the loop is said to be "tracking." Actually, $\epsilon_s$ may fluctuate out of the gate and back in again in such a way that the system is still "tracking" according to the above definition. However, a fluctuation outside the gate when the target is accelerating (i. e., $\dot{f}_d > 0$) increases the probability of loss on such a fluctuation (if $\dot{f}_d$ and the fluctuation are in the same direction). Furthermore, experimental investigations have shown that the target actually is lost most of the time when the signal fluctuates out of the gate. Hence, loss will be defined as occurring whenever $\epsilon_s$ fluctuates out of the gate (i. e., when $|\epsilon_s| > \beta$), regardless of whether or not it fluctuates back in. Although the noise on $\epsilon_s$ contributes slightly to the noise on $f_f$, the noise $\epsilon_N$ is the principal contributor. The noise spectrum of $f_f$ will therefore be derived from $\epsilon_N$ alone.

By assumption, the velocity gate has no effect on $\epsilon_s$. If B is the audio bandwidth of the spectrum of $f_N$, the effect of the velocity gate on $\epsilon_N = f_N$ is to narrow the audio spectral width to β. The output of the velocity gate is therefore

$$\epsilon' = \epsilon_s + f_N' \tag{67}$$

But if frequencies inside the gate only are considered, $f_N' = f_N$,

$$f_N' = f_N \left[u(f_N) - u(f_N - \beta)\right] \tag{68}$$

Since no limiter preceding the discriminator has been assumed, the discriminator output is proportional to the amplitude of the input as well as its frequency. Furthermore, the standard type of frequency discriminator (Foster-Seeley, slope, etc.) is nonlinear in that the superposition law does not hold for frequencies even though the slope is linear. This effect introduces a degradation of the weaker signal. Since $S < N$ in this case, the signal is degraded by the S/N ratio. If incoherent limiting is used, the degradation is even worse. The commonly used phase detectors, on the other hand, do not introduce nonlinear degradation, and this fact is an argument in favor of phase-locked loops. However, it is possible to build frequency discriminators which are very nearly ideal in that the voltage output to the sum of two (or more) frequencies is linearly proportional to their sum. One possible method of instrumenting an approximation to this ideal discriminator is to pass the signal through a bank of narrow frequency filters, then detect each output and sum the resultant outputs. The voltage output of each filter must be linearly proportional to the frequency offset from crossover as well as to the amplitude of the signal present in the filter. For simplicity in analysis, this assumption will be made. Now if $V_s$ is the amplitude of the signal and $V_N$ is the amplitude of the noise at time t, the ideal discriminator just assumed develops an output

$$V_1 = k_1\left(\frac{V_s}{\sqrt{2}}\,\epsilon_s + V_N f_N'\right)$$

$$= K_s\,\epsilon_s + K_N\,\epsilon_N \text{ for } \beta \geq \epsilon_N \geq 0 \qquad (69)$$

Note that although $K_s$ is a nonrandom constant for $V_s$ a constant, $K_N$ is a random variable.

The voltages $V_1$ and $V_2$ are related by

$$V_2(s) = Y_f(s)\,V_1(s) \qquad (70)$$

For the one-integrator case

$$Y_f(s) = \frac{1}{s} \qquad (71)$$

For the two-integrator-plus-lead case

$$Y_f(s) = \frac{s + a}{s^2} \qquad (72)$$

An ideal VCO develops a frequency which is proportional to the input control voltage. Hence

$$f_f = k_2 V_2 \qquad (73)$$

The VCO output voltage is then

$$V_f(t) = A_f \cos(\omega_f t + \phi_f) \qquad (74)$$

From Eqs. (69), (70), and (73), in the region where $0 \leq \epsilon_N \leq \beta$,

$$f_f = k_2 Y_f V_1 = k_2 Y_f(K_s \epsilon_s + K_N \epsilon_N) = Y_s \epsilon_s + Y_N \epsilon_N \quad (75)$$

where

$$Y_s = k_2 K_s Y_f \quad (76)$$

$$Y_N = k_2 K_N Y_f \quad (77)$$

Observe that

$$Y_N = \frac{Y_s K_N}{K_s} \quad (78)$$

But from Eqs. (65), (66), and (75),

$$f_f = Y_s(f_d - f_f) + Y_N f_N$$

or

$$f_f = \frac{Y_s f_d + Y_N f_N}{1 + Y_s} = \frac{Y_s}{1 + Y_s} \left(f_d + \frac{K_N}{K_s} f_N\right) \quad (79)$$

Similarly

$$f_d - \epsilon_s = Y_s \epsilon_s + Y_N f_N$$

or

$$\epsilon_s = \frac{f_d - Y_N f_N}{1 + Y_s} = \frac{f_d - \frac{K_N}{K_s} Y_s f_N}{1 + Y_s} \quad (80)$$

Equation (80) shows that the effect of the noise is reduced as $K_s/K_N$ increases. $K_s/K_N$ is related to the S/N ratio. However, since $K_N$ is a random variable, Eqs. (79) and (80) are not in usable form for calculation.

For convenience, let us neglect the fluctuations in $V_1$ due to input amplitude fluctuations. In other words, the noise spectral output of the discriminator depends only on frequency variations on the input. The mean output should still depend on the input amplitude, and this is accomplished by assuming that the noise voltage output of the discriminator is proportional to the rms noise amplitude and the instantaneous noise frequency. Since the noise input voltage amplitude and frequency are independent, Eq. (69) becomes

$$V_1 = k_1 \left( \frac{V_s \epsilon_s}{\sqrt{2}} + \sqrt{\overline{V_N^2}}\; f_N' \right)$$

$$= K_s \epsilon_s + \sqrt{\overline{K_N^2}}\; \epsilon_N \text{ for } \beta \geq \epsilon_N \geq 0 \qquad (81)$$

Equations (79) and (80) then become, respectively,

$$f_f = \frac{Y_s}{1 + Y_s} \left( f_d + \frac{\sqrt{\overline{K_N^2}}}{K_s} f_N \right) = Y_o \left( f_d + \frac{f_N}{\gamma} \right) \qquad (82)$$

$$\epsilon_s = \frac{f_d}{1 + Y_s} - \frac{Y_s}{1 + Y_s} \frac{\sqrt{\overline{K_N^2}}}{K_s} f_N = \frac{Y_o}{Y_s} f_d + \frac{Y_o f_N}{\gamma} \qquad (83)$$

where

$$Y_o = \frac{Y_s}{1 + Y_s}$$

$$Y_s = k_2 K_s Y_f = \frac{k_1 k_2 V_s}{\sqrt{2}} Y_f$$

$$\gamma^2 = \frac{K_s^2}{\overline{K_N^2}} = \frac{k_1^2 V_s^2}{2k_1^2 \overline{V_N^2}} = \frac{V_s^2}{2 \overline{V_N^2}} \qquad (84)$$

$\gamma^2$ is therefore the power S/N ratio at the gate output.

Rice (1) shows that for normally distributed noise of mean zero, variance $\sigma^2$, and spectral density G(f), the expected number of positive-going crossings per second of a level, I, is

$$\lambda = \left[ \frac{\int_0^\infty f^2 G(f) df}{\int_0^\infty G(f) df} \right]^{1/2} e^{-\frac{I^2}{2\sigma^2}} \tag{85}$$

where

$$\sigma^2 = \int_0^\infty G(f) df \tag{86}$$

In the particular case at hand, $\lambda$ is the loss rate, since the reciprocal of the mean time to loss is simply the expected number of losses per second. A reasonable loss rate might be one loss in 100 sec, or $\lambda = 0.01 \text{ sec}^{-1}$. It has already been shown that $\epsilon_s$ is (approximately) normally distributed. Since Eq. (85) assumes a normal distribution with zero mean, we will be concerned with the variable $\epsilon_s - \overline{\epsilon}_s$. Loss occurs if the "signal" $\epsilon_s$ exceeds the velocity gate cutoff frequency β. Therefore $I = \beta - \overline{\epsilon}_s$. In Eq. (85) the spectral density of G(f) is $G_{\epsilon_s - \overline{\epsilon}_s}(f)$. Since $f_d$ is nonrandom and $\overline{f_N} = 0$, from Eq. (83),

$$\overline{\epsilon}_s = \frac{Y_o}{Y_s} f_d \tag{87}$$

Hence

$$\epsilon_s - \overline{\epsilon}_s = \frac{Y_o f_N}{\gamma} = z \tag{88}$$

Let the spectral width of $f_N$ be sufficiently wide such that the spectral density of $f_N$ is a constant $w_o$ over the velocity gate-width $0 \leq f_N \leq \beta$. Hence

$$G_z(f) = \frac{G_{f_N}}{\gamma^2} \left| Y_o(j\omega) \right|^2 = \frac{w_o}{\gamma^2} \left| Y_o(j\omega) \right|^2 \tag{89}$$

## Single Integrator Case

At this point it is necessary to consider what $Y_o(j\omega)$ is. Let us first consider the single integrator case. From Eqs. (79) and (71),

$$Y_s = k_2 K_s Y_f(s) = \frac{k_2 K_2}{s} = \frac{1}{st_o} \tag{90}$$

where the S/N ratio is varied by varying the noise power while holding the signal amplitude, and hence $K_s$, constant, $t_o$ is therefore the time constant associated with the integrator divided by the open-loop gain. Hence

$$Y_o(s) = \frac{Y_s}{1+Y_s} = \frac{1}{1+st_o} \tag{91}$$

From Eq. (87), the steady-state average error is

$$\overline{\epsilon_s}(t \to \infty) = \lim_{s \to 0} s\overline{\epsilon_s}(s)$$

$$= \lim_{s \to 0} \frac{sY_o(s)}{Y_s(s)} f_d(s) = \frac{s^2 t_o}{1+st_o} f_d(s)\Bigg|_{s \to 0} \tag{92}$$

Suppose the target is undergoing a constant acceleration, "a," relative to the missile. The maximum Doppler shift is

$$f_d = \frac{2f_c v}{c} = \frac{2f_c}{c}\int_o^t a\,dt = \frac{2f_c at}{c} = k_o t \tag{93}$$

Therefore

$$f_d(s) = \frac{k_o}{s^2} \tag{94}$$

and

$$\overline{\epsilon_s}(t \to \infty) = \frac{t_o k_o}{1+st_o}\Bigg|_{s \to 0} = k_o t_o \tag{95}$$

Similarly, from Eqs. (89) and (91),

$$G_z(f) = \frac{w_o}{\gamma^2} \quad \frac{1}{1 + \omega^2 t_o^{\ 2}} \tag{96}$$

$$\sigma^2 = \int_o^\beta G_z(f)df \cong \int_o^\infty G_z(f)\,df$$

$$= \frac{w_o}{\gamma^2} \int_o^\infty \frac{df}{1+\omega^2 t_o^{\ 2}} = \frac{w_o}{4t_o\gamma^2} \tag{97}$$

where $G_z(f) \cong 0$ at $f = \beta$ so that the upper limit $\beta$ can be replaced by $\infty$ to give an approximate result. Similarly

$$\int_o^\beta f^2 G_z(f)\,df = \frac{w_o}{(2\pi t_o)^3 \gamma^2} \int_o^{2\pi t_o \beta} \frac{x^2 dx}{1+x^2}$$

$$= \frac{w_o}{(2\pi t_o)^3 \gamma^2} \left(x - \tan^{-1} x\right) \Big|_o^{2\pi \beta t_o} \cong \frac{w_o}{16\pi^2 t_o^{\ 3} \gamma^2} (4\beta t_o - 1) \tag{98}$$

From Eq. (95)

$$I = \beta - \overline{\epsilon}_s = \beta - k_o t_o \tag{99}$$

Hence, substituting Eqs. (97), (98), and (99) in Eq. (85),

$$\lambda = \left[\frac{\dfrac{w_o}{16\pi^2 t_o^{\ 3}\gamma^2} (4\beta t_o - 1)}{\dfrac{w_o}{4t_o\gamma^2}}\right]^{1/2} \exp\left[\frac{-(\beta - k_o t_o)^2}{\dfrac{w_o}{2t_o\gamma^2}}\right]$$

$$= \left(\frac{4\beta t_o - 1}{4\pi^2 t_o^{\ 2}}\right)^{1/2} \exp\left[\frac{-2t_o\gamma^2}{w_o}(\beta - k_o t_o)^2\right] \tag{100}$$

But it is assumed that $\beta >> \frac{1}{t_o}$, hence

$$\lambda \cong \frac{1}{\pi}\sqrt{\frac{\beta}{t_o}} \quad \exp\left[\frac{-2t_o\gamma^2}{w_o}(\beta - k_o t_o)^2\right] \quad \beta t_o >> 1 \tag{101}$$

Now the procedure is to minimize the loss rate $\lambda$ with respect to $t_o$. This can be done approximately by maximizing the exponent with respect to $t_o$. Thus

$$-k_o 2t_o(\beta - k_o t_o) + (\beta - k_o t_o)^2 = 0$$

$$t_{o\,opt} = \frac{\beta}{3k_o} \tag{102}$$

In this particular case, from Eq. (95), for a = 50g,

$$k_o = \frac{2f_c a}{c} = \frac{2a}{\lambda} = \frac{2\text{x}50\text{x}32}{0.1} = 32000 \text{ cycles/sec}^2 \tag{103}$$

and $\beta$ = 1000 cps. Hence, from Eq. (102)

$$t_{o_{opt}} = \frac{1000}{3 \text{ x } 32000} = \frac{1}{96} \text{ sec} \tag{104}$$

The corresponding "closed loop bandwidth" is

$$B_c = \frac{1}{2\pi t_o} = \frac{96}{2\pi} \cong 15 \text{ cps} \tag{105}$$

Note that $\beta t_o = \frac{1000}{96} \cong 10 >> 1$ as sssumed. $\overline{\epsilon}_s = k_o t_o = \beta/3 = 333$ cps. It now remains to find the voltage S/N ratio needed to maintain track in this optimized system. From Eq. (101),

$$\gamma^2 \cong \frac{w_o}{2t_o(\beta - k_o t_o)^2} \quad \ln \frac{1}{\pi\lambda}\sqrt{\frac{\beta}{t_o}} \tag{106}$$

where

$$k_o = 32 \times 10^3 \text{ cycles/sec}^2$$

$$\beta = 10^3 \text{ cycles/sec}$$

$$t_{o_{opt}} = 1/96 \text{ sec}$$

$$\lambda = 0.01 \text{ sec}^{-1}$$

It remains to determine $w_o$, the noise frequency spectral density. It is shown in Threshold Signals (2) that the frequency spectral density of Gaussian noise after passage through a square passband of width $\beta$ is

$$G(f) = 2\pi\beta \int_0^\infty dx \cos\frac{2fx}{\beta} \; \frac{\sin^2 x - x^2}{x^2 \sin^2 x} \; \ln\left(1 - \frac{\sin^2 x}{x^2}\right) \tag{107}$$

This integral is done numerically with the results:

| $\frac{f}{\beta} = y$ | $\frac{G(f)}{4\pi\beta} = G(y)$ |
|---|---|
| 0 | 0.955 |
| 0.1 | 0.816 |
| 0.2 | 0.698 |
| 0.3 | 0.586 |
| 0.4 | 0.501 |
| 0.5 | 0.428 |
| 0.6 | 0.373 |
| 0.7 | 0.329 |
| 0.8 | 0.295 |
| 0.9 | 0.266 |
| 1.0 | 0.242 |

Since it has already been assumed in this simplified analysis that $w_o$ is uniform across the velocity gatewidth $\beta$, the equivalent constant noise density $w_o$ will be found from the above table by equating $w_o\beta$ to the noise power in the band of width $\beta$. This procedure is valid since $w_o$ is actually the spectral density of $f_N$' which means the spectral density of that portion of $f_N$ lying in the region $0 \leq f_N \leq \beta$. Thus

$$w_o = \frac{1}{\beta} \int_0^\beta G(f)\, df = 4\pi\beta \int_0^1 G(y)\, dy = 1670 \text{ cps}^2/\text{cps} \tag{108}$$

Hence, from equations (106) and (108)

$$\gamma^2 = \frac{(6.6 \times 10^3)(96)}{4\pi^2 \cdot 2(667)^2} \ln \frac{100}{\pi}\sqrt{96000} \cong \frac{6.6}{39.6} = 0.167$$

$$\gamma \cong 0.41 \cong -8\text{db} \qquad (a = 50g) \qquad (109)$$

To track 5g with this same (no longer optimized) loop time constant would require $\gamma \cong 0.273$. However, if the loop time constant were optimized for a maximum missile-launcher acceleration of 5g,

$$t_o = \frac{\beta}{3k_o} = \frac{1}{9.6} \text{ sec}$$

$$\gamma^2 = \frac{(6.6 \times 10^3)(9.6)}{4\pi^2 \, 2(667)^2} \ln \frac{100}{\pi} \sqrt{9600} \cong 0.0144$$

$$\gamma \cong 0.12 \cong -18\text{db} \qquad (110)$$

Experimental results show that, for a loss ratio of about 0.01, a 14g target was tracked at -6 db S/N ratio with a loop time constant of 1/500 sec. The theoretical result (110) agrees quite well with this S/N ratio but not with the loop gain $1/t_o$. With the numbers from the experiment used in Eq. (101), a high loss rate is indicated. However, the loss rate is a very strong function of $\gamma$, decreasing as $\gamma$ increases. In fact, holding the other parameters constant, doubling the voltage S/N ratio divides the loss rate by a factor of 55! The loss rate is also a strong function of $t_o$, particularly for small values of $t_o$. A plot of $\lambda$ versus $t_o$ for $k_o = 64 \times 10^3$ cycle/sec$^2$ = 100 g, $\beta = 10^3$ cps, and $\gamma = 3.69$ is shown in Fig. 8. Thus small experimental errors in measurement will have a very great effect on loss rate. In the absence of noise, the maximum time constant is

$$t_o = \frac{\beta}{k_o} = \frac{3}{96} = \frac{1}{32} \text{ sec}$$

The loss rate for this case is

$$\lambda = \frac{1}{\pi}\sqrt{\frac{\beta}{t_o}} = \frac{1}{\pi}\sqrt{32000} \cong 56$$

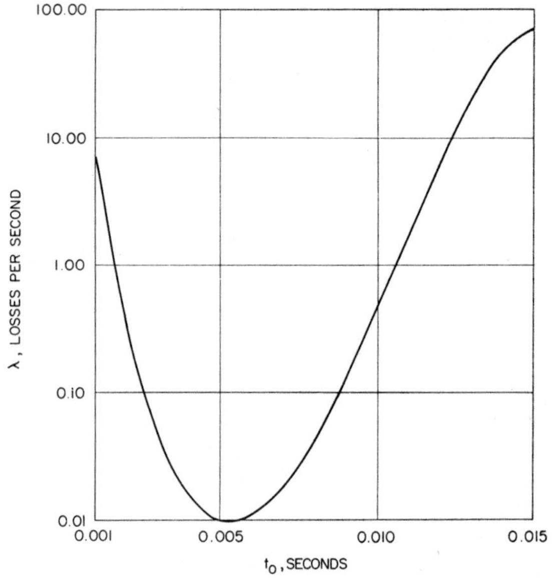


Fig. 8. Loss Rate λ Variation with Loop Time Constant $t_o$

Hence the effect of noise is to increase the loop gain from the minimum needed for steady-state tracking at the edge of the gate. Furthermore, the steady-state error is the largest error to a ramp input in frequency. Consequently, both the transient and steady-state behavior at a loop gain of $1/t_o = 32$ would be satisfactory in the absence of noise. The loss rate increases from the optimum $t_o$ as the gain $1/t_o$ decreases since the mean of the noise (i.e., the signal) is close enough to the edge of the gate to cause many crossings. The loss rate increases as the gain $1/t_o$ increases from the optimum because the noise distribution about the signal is so wide that even though the mean is near the center of the gate a large number of crossings occur providing $\beta t_o >> 1$, i.e., providing the gate-width is still large compared to the loop gain in $\sec^{-1}$. Expressions (100) and (101) are incorrect for $\beta t_o << 1$. In this case, Eq. (97) becomes

$$\sigma^2 = \frac{w_o}{2\pi t_o \gamma^2} \left( \tan^{-1} 2\pi \beta t_o - \tan^{-1} 0 \right) \cong \frac{w_o \beta}{\gamma^2} \qquad (111)$$

and Eq. (98) becomes

$$\int_o^{\beta} f^2 G_z(f)\, df = \frac{w_o}{(2\pi t_o)^3 \gamma^2} \left[ \beta t_o - \tan^{-1} 2\pi \beta t_o \right] \cong \frac{w_o}{3\gamma^2} \beta^3 \qquad (112)$$

and the loss rate becomes

$$\lambda \cong \left[ \frac{w_o \beta^3}{3\gamma^2} \; \frac{\gamma^2}{w_o \beta} \right]^{1/2} \exp \left[ \frac{-(\beta - k_o t_o)^2}{\dfrac{w_o \beta}{\gamma^2}} \right]$$

or

$$\lambda = \frac{\beta}{\sqrt{3}} \exp \left[ \frac{-\gamma^2 (\beta - k_o t_o)^2}{w_o \beta} \right] \qquad \beta t_o << 1 \qquad (113)$$

Note that if $\beta t_o << 1$, $\gamma^2$ = constant, as $t_o \rightarrow 0$, the loss rate becomes independent of the loop gain and dependent (linearly dependent, since $\omega_o = \text{const} \times \beta$) only on the velocity gatewidth, since this is now the limiting factor on the noise width and hence the noise power.

It is interesting to investigate the variation of $\lambda$ with the gatewidth $\beta$. If the system is tracking near the edge of the gate, the loss rate increases with increasing $\beta$ because more noise is passed by the wider gate. However, for $\beta > k_o t_o$, $\beta > \omega_o/\gamma^2$, $\beta t_o >> 1$, the loss rate decreases with increasing $\beta$ because, despite additional noise, the signal can fluctuate over a wider region without loss.

Double Integrator Case

For this case the problem is identical with the single integrator problem up to Eq. (89). From Eqs. (72) and (76),

$$Y_s = k_2 K_s Y_f(s) = \frac{k_2 K_s (s+a)}{s^2} = \frac{2st_o + 1}{s^2 t_o^2} \tag{114}$$

where $t_o = \frac{1}{2a} = \frac{2}{K_a k_2}$ for the loop to be critically damped (115)

Thus

$$Y_o(s) = \frac{Y_s}{1+Y} = \frac{2st_o + 1}{(st_o+1)^2} \tag{116}$$

and, from Eq. (87)

$$\bar{\epsilon}_s 2 = \frac{Y_o}{Y_s} f_d(s) = \frac{s^2 t_o^2}{(st_o+1)^2} f_d(s) \tag{117}$$

The average error in the steady state is

$$\bar{\epsilon}_s (t \to \infty) = \lim_{s \to 0} s \bar{\epsilon}_s (s) = \lim_{s \to 0} \frac{s^3 t_o^2}{(st_o+1)^2} f_d(s) \tag{118}$$

For a constant target acceleration, Eq. (90) shows $f_d(s) = k_o/s^2$. Therefore

$$\bar{\epsilon}_s (t \to \infty) = 0 \tag{119}$$

From Eq. (89),

$$G_z(f) = \frac{w_o}{\gamma^2}\left|Y_o(j\omega)\right|^2 = \frac{w_o}{\gamma}\,\frac{4\omega^2 t_o^{\,2}+1}{(\omega^2 t_o^{\,2}+1)^2} \tag{120}$$

$$\sigma^2 = \int_o^\beta G_z(f)\,df = \frac{w_o}{\gamma^2}\int_o^\beta \frac{4\omega^2 t_o^{\,2}+1}{(\omega^2 t_o^{\,2}+1)^2}\,df$$

$$= \frac{w_o}{2\pi t_o \gamma^2}\left\{-\frac{1.5(2\pi t_o\beta)}{4\pi^2 t_o^{\,2}\beta^2+1} + 2.5\tan^{-1} 2\pi t_o\beta\right\} \tag{121}$$

$$\int_o^\beta f^2 G_z(f)\,df = \frac{w_o}{(2\pi t_o)^3\gamma^2}\int_o^{2\pi t_o\beta}\frac{x^2(4x^2+1)\,dx}{(x^2+1)^2}$$

$$= \frac{w_o}{(2\pi t_o)^3\gamma^2}\left\{-\frac{1.5(2\pi t_o\beta)^3}{(2\pi t_o\beta)^2+1} + 5.5(2\pi t_o\beta) - 5.5\tan^{-1} 2\pi t_o\beta\right\} \tag{122}$$

From Eq. (85)

$$I = \beta - \overline{\epsilon}_s = \beta \tag{123}$$

Hence, substituting Eqs. (121) and (122) in Eq. (85)

$$\lambda = \frac{1}{2\pi t_o}\left\{\frac{4(2\pi t_o\beta)^3 + 5.5(2\pi t_o\beta) - 5.5\left[(2\pi t_o\beta)^2+1\right]\tan^{-1} 2\pi t_o\beta}{-1.5(2\pi t_o\beta) + 2.5\left[(2\pi t_o\beta)^2+1\right]\tan^{-1} 2\pi t_o\beta}\right\}^{1/2}$$

$$\exp\left\{\frac{-\pi\beta^2 t_o\gamma^2}{w_o}\cdot\frac{4\pi^2 t_o^{\,2}\beta^2+1}{-1.5(2\pi t_o\beta) + 25\left[(2\pi t_o\beta)^2+1\right]\tan^{-1} 2\pi t_o\beta}\right\} \tag{124}$$

Equation (124) is minimized for $t_o \rightarrow \infty$. Since the steady-state error is zero, the loss rate in the steady state can be made zero by having a zero bandwidth servo. Unfortunately, the transient response sets an upper limit of 1/16.8 sec for $t_o$. If the servo were asked to follow a parabola in frequency (i.e., a constant time rate of change of acceleration) of magnitude $\ddot{f}_d = 2a/\lambda$, Eq. (117) becomes

$$\bar{\epsilon}_s = \lim_{s \rightarrow 0} \frac{s^3 t_o}{(st_o + 1)^2} \frac{|\ddot{f}_d|}{s^3} = |\ddot{f}_d| \, t_o^2 \qquad (125)$$

and Eq. (123) becomes

$$I = \beta - \bar{\epsilon}_s = \beta - |\ddot{f}_d| \, t_o^2 \qquad (126)$$

If $t_o \beta >> 1$, Eq. (85) becomes approximately

$$\lambda = \frac{1}{\pi} \sqrt{\frac{4\beta}{2.5t_o}} \exp\left[\frac{-0.8t_o \gamma^2}{\omega_o} (\beta - |\ddot{f}_d| t_o^2)^2\right] \qquad (127)$$

Again minimizing the loss rate by maximizing the exponent with respect to $t_o$,

$$-2t_o(\beta - |\ddot{f}_d| \, t_o^2)(2t_o |\ddot{f}_d|) + (\beta - |\ddot{f}_d| \, t_o^2)^2 = 0$$

or

$$t_o = \sqrt{\frac{\beta}{5 |\ddot{f}_d|}} \qquad (128)$$

The optimum steady-state displacement is therefore $\beta/5$ in this case. If $|\ddot{f}d| = 0$ as initially assumed, $t_o \rightarrow \infty$. Thus $\beta t_o >> 1$ and Eq. (127) applies very well. The S/N ratio is then

$$\gamma^2 \cong \frac{w_o}{0.8 t_o \beta^2} \ln \frac{1}{\pi\lambda} \sqrt{\frac{1.6\beta}{t_o}} \qquad (129)$$

From Eq. (108), $w_o = 6.6 \times 10^3/4\pi^2$ cps$^2$/cps. Let $t_o$ = 1/16.8, $\lambda = 0.01$, $\beta = 1000$ cps. Then

$$\gamma^2 = \frac{6.6 \times 10^3 (16.8)}{4\pi^2 \left(0.8(10^6)\right)} \quad \ln \quad \frac{1}{0.01\pi} \quad \sqrt{1.6 \times 10^3 (16.8)}$$

$$= 0.00285$$

$$\gamma = 0.0535 = -25 \text{ db}$$

Note the very significant improvement in S/N ratio (18-db improvement) introduced by the use of two integrations. The principal reason for this improvement is the much longer time constant allowable for tracking a constant acceleration.

## References

1. Rice, S.O., "Mathematical Analysis of Random Noise," from Noise and Stochastic Processes, by Wax (Dover, 1954) p. 193.

2. Lawson and Uhlenbeck, Threshold Signals, MIT Rad Lab Series, Vol. 24, (McGraw-Hill) p. 374.

# ANALOG SIMULATION OF RADIO GUIDANCE AND SPACE COMMUNICATION SYSTEMS

Joseph P. Frazier and John M. Lambert
General Electric Company
Syracuse, New York

## Abstract

The purpose of this paper is to reveal a new approach to the development and evaluation of radio guidance and communication systems. This approach is the Electronic System Evaluator, a tool which is proving to be highly effective in the development of electronic systems.

Examples are given to show how the Electronic Systems Evaluator is applied to radio guidance and space communications systems development, and to systems synthesis and evaluation.

## Introduction

The Electronic System Evaluator is best introduced by means of an analogy. Airplane models are tested in wind tunnels under simulated environmental conditions to predict performance and behavior characteristics early in the development program. As the development of the design and the prototype progress, changes for refinement and improvement of the aircraft are embodied in the model and tested in the wind tunnel to determine the effects. The Electronic System Evaluator is a tool similar to the wind tunnel but is applicable to the electronic field. Models of the proposed electronic systems are quickly breadboarded and operated under simulated conditions of electronic environment and evaluated early in the development program. Changes can be quickly made in the model and environment to determine the effects on the system.

The Electronic System Evaluator (ESE) is a special purpose electronic analog computer, a well known and widely used engineering tool. The analog computer is used by aircraft and missile manufacturers to predict dynamic performance of servomechanisms, aircraft and missiles prior to construction. ESE extends electronic analysis to electronic systems.

It is very interesting to note that the same electronic engineers who have developed the analog computer have not utilized these techniques in their own field--the prediction of the performance of radar, radio guidance, and communication systems. The usual method has been one of building operational equipment and then testing it in actual field conditions.

ESE, however, now extends the use of the analog computer to enable the systems engineer to accurately predict the performance of radar and communications systems prior to construction of the hardware.

## Development of the Electronic System Evaluator

Early in the development of the Atlas Radio Guidance System it was appreciated that the system would have to be designed to minimize susceptibility to enemy countermeasures and normal environment interferences. Accordingly, General Electric recognized the need for a tool to investigate and to experiment with these effects. The Electronic System Evaluator was developed and established as a tool. The facility, located in Syracuse, New York, is a prime tool in the development and investigation of the electronic subsystems. Forty percent of the major weapon systems are electronic subsystems.

The Electronic System Evaluator is used to develop radar, communications, and radio guidance systems. ECCM circuits and techniques of existing systems are optimized and new techniques and systems are evaluated. Typical applications are:

- ECM Evaluation and Test
- ECCM Optimization
- Satellite Communication System Design
- Electromagnetic Reconnaissance Systems
- Wide Band Versus Narrow Band Communication Study
- Evaluation of Foreign Radars
- Guidance Systems
- Electromagnetic Compatibility
- Flight Test Planning and Extrapolation
- Communication Techniques Evaluation.

## Theory

To understand the Electronic System Evaluator and to appreciate how it can be applied, it is necessary to understand the fundamental theory. Figure 1 is the present facility. Figure 2 is an artist's concept of the expanded facility which is being implemented by General Electric. This single facility has the capability of building low frequency electronic models of virtually any communication, radar or radio guidance system.

Unit (a) is one of the two special magnetic tape recorders. One of these recorders is a 14 channel continuous loop recorder used to simulate such things as tapped delay lines and

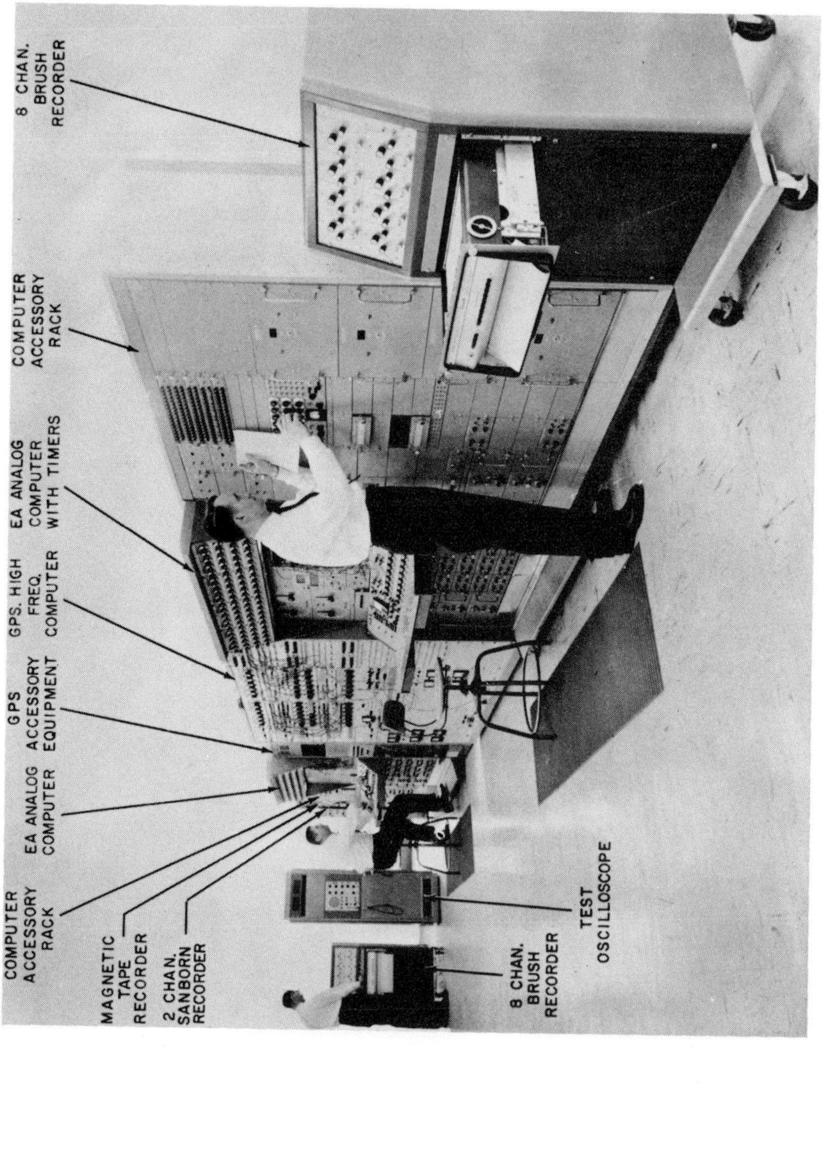
COMPUTER ACCESSORY RACK
MAGNETIC TAPE RECORDER
2 CHAN. SANBORN RECORDER
EA ANALOG COMPUTER
GPS ACCESSORY EQUIPMENT
GPS. HIGH FREQ. COMPUTER
EA ANALOG COMPUTER WITH TIMERS
COMPUTER ACCESSORY RACK
8 CHAN. BRUSH RECORDER
8 CHAN. BRUSH RECORDER
TEST OSCILLOSCOPE

Figure 1

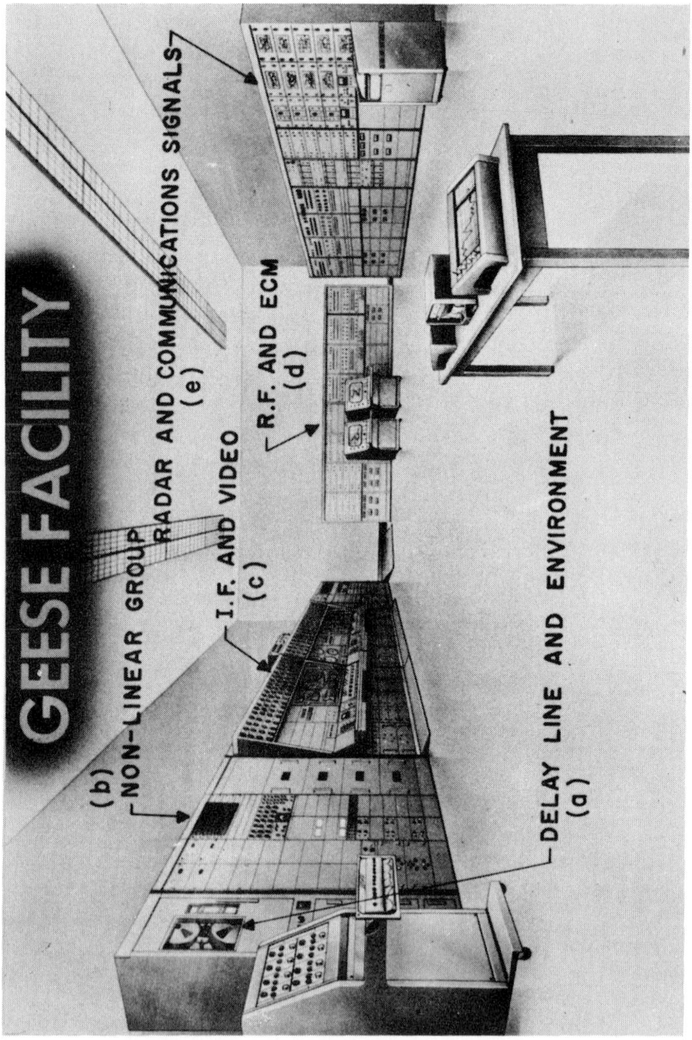
GEESE FACILITY
(b)
NON-LINEAR GROUP
RADAR AND COMMUNICATIONS SIGNALS
(e)
I.F. AND VIDEO
(c)
R.F. AND ECM
(d)
DELAY LINE AND ENVIRONMENT
(a)

Figure 2

multipath propagation, where time delays are required. An additional tape recorder is installed to record electronic signals such as radar signals, jamming signals, and friendly interference. The next unit shown (b) is a Non-Linear Group whereby any non-linear function such as diode mixer characteristics, AGC characteristics, overload characteristics, and similar functions can be reproduced to an accuracy of one percent. Unit (c) consists of two consoles of modified electronic analog computers which are used to simulate intermediate frequency and video amplifiers. To the rear of the room, unit (d) is the special high-frequency analog equipment which is used to simulate high-frequency circuits such as waveguide filters, radio frequency stages, and so forth. On the right, unit (e) is some of the special purpose equipment referred to as the Electromagnetic Spectrum Generator (ESG). The ESG is a bank of special audio frequency oscillators which can be programmed to simulate AM, FM, pulse modulation, single sideband, double sideband, spread spectrum, and other types of electronic signals.

The basic principle is that all tests are made on a low frequency electronic model of the system. In other words, the actual frequencies are scaled down to audio frequencies. The highest frequencies in an ESE model of an electronic system are in the order of 20 kilocycles. Electronic countermeasure and friendly interference signals are scaled by the same scale factor as the system model.

Let's take some specific examples. These are typical scale factors. In the case of radar, a nominal scale factor is $10^6$. X Band (10,000 megacycles per second) becomes 10,000 cycles per second. S Band (3000 megacycles per second) becomes 3000 cycles per second. L Band (1000 megacycles per second) becomes 1000 cycles per second. A typical IF center frequency of 60 megacycles per second becomes 60 cycles per second. A typical bandwidth of 2 megacycles per second becomes 2 cycles per second.

The result of scaling center frequencies and bandwidth down by a factor of one million is that time is stretched by the same scale factor. One microsecond becomes one second. This turns out to be one of the big advantages of the approach. In real life the transient phenomena occurs in microseconds; in the model the same transient occurs in seconds.

In scaling communication problems, a different scale factor is required, usually a scale factor of $10^3$ to $10^6$. A typical communication bandwidth of 10 kilocycles becomes 10 cycles per second, for instance.

The reason that a single facility can be utilized to simulate virtually any electronic system is that all radar and communication systems consist of some combination of only 15 building blocks:

RF Amplifier
IF Amplifier
Delay Line
CW Oscillator
Mixer
Voltage Controlled Oscillator
Balanced Mixer
Integrator
Audio Amplifiers
Limiter
Correlator
Second (Amplitude) Detector
Phase Detector
Video Amplifier
Discriminator.

The transfer functions of each type of building block are solved directly on the facility.

## Application to Radio Guidance Systems

Radio guidance systems are utilized for ballistic missile and space vehicle guidance whenever extremely high accuracy is required. A typical guidance system consists of a monopulse radar tracking system and a continuous wave rate measuring system (Figure 3). Radio guidance systems operate in an electromagnetic environment consisting of many signals sharing the same frequency band. To show how the Electronic System Evaluator is utilized to optimize guidance system performance, a simple rate measuring system will be used for an example.

Figure 4 shows how the electronic countermeasure and friendly interference performance of a rate transponder is evaluated by using a low frequency analog model.

The first step is to scale the frequencies and bandwidths of the rate transponder. Referring to Figure 5, there are three types of signals. First, signals from the rate station at the guidance site (this is the desired signal). A potentiometer is used to adjust signal level that the rate transponder in the missile sees during any particular part of its trajectory. Similarly by knowing the position of the jammer, its power antenna pattern and type of jamming, a jamming signal is introduced into the rate transponder model of the same strength that the rate transponder would see at any particular point in the trajectory. By using electromagnetic environmental data published by Rand Corporation and Project Monmouth, interference from other U.S. radar and communication sites can also be introduced.

Figure 5 is a block diagram of a typical rate transponder. For security reasons, the block diagram is very simple and ECCM features have been removed. But this example is close

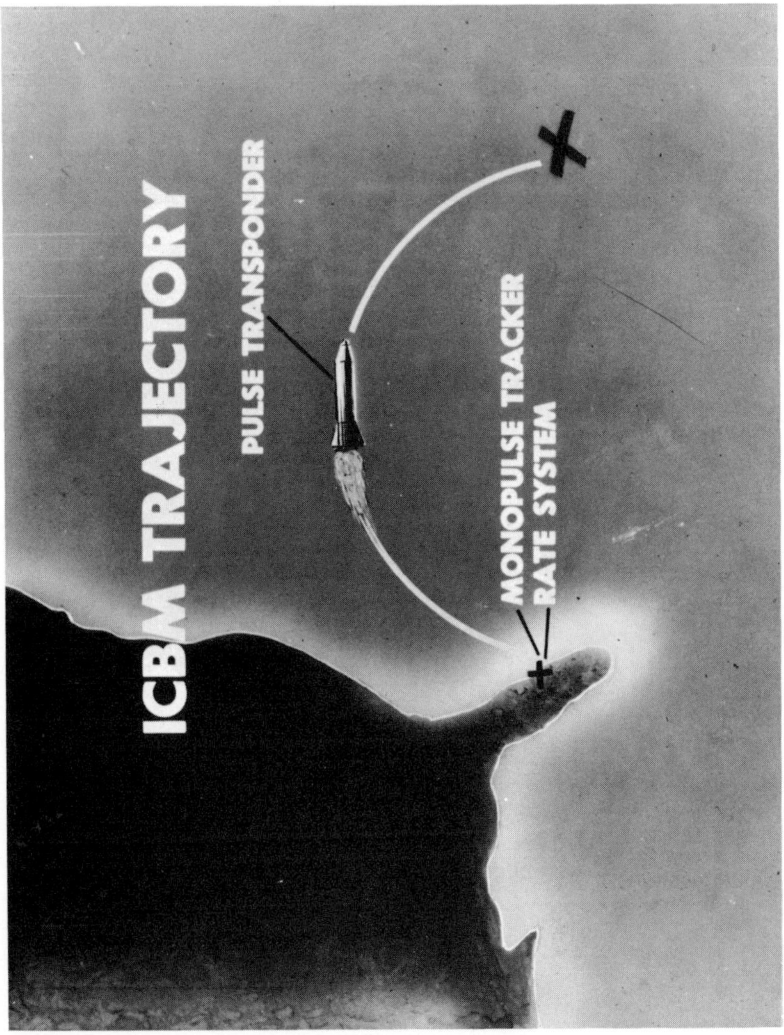
ICBM TRAJECTORY
PULSE TRANSPONDER
MONOPULSE TRACKER
RATE SYSTEM

Figure 3

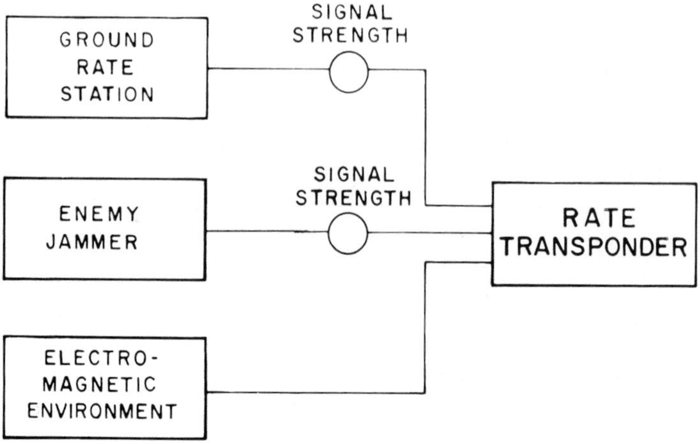


Figure 4

# PHASE LOCKED RECEIVER

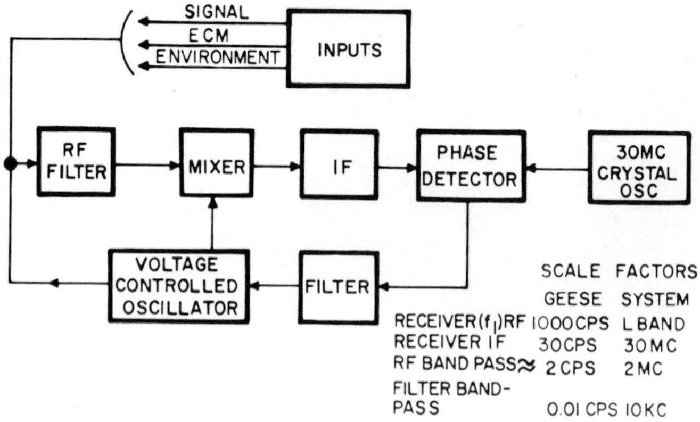


Figure 5

enough to actual rate transponders to illustrate the concept.

Coming from the rate transmitter on the ground is a CW signal which comes into the RF filter through the antenna system on the missile. The signal is heterodyned with a local oscillator in the mixer. The intermediate frequency is passed through the intermediate frequency amplifier where the phase is compared with a 30 megacycle crystal oscillator. The output of the phase detector is a control frequency which locks the voltage controlled oscillator exactly 30 megacycles above the incoming radio frequency. This signal is sent back to the rate receiver on the ground and by using a similar circuit in the rate receiver the velocity of the missile can be measured very accurately to about 0.1 foot per second. But, this system has to work in the presence of electronic countermeasure signals and friendly interference.

Figure 6 and 6A depict the Electronic System Evaluator equivalent circuit of the rate transponder block diagram. There are three input signals: the desired signal, the jamming signal, and the friendly interference signal. The signals are filtered by the radio frequency filter, which is simulated by an operational amplifier with a bridged T-feedback filter. The output of the mixer (simulated with an electronic multiplier) goes to the intermediate frequency amplifier. The control signal from the phase detector controls the klystron local oscillator (voltage controlled oscillator) and is also the transmitter signal which is transmitted back to the tracking site.

The output of the mixer goes into six stages of intermediate frequency amplification. Since they are identical stages, only one stage is shown on this diagram to keep it simple. This is a good place to explain the symbols. A triangle with a double bar represents an integrator, a triangle with a single bar is an operational amplifier. The circles are coefficient potentiometers. The rest of the symbols are conventional. The Electronic System Evaluator utilized the transfer function of each block of the block diagram of the actual system and solves the transfer function using analog computer techniques. (See appendix.) This approach results in flexibility and convenience. For example, potentiometer 4a adjusts the bandwidths of the stage from 0 to 50 megacycles per second. Potentiometer 4b adjusts the center frequency of the stage from 0 to 200 megacycles per second. (On the ESE, this is only from 0 to 200 cycles per second.) A low frequency model of any subsystem can be built up within a few hours.

The phase detector compares the output of the intermediate frequency amplifier with a 30 megacycle oscillator. The output of the phase detector goes through a low pass filter and is used to control the klystron simulator (voltage controlled

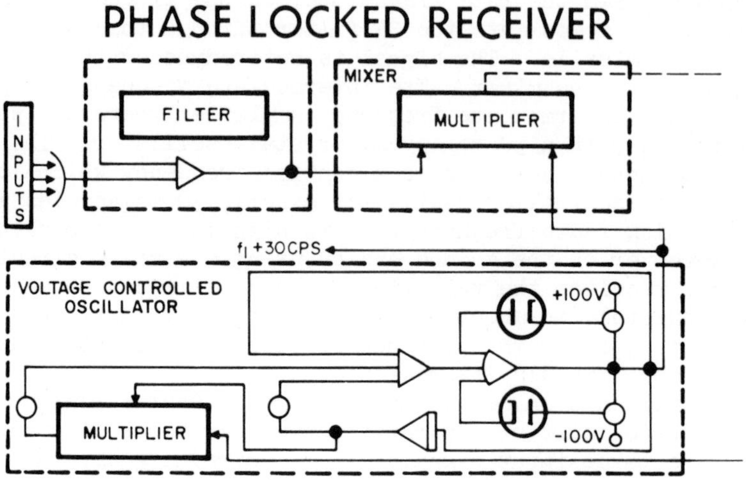


Figure 6

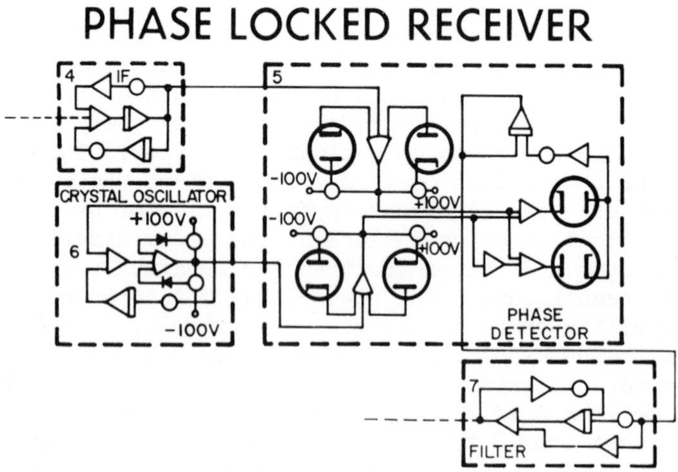


Figure 6a

oscillator).

By using the approach described, the performance of the Atlas guidance system in the presence of electronic countermeasure and friendly interference was predicted 15 months before the system was available for laboratory tests. The question is asked: "How well did the predicted test results correlate with laboratory tests made on the actual equipment?" Figure 7 shows typical test result correlation. The jammer sweep rate is shown on the ordinate from 0 to 500 kilocycles. On the abscissa is plotted the relative signal to jamming ratios in db. In order to declassify the figure there has been a bias added to these test results so that only the correlation rather than the actual test results are shown. The correlation is shown accurately. The middle curve was predicted 15 months before a rate transponder was available. The laboratory test results are shown on the left and a flight test is shown on the right. The correlation of test results is within 3 db. This particular curve is typical. Ninety-five percent of the test results which were predicted by the ESE correlate with laboratory data within 3 db.

## Satellite Application

Another application which has been programmed is an active satellite orbiting around the earth (Figure 8) receiving signals from the ground communication transmitter and being jammed by an enemy jammer. This problem is programmed in the following manner:

First, the satellite receiver is programmed. (See Figure 9.) This is done by building an audio frequency model of the satellite receiver using the techniques previously described. An audio frequency signal generator is programmed to generate the same modulation characteristics, signal strength, etc., as the ground transmitter. Another special purpose signal generator is programmed to simulate the enemy jammer. In addition, a recorded electromagnetic environment is introduced from a tape recorder to simulate the thousands of radio and radar signals which would be received by a satellite. The signal strength of the electromagnetic spectrum received by the satellite receiver consists of all three inputs. The effects of propagation, antenna patterns (ground transmitter, enemy jammer and the satellite), as well as the trajectory and the XYZ coordinates of the jammer and the ground transmitter are programmed. Typical parameters which are varied in this problem are the satellite orbit, different altitudes, circular or elliptical, modulation type (FM, AM Spread Spectrum), transmitter power, receiver noise figure, receiver selectivity, jammer power, jammer modulation, electromagnetic environmental density, antenna patterns, AGC optimization.

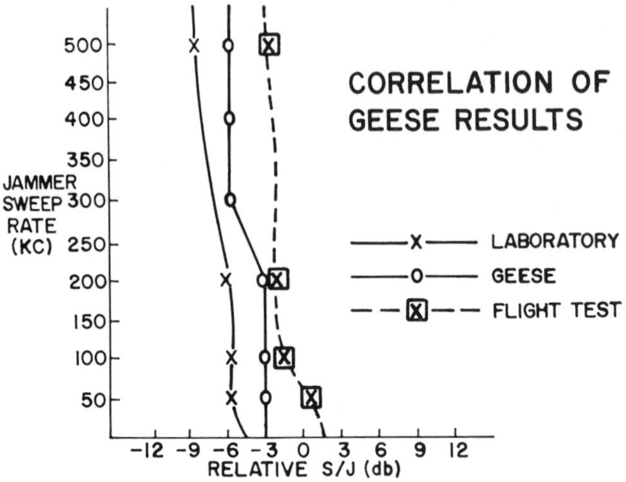


Figure 7

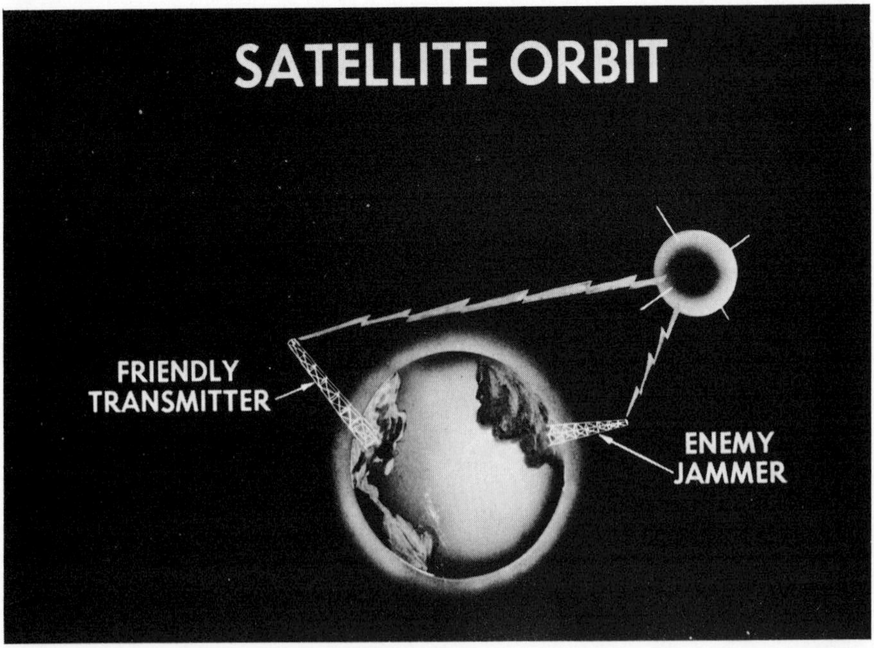


Figure 8

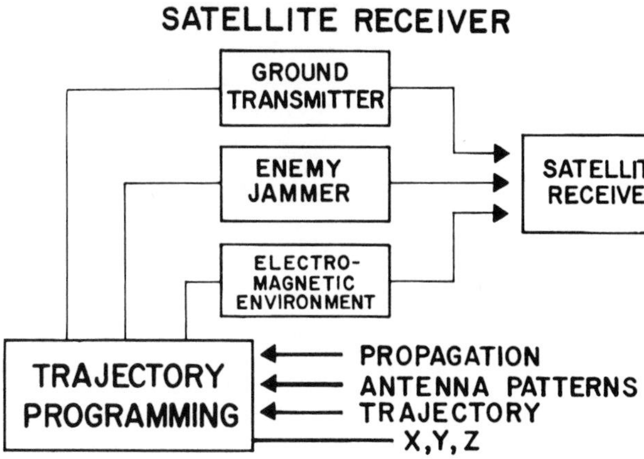


Figure 9

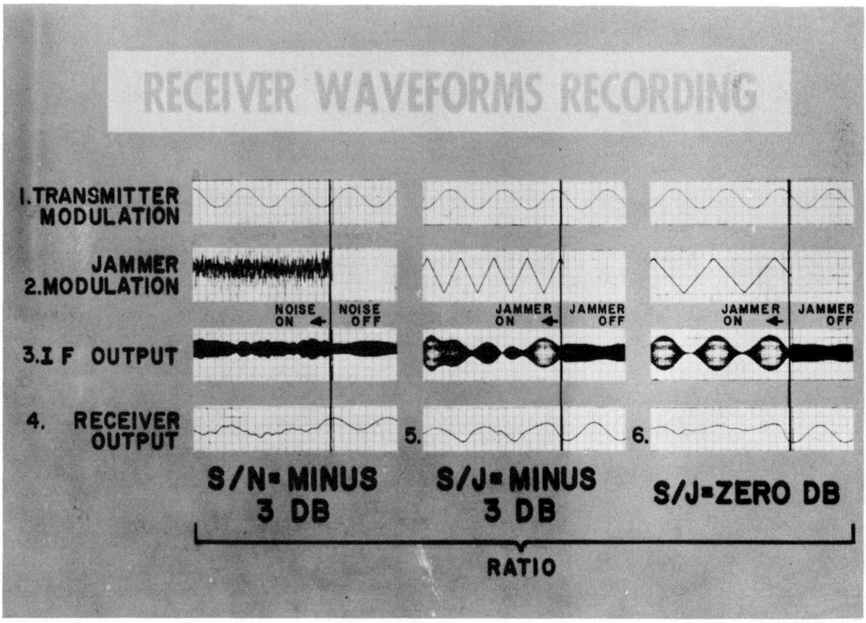


Figure 10

The electromagnetic density (which is the function of the satellite location and altitude as well as antenna patterns) is an important variable. The receiver characteristics such as anti-jamming and anti-interference circuits are thereby optimized.

Figure 10 shows actual Electronic System Evaluator recordings on the satellite problem. Number 1 shows the modulation being transmitted to the satellite. This could be voice modulation, pulse modulation, etc. The modulation is a 1000 cycle sine wave. (Don't confuse this with the carrier which is also a sine wave.) Three types of jamming tests were performed: noise jamming, carcinatron jamming and slow sweep jamming. The noise jammer modulation is shown in number 2 and the effects of the jamming modulation on the intermediate frequency carrier are shown in number 3. The noise jamming introduces noise amplitude modulation into the intermediate frequency carrier. To the right of the vertical line the jamming was removed and the effect of the noise jamming disappeared. The effects of noise jamming on the video output are shown in number 4. When the noise jamming is removed the received signal modulation is identical to the transmitter signal modulation. The signal-to-noise ratio on this particular test was -3 db.

Using the same transmitter signal the effects of carcinatron sweep jamming were investigated. The carcinatron sweep jammer sweeps through the receiver bandpass in a fraction of a microsecond. Depending on whether the instantaneous phase between the signal carrier and the jammer carrier is in addition or subtraction, the jammer will either add to or subtract from the intermediate frequency signal. This shows a unique capability of the ESE in that a better physical understanding of the performance of the system is inherent since both radio frequency and intermediate frequency carriers are recorded. For example, by running the recorder at a faster speed the intermediate frequency carrier can be examined.

The effects of the carcinatron jammer on the receiver output are seen in number 5. A sine wave modulation was transmitted. A rather poor sine wave was received due to the effects of the carcinatron jamming. Number 6 shows the effect of very low sweep speed jammer on the satellite receiver output. The sweep jammer remains within the receiver bandpass for a much longer period of time. With a signal-to-noise ratio of 0 db the satellite receiver performance is deteriorated to the point where the signal modulation is unintelligible.

## Programming System Problems

Figure 11 shows how system problems are programmed on the ESE facility. The digital computer shown in the block diagram is currently an IBM-704. Such factors as the propagation,

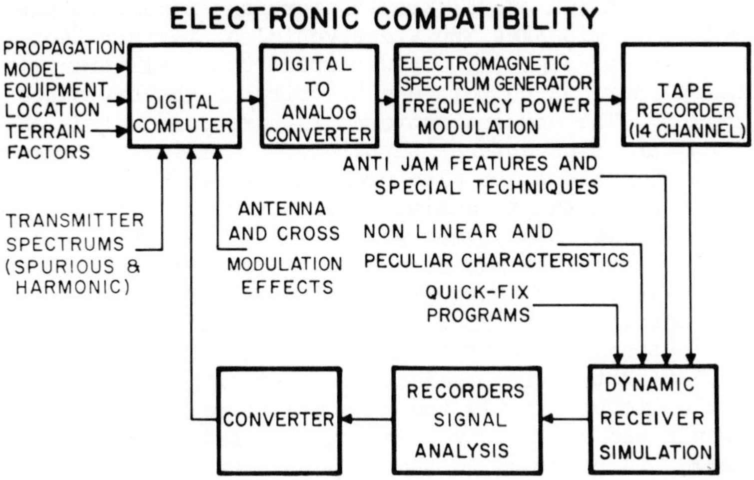


Figure 11

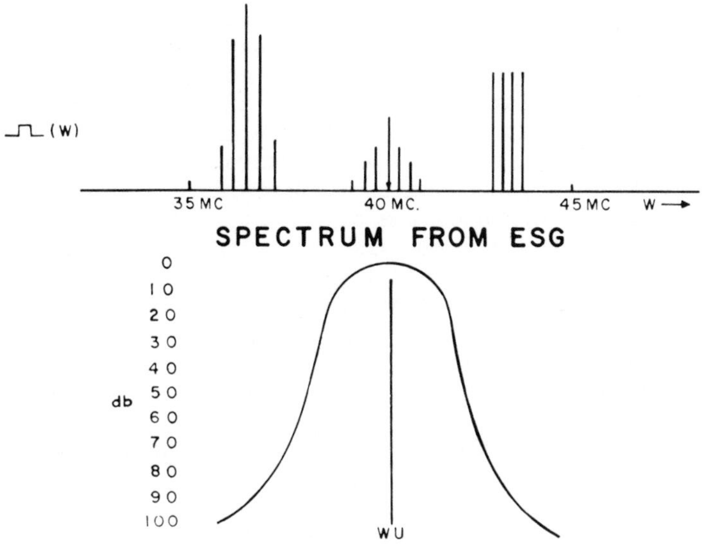


Figure 12

equipment location of all transmitters and receivers plus the trajectory of missiles and space vehicles, terrain factors such as line-of-sight, the power spectrum of all transmitters including spurious outputs and the first eight harmonics are programmed. The antenna patterns in three dimensions of each radar antenna plus antenna pattern of the missile transponder in three dimensions are also programmed. The output of the 704 feeds a digital to analog converter which supplies analog control signals to a device we call the Electromagnetic Spectrum Generator. The ESG is a bank of voltage controlled oscillators which are controlled by the digital computer to simulate transmitters. The output of the ESG consists of the total electromagnetic spectrum seen by the transponder at any particular spot on its trajectory. The signal strengths are controlled to be exactly the same as the receiver in the missile would see as it travels along its trajectory. The output of the ESG is recorded so that a permanent record of the electromagnetic environment of a complete test may be kept. In this manner the recorded environment is fed into the receiver simulation. This dynamic receiver simulation is a low frequency model of the receiver such as was described in the Atlas example. In other words, this whole problem is working at audio frequencies. Typical parameters which can be optimized in the dynamic receiver simulation are the anti-jam features, receiver selectivity characteristics, non-linear characteristics, and proposed quick-fixes. The output of the low frequency model is analyzed to determine such things as a single-to-noise ratio, signal spectrum, decoder performance, and so forth. This output information is converted back into digital form for statistical analysis by the digital computer. Figure 12 shows what the output of the ESG typically looks like. Let's take a simple example where we have the desired signal at 40 megacycles and two interference signals. The digital computer computes the signal strengths seen by the receiver at the antenna terminals and sends control voltages through the D-A converter to adjust the signal strength, center frequency, and type of modulation of each of the three signals. The total environment consisting of the desired signal plus the undesired signals are then played into the low frequency model of the receiver under test.

## Future of the Electronic System Evaluator

Figure 13 illustrates what the ESE equipment under development will probably look like. For example, the Barrage Noise Jammer will have the capability of generating a low frequency noise jamming signal which will simulate a spot jammer or noise jammer at any frequency up to 30 thousand megacycles per second. The controls will adjust the center frequency

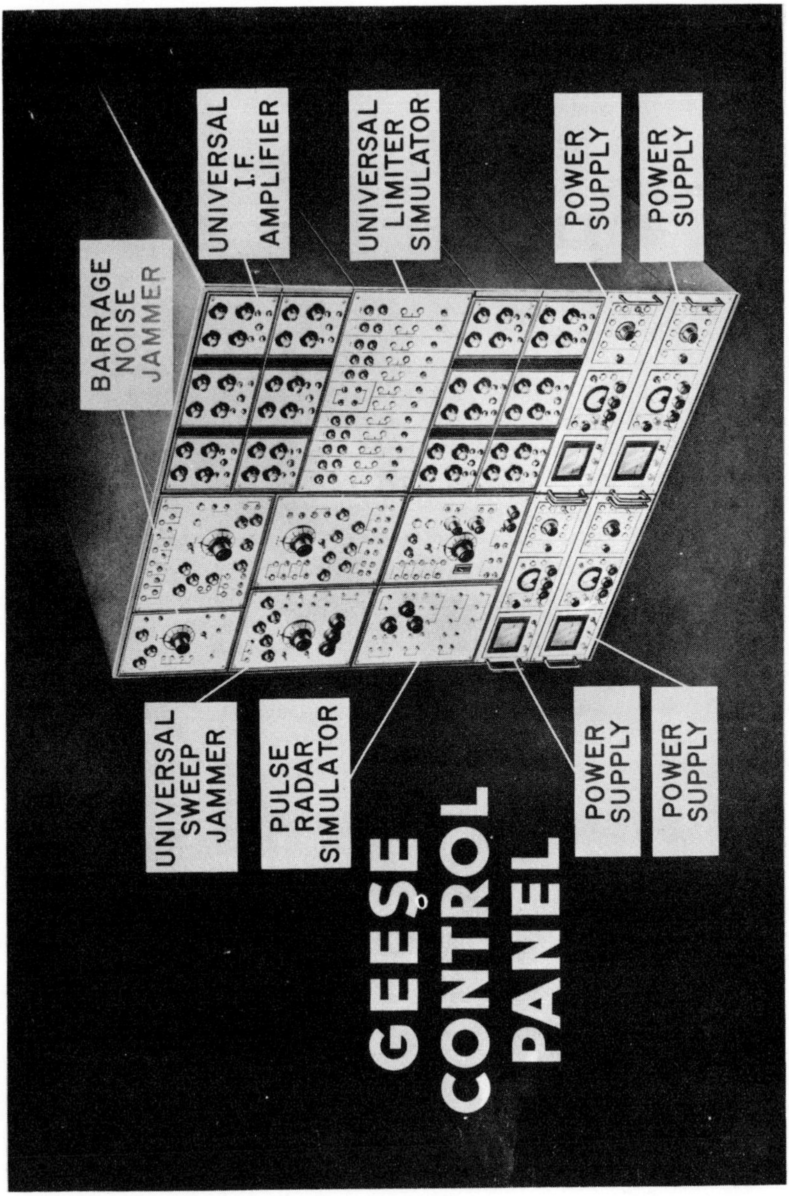
GEESE CONTROL PANEL
BARRAGE NOISE JAMMER
UNIVERSAL I.F. AMPLIFIER
UNIVERSAL LIMITER SIMULATOR
POWER SUPPLY
POWER SUPPLY
UNIVERSAL SWEEP JAMMER
PULSE RADAR SIMULATOR
POWER SUPPLY
POWER SUPPLY

Figure 13

and the width of the noise spectrum. The next module is a Universal Sweep Jammer. The single module will simulate approximately two hundred different types of sweep jammers currently in existence, ranging from HF to K band. Sweep deviations up to several thousand megacycles per second are available to simulate any known sweep jammer. The reason that this is quite simple is the fact that going from 0 cycles per second to 30 thousand megacycles in real life is equivalent to going from 0 cycles per second to 30 thousand cycles per second on the ESE. It is certainly much easier to build an audio frequency oscillator which will sweep from 0 cycles per second to 30 thousand cycles per second than from 0 cycles per second through the LF, HF, VHF, UHF, L band, S band, C band, X band, and K band. The Pulse Radar Simulator (PRF) is adjustable from 0 to one hundred kilocycles and has pulse widths from 0.01 to 1000 microseconds. Any carrier frequency from 30 megacycles to 100,000 megacycles is available. The design philosphy is that either manual operation or digital computer controlled operation can be utilized to set in the frequency power level, types of modulation and so forth for each signal. Twelve modules of the Universal Intermediate Frequency Amplifier simulator are also shown. Each module will be used to simulate one stage of an intermediate frequency strip. As an example, if the intermediate frequency strip consists of two staggered triples a total of six modules are required. By individual adjustment of the center frequency and gain of each stage, the characteristic of the actual intermediate frequency strip can be exactly matched. The Universal Limiter Simulator uses diode function generators to introduce non-linearities into the model. Typical non-linearities are AGC characteristics, mixer characteristics, overload characteristics and so forth. Using this approach any physically reliable non-linearity can be simulated within 1 percent.

## Summary

The ESE is a useful tool for:

(1) Evaluation and optimization of satellite and space communication subsystems.

(2) Evaluation of advanced radio guidance systems.

(3) Invulnerability optimization of subsystems to electronic countermeasures.

(4) Generic system studies to obtain quantitative performance data of proposed systems prior to hardware construction.

(5) Electromagnetic compatability studies.

The basic techniques described in this report are incorporated into a special analog computer facility, the Electronic System Evaluator. Many of the techniques are applicable to standard analog computers. The primary limitation of standard computers in electronic system evaluation is bandwidth. This limitation has been overcome in the ESE.

## Appendix

### Frequency and Bandwidth Scaling

Typical radar systems use frequencies ranging from 20 megacycles per second to 56 kilomegacycles per second. In simulating a radar system, there is no need to scale carrier frequencies, since the carrier contains no "information." Therefore the RF carrier frequency of the simulation is any convenient audio frequency. The only restriction on the RF frequency is that it be high enough to allow the use of a convenient IF frequency and bandwidth.

The IF center frequency is usually in the order of one-millionth of the radar IF frequency. Typical IF frequencies on the simulator are 30 and 60 cycles per second.

Although the choice of RF and IF center frequencies is more or less arbitrary, all bandwidths (RF, IF, video and servo) in a radar system must be scaled by the same scale factor. A convenient scaling is to make all simulator bandwidths one-millionth of the corresponding radar bandwidth. Since bandwidth determines the response time of a system, computer time is then one million times real time. A one-microsecond pulse is a one-second pulse on the ESE for instance.

An important advantage of the ESE is that all transient phenomena as well as steady state conditions can be recorded with standard oscillographs. In analyzing system performance it is very convenient to run off samples of RF, IF, video, and servo waveforms. Thermal noise can also be introduced so that the tracking errors of a radar can be recorded at different signal-to-noise ratios.

To simulate communication systems, a frequency scaling of $10^3$ to $10^5$ is used.

### Stability Requirements

The frequency stability of audio generators used to simulate signals must be very good unless care is used in picking the RF center frequency. For example, if a magnetron in a 3,000 megacycle radar has a frequency stability of 2 megacycles per second, scaling the carrier by $3 \times 10^6$ and scaling the bandwidth by a factor of $10^6$ would require a stability of 2 cps/1000 cps = 0.2 percent for the audio oscillator simulating the magnetron.

## Component Simulation

All of the basic electronic building blocks can be simulated by low frequency analog models. A short derivation of the basic models is presented in the remainder of the appendix.

## RF Filters and IF Amplifiers

RF filters, and IF amplifiers are scaled to audio frequencies by direct transfer function scaling. Single-tuned, double-tuned and staggered tuned amplifiers are simulated by cascading single-tuned stages such as Figure A-1.

A nodal analysis of this circuit yields

$$\frac{E_i}{R_g} = \frac{E_o}{R_g} + \frac{E_o}{R} + \frac{E_o}{LS} + CSE_o \qquad (1)$$

so that

$$\frac{E_o}{E_i} = \frac{1}{F_g C} \frac{S}{S^2 + \frac{1}{R_p C} S + w_o^2} \qquad (2)$$

However, since the computer will solve differential equations directly, it may be best to solve Equation (1) for its highest order derivative.

$$\frac{dE_o}{dt} = \frac{E_i}{R_g C} - \frac{E_o}{R_p C} - \frac{1}{LC} \int E_o dt \qquad (3)$$

Equation (5) may be solved on an analog computer using a circuit set up as shown in Figure A-2. This, then, is the simulation for the bandpass filter.

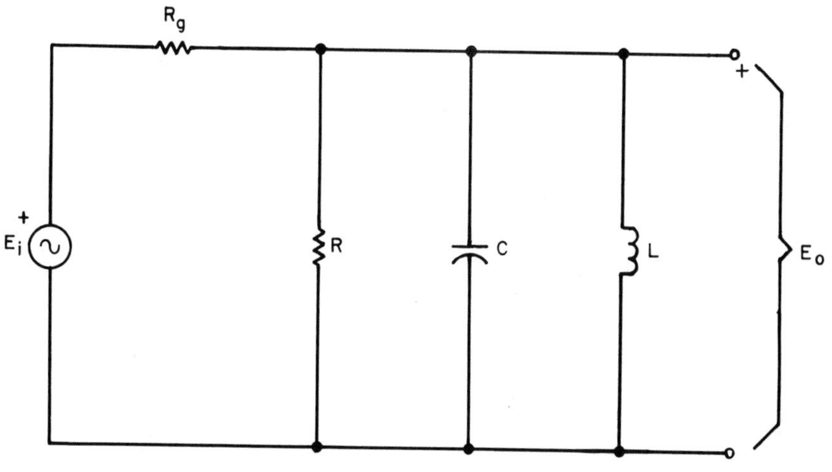


Figure A-1. Narrow Bandpass Filter

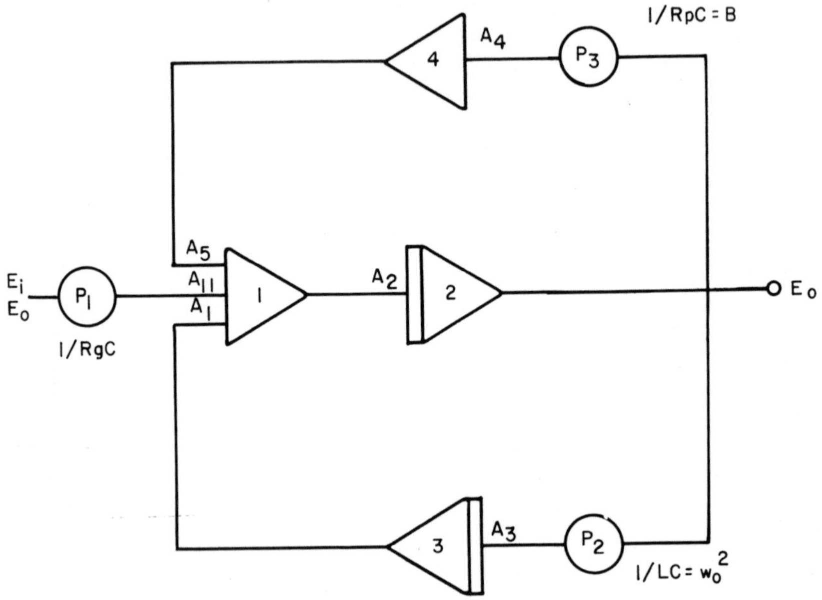


Figure A-2. ESE Equivalent Circuit

Referring to Figure A-1 it is seen that the Q of the circuit is

$$Q_c = w_o R_p C \tag{4}$$

The natural frequency (in radians/sec) of this circuit is

$$w_o^2 = \frac{1}{LC} \tag{5}$$

while the bandwidth (in radians/sec) is given by

$$B = \frac{1}{R_p C} \tag{6}$$

Referring to Figure A-2, the center frequency is adjusted by changing the gain of the loop containing $P_2$. The bandwidth is controlled by the gain of the loop containing $P_3$.

$$w_o^2 = (P_2)\,(A_1)\,(A_2)\,(A_3) \tag{7}$$

$$B = (P_3)\,(A_1)\,(A_2)\,(A_4) \tag{8}$$

Using wide band operational amplifiers and stabilizing networks, filters can be operated up to 20,000 cps.

## Mixers

Frequency conversion is accomplished in a receiver by using either vacuum tube or crystal mixers. The output of such a mixer consists of harmonic components as well as the desired signal. By filtering, the desired difference frequency of the two signals can be obtained. In the simulation, the desired difference frequency can be obtained by multiplying the two signals together.

Assuming the RF signal is A = asin $w_1t$ and the LO is B = bsin $w_2t$ the desired IF frequency is found by multiplying and filtering.

$$w_1 < w_2 \tag{9}$$

$$AB = ab \sin w_1t \sin w_2t$$

$$= \frac{ab}{2} \cos (w_1 - w_2)\, t - \frac{ab}{2} \cos (w_1 + w_2)\, t$$

In the computer there are two types of multipliers, servo and electronic. Due to the frequency limitations of the electro-mechanical components of the servo multiplier, it is required that a non-multiplier be used when "high" frequencies (2 cps or greater) are mixed.

A superior method of simulating a mixer in electromagnetic compatability problems is to use diode function generating equipment to duplicate the actual non-linear mixer characteristics. Spurious receiver modes are thereby simulated.

## Phase Detectors

A phase detector is a circuit whose output voltage is proportional to the phase difference between two input signals. The phase detector simulation of Figure A-3 operates in the following manner. First, two input signals of different phases ($E_1$ and $E_2$) are fed into limiting circuits. Waveforms $E_3$ and $E_4$ are the results of the limiting operations. These two voltages are then added and subtracted resulting in the waveforms $E_5$ and $E_6$. The negative part of the sum signal and the positive portion of the difference signal is also cut off. The resulting half-waves are added (waveform $E_7$) and then filtered ($E_8$). The resulting voltage is proportional to the phase difference of the input signal. The slope of this curve is defined as the phase detector sensitivity $k_\phi$.

## Voltage Controlled Oscillators

A voltage controlled oscillator circuit is used to simulate magnetrons, klystrons, carcinotrons, crystal oscillators, etc. Either frequency modulation or CW can be produced. Figure A-4 is the diagram of a simple VCO circuit which generates

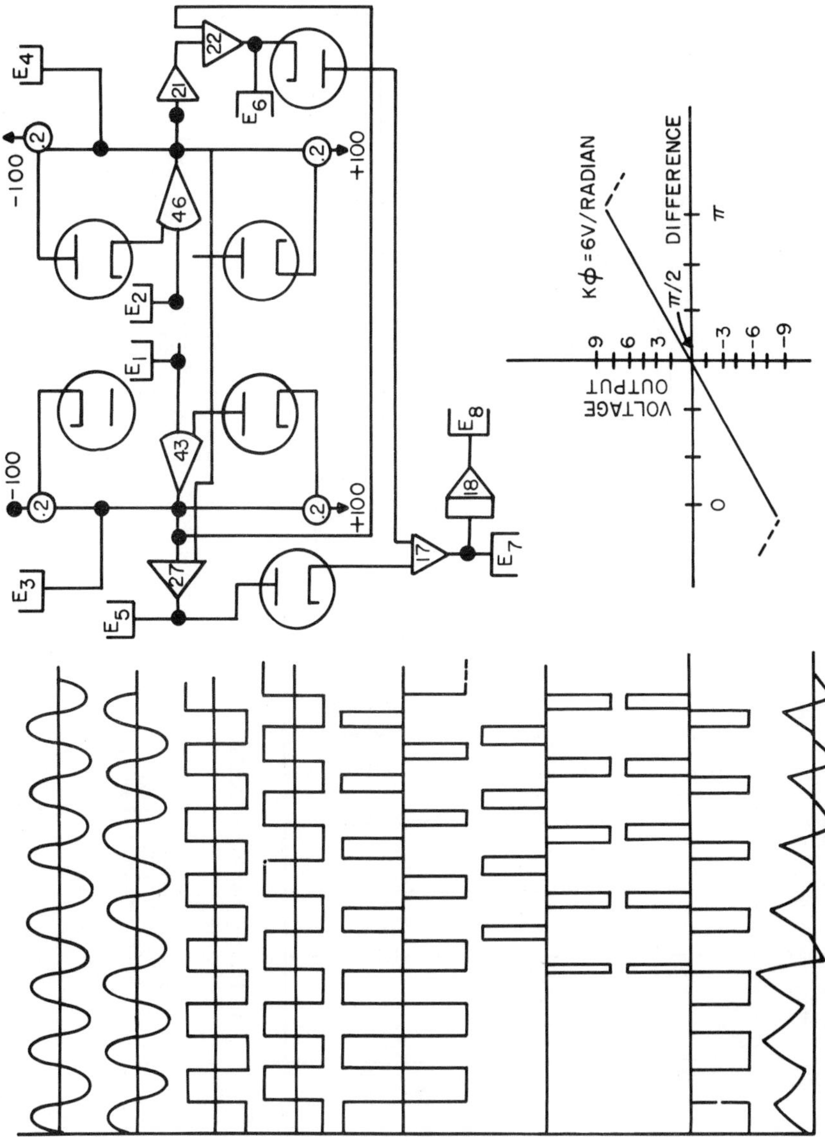


Figure A-3. Phase Detector Waveforms and Sensitivity

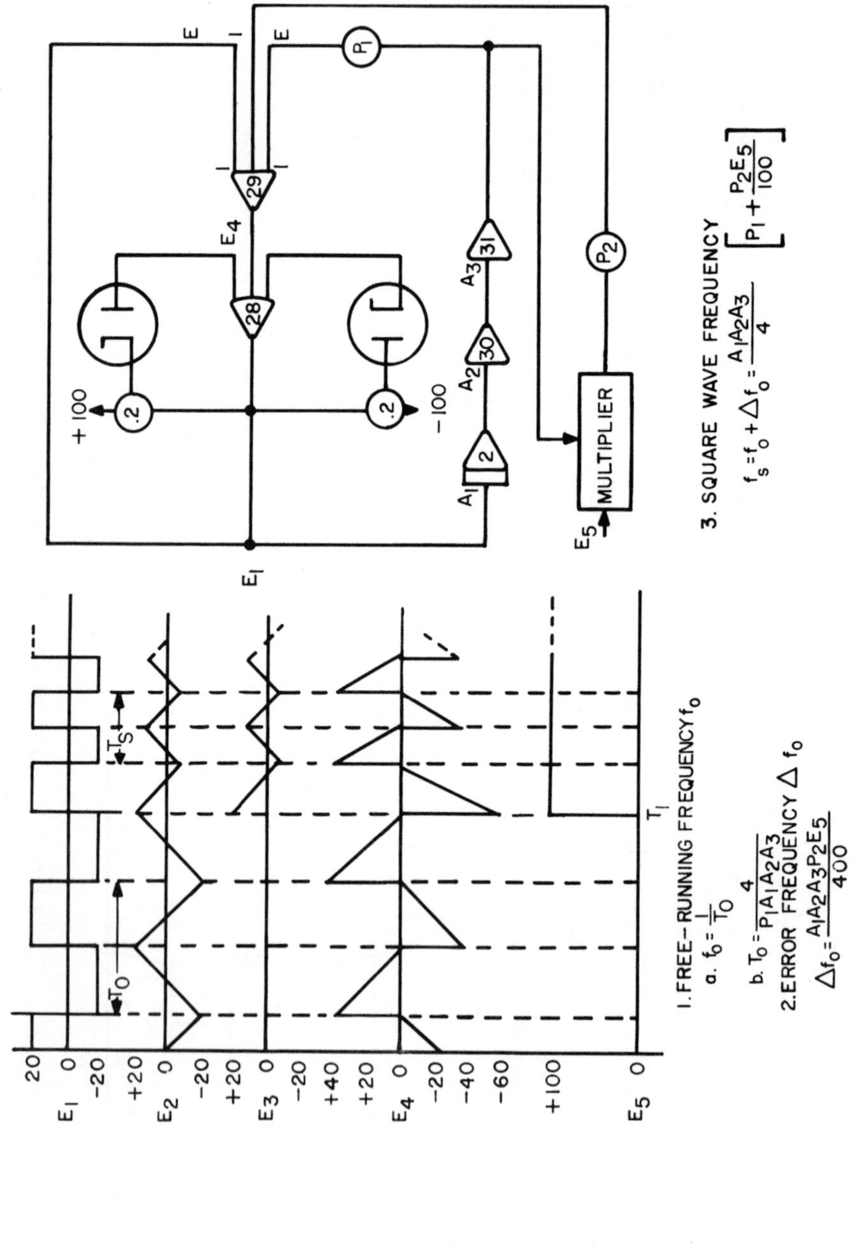

Figure A-4. Waveforms of Voltage Controlled Oscillator

1. FREE-RUNNING FREQUENCY $f_o$

a. $f_o = \dfrac{1}{T_o}$

b. $T_o = \dfrac{4}{P_1 A_1 A_2 A_3}$

2. ERROR FREQUENCY $\Delta f_o$

$\Delta f_o = \dfrac{A_1 A_2 A_3 P_2 E_5}{400}$

3. SQUARE WAVE FREQUENCY

$f_s = f_o + \Delta f_o = \dfrac{A_1 A_2 A_3}{4}\left[P_1 + \dfrac{P_2 E_5}{100}\right]$

MULTIPLIER

rectangular output waveforms at $E_1$. $E_5$ is the frequency modulation signal. If $E_5$ is zero, the circuit will generate a CW. $E_1$ is the rectangular waveform output signal. $E_1$ is filtered if a sine wave is required.

Figure A-5 shows a VCO circuit which generates sine waves directly. The basic circuit is derived from the low frequency analog sine wave generator which is normally limited to a frequency range of less 2 or 3 cps. The operating frequency is given by

$$f_o = \frac{\omega_o}{2\pi} = \frac{1}{2\pi}\sqrt{G_L} = \frac{\omega}{2\pi}\sqrt{A_1A_2A_3} \quad (10)$$

In as much as the frequency can be varied by changing the coefficient potentiometer they can be replaced by multipliers with no change in the normal operation. The VCO version of the basic circuit uses multipliers in place of coefficient potentiometers. The gain in the loop is controlled by the potentiometer and can therefore be controlled by the voltage into amplifier D. The frequency of operation is

$$f_o = \frac{\omega_o}{2\pi} = \frac{1}{2\pi}\sqrt{G_L} = \frac{\omega}{2\pi}\sqrt{\frac{A_1A_2A_3}{10^4}} \quad (11)$$

To operate at high audio frequencies an amplitude stability loop is used. (See Figure A-5.) This circuit has been operated at 1500 cps with one decade frequency deviation. The dynamic range of the multipliers limit the range of operation.

The stabilizing loop utilizes the variations in the signal amplitude within the loop to vary the feedback. Potentiometer A determines the amplitude level within the loop. This voltage A serves to cancel the average voltage out of the full wave rectifier and keep the average voltage level out of amplifier E at zero.

## Discriminator

The discriminator circuit (Figure A-6) utilizes two tuned circuits and an amplitude detector. The upper circuit is tuned to $\omega_1$ and the lower tuned to $\omega_2$ so that the center frequency is

$$\omega_o = \frac{\omega_1 + \omega_2}{2} \quad (12)$$

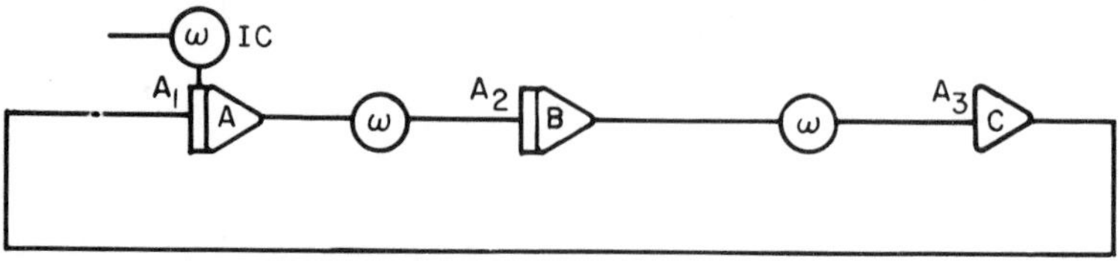


BASIC SINE WAVE OSCILLATOR

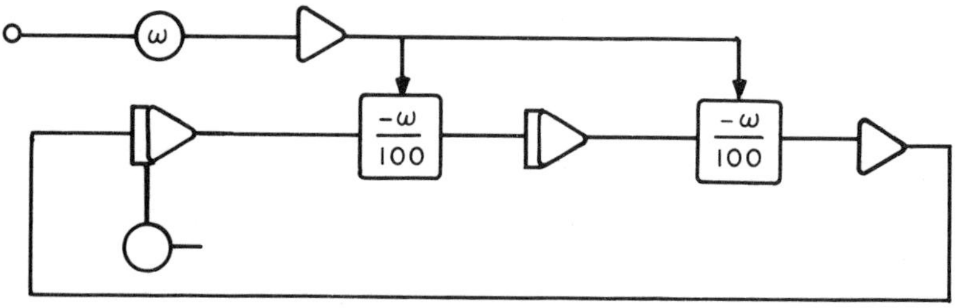


VCO VERSION

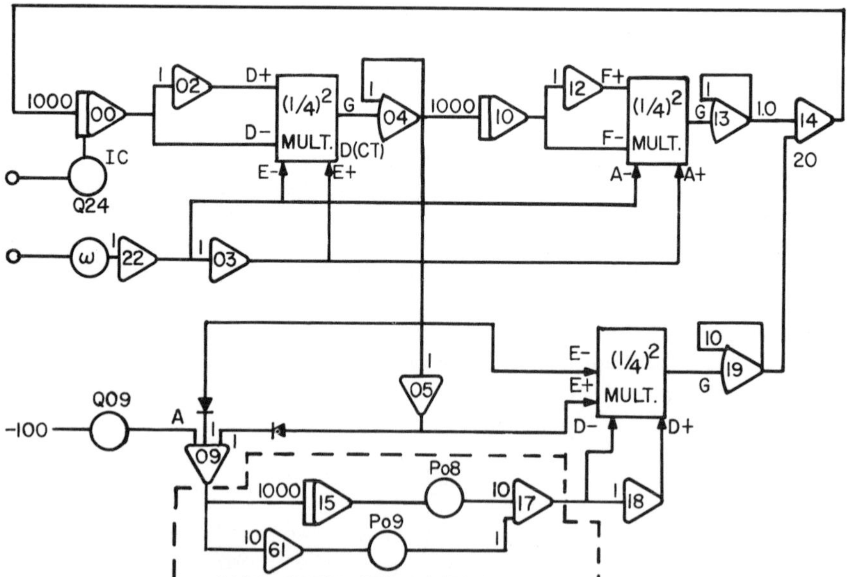


VCO WITH STABILIZING LOOP

Figure A-5

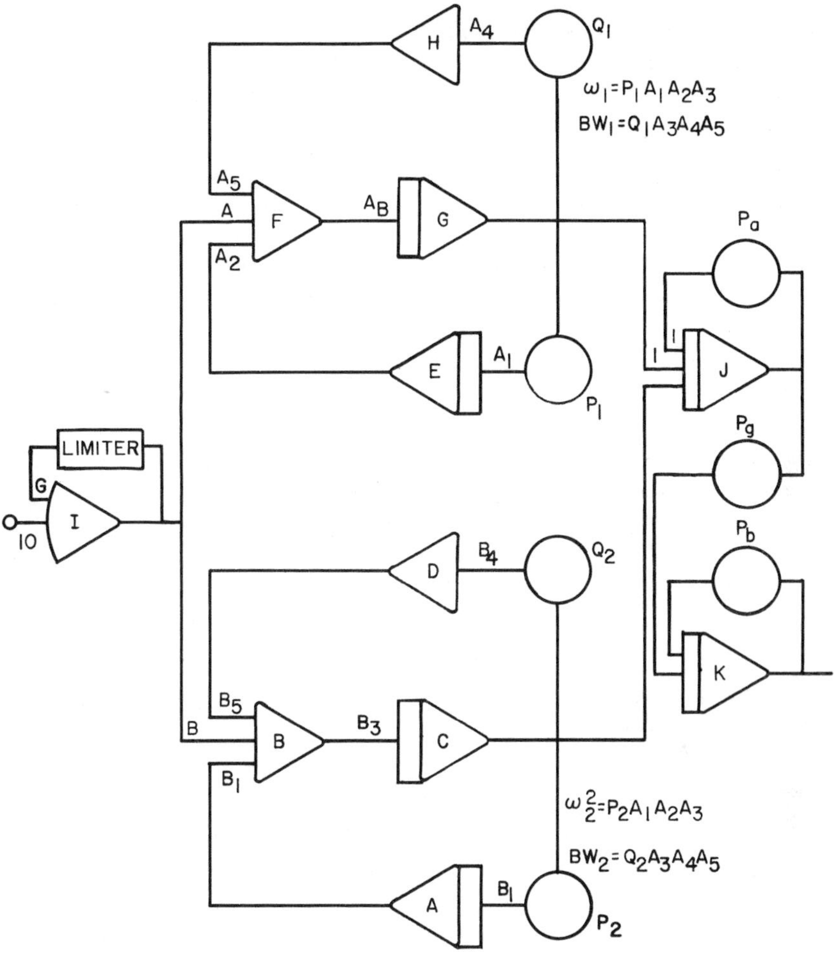


DISCRIMINATOR CIRCUIT

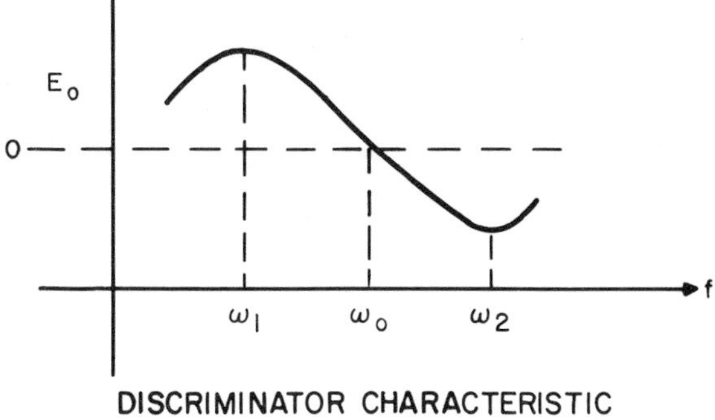


DISCRIMINATOR CHARACTERISTIC

Figure A-6

and the general characteristic is shown in Figure A-6.

The discriminator characteristic curve is adjusted by tuning the upper loop to $\omega_1$ with a 3 db bandwidth of $2(\omega_o - \omega_1)$. The lower loop has the same 3 db bandwidth but is tuned to $\omega_2$.

The output and slope of this discriminator is proportional to the limit level out of limiter 1 and can be varied directly by potentiometer $P_g$. The two low pass filters on the output serve to eliminate the high frequency components and therefore determine the time response of the discriminator.

## Second Detector

The circuit of a typical diode detector is shown in Figure A-7. More complicated filter networks can also be simulated with the computer by using additional operational amplifiers. The transfer function of such filters can be used to determine the equivalent simulator circuit. An example of this procedure is given in the discussion of the single-tuned band-pass filter.

## Video Amplifiers

Video amplifiers can be simulated by using operational amplifiers programmed as low pass filters.

## Tapped Delay Lines

Tapped delay lines are used in matched filter radar systems, and can be simulated by a magnetic tape recorder using continuous tape loop. 100 or more evenly spaced taps can be simulated using multiple recording on a single tape loop.

## Checking

In simulating large radar systems, it is expedient to consider subsystem by subsystem, checking out each loop independently. It is also desirable to check the computer solution mathematically at several points where the solution is amenable to analysis. Accuracies in the order of 5 to 10 percent are typical.

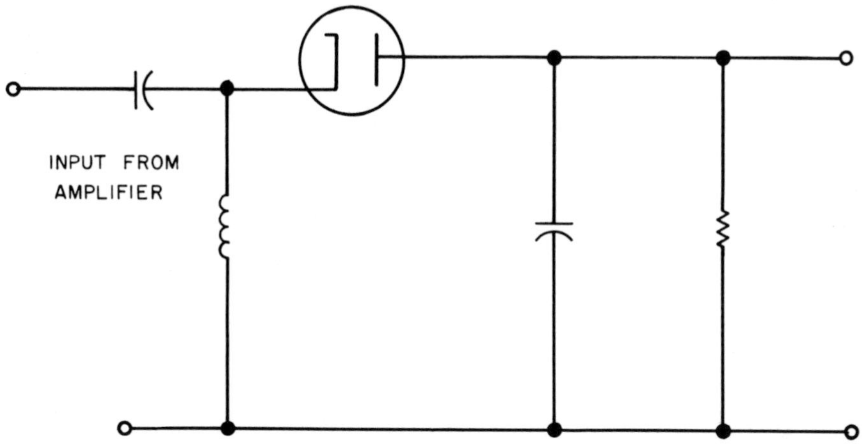


TYPICAL RADAR SECOND DETECTOR

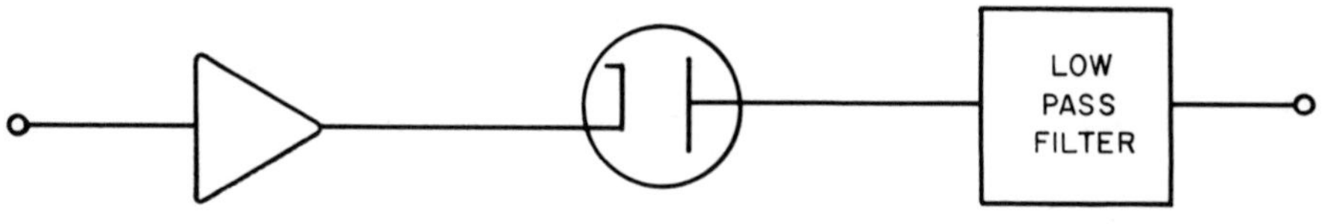


COMPUTER EQUIVALENT CIRCUIT

Figure A-7

SPACE TRAJECTORIES

# ANALYTICAL PERTURBATION EXPRESSIONS FOR THE RESTRICTED THREE-BODY PROBLEM

Paul A. Penzo
Space Technology Laboratories, Inc.
Los Angeles 45, California

## Abstract

Based on the restricted three-body problem and the added assumption that the infinitesimal body moves in the vicinity of one of the finite bodies, and in near-Keplerian motion, the perturbations on the motion of the infinitesimal body is found due to the gravitational effects of the other finite body. For example, if the infinitesimal body is a satellite of the Earth, then the perturbation expressions will represent deviations of the motion of the satellite from a pure elliptic orbit due to the effects of the Moon. All other perturbations such as those due to drag and oblateness have been neglected.

The approach taken here is to assume that the unperturbed motion is a conic trajectory and then to write the perturbation expressions in integral form. A transformation of coordinates is then applied to the orbital elements in order to simplify the actual integration and the final perturbation expressions.

Some suggestions as to possible applications and the effects of the restricting assumptions on these applications is then presented. These include application to Earth and Moon satellites and circumlunar trajectories. Finally, the general analytical expressions are reduced to several usable forms, including the special cases of circular and parabolic trajectories.

## Introduction

The need for methods of calculating lunar and solar perturbations on high-altitude satellite orbits around the Earth made itself felt, in a practical way, with the launching of 1959 Delta, STL's paddlewheel satellite placed in a highly eccentric orbit. In this case, soon after launch, Y. Kozai (1) of the Smithsonian Astrophysical Observatory predicted that the lifetime of this satellite would be greatly shortened due to perturbations of the Moon on the satellite's perigee distance. On the basis of his calculations, the perigee altitude (approximately 135 n mi) of the satellite's orbit would gradually decrease, allowing drag effects to become significant and resulting in a total lifetime of about 2 years. These results have since been confirmed by M. Moe (2) at STL and have led to increasing interest in the general problem of lunar and solar perturbations.

Prior to the launching of 1959 Delta, computer programs existed at STL which could calculate the drag and oblateness effects on an Earth satellite after many turns; however, no analytical scheme existed which could include lunar and solar perturbations. At this time, STL's Interplanetary Program, which solves the differential equations of the n-body problem by numerical methods, was used to calculate the orbit of an Earth satellite, including the effects of the Sun and Moon, but the machine time required to calculate the trajectory over many revolutions is exorbitant. This problem was relieved by M. Moe who derived approximate analytical expressions for lunar and solar perturbations on an Earth satellite and incorporated them into STL's Satellite Lifetime Program.

These analytical expressions are special cases of the general expressions derived here, and although the following theory has been developed on the basis of an Earth satellite perturbed by the Moon, the general nature of these expressions will allow application to other than satellite motion. These possibilities are discussed in the final section.

## Notation and Method

The perturbation procedure used here is the standard one, in which the motion of the satellite about the central body, the Earth, is known and the deviations of the orbital elements due to the perturbing body, the Moon, are found. Ignoring drag and oblateness effects and assuming that the central and perturbing bodies are point masses, the unperturbed motion of the satellite (whose mass is negligible) will be a Kepler ellipse. Following the notation used in Moulton and assuming the Earth to be the central body, the orbital elements are given by

- $q$ the perigee distance of the ellipse
- $e$ the eccentricity of the ellipse
- $\Omega$ the longitude of the ascending node (measured from some reference direction in the Moon's plane)
- $\omega$ the argument of perigee from the ascending node
- $i$ the inclination of the satellite plane to the Moon's orbital plane
- $v$ the angular distance of the satellite from perigee.

The first five elements describe the size, shape, and orientation of the ellipse, whereas the position of the satellite on the ellipse is specified when the true anomaly v is given. These six quantities, then, determine the unperturbed motion of the satellite. The reason for the choice of the element q instead of the semimajor axis, a, will become apparent when the results are applied to parabolic and hyperbolic motion. The radial distance, r, of the satellite from the center of the Earth is given by:

$$r = \frac{q(1 + e)}{1 + e \cos v} \tag{1}$$

Also, the satellite's energy per unit mass, $\epsilon$, and its angular momentum per unit mass, h, are given by the two equations:

$$\epsilon = -\frac{\mu}{2a} = -\frac{\mu(1 - e)}{2q} \tag{2}$$

and

$$h = r^2 \dot{v} = \sqrt{\mu a(1 - e^2)} = \sqrt{\mu q(1 + e)} \tag{3}$$

where $\mu = GM = 1.4077 \times 10^{16}\ ft^3/sec^2$ is the product of the gravitational constant and Earth's mass.

The orbital elements have been defined with reference to the Moon's plane and, therefore, the Moon will be in the x-y plane (see Figure 1). The components of the disturbing acceleration (3) as seen by the satellite will be

$$R = \mu_D \left[ -\frac{r}{\rho^3} + a_D \left( \frac{1}{\rho^3} - \frac{1}{a_D^3} \right) (\cos \gamma \cos u + \sin \gamma \sin u \cos i) \right] \tag{4}$$

$$S = \mu_D a_D \left( \frac{1}{\rho^3} - \frac{1}{a_D^3} \right) (-\cos \gamma \sin u + \sin \gamma \cos u \cos i) \tag{5}$$

and

$$W = -\mu_D a_D \sin \gamma \sin i \left( \frac{1}{\rho^3} - \frac{1}{a_D^3} \right) \tag{6}$$

where

$\mu_D$ = $GM_D$, the product of the gravitational constant and the mass of the disturbing body (Moon)
u = $\omega + v$, see Figure 1
$\rho$ = the distance from the satellite to the Moon
$a_D$ = the distance between the Earth and the Moon
$\gamma$ = the angle between the line of nodes and $a_D$.

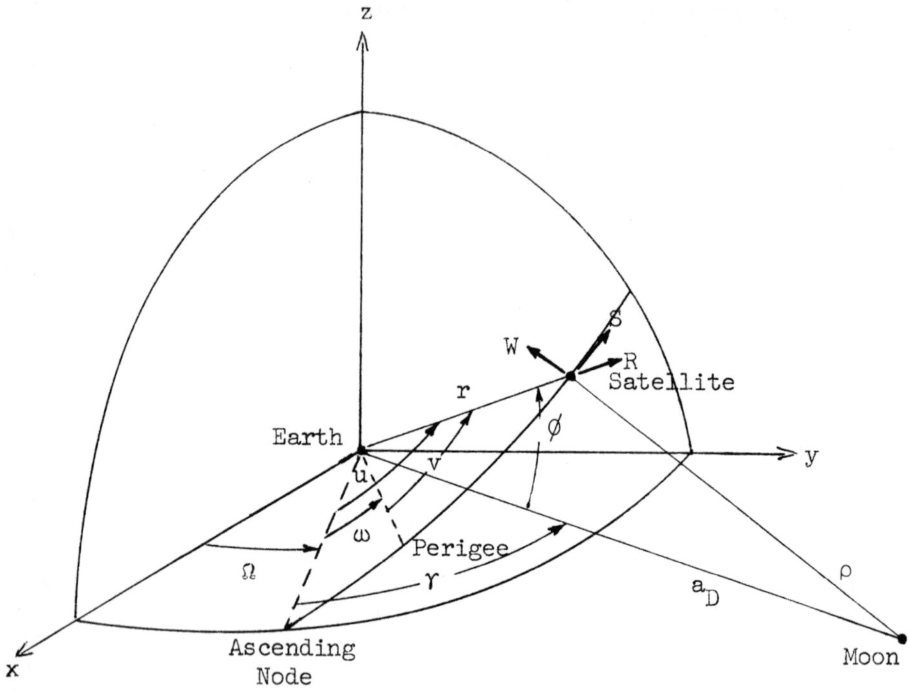


Figure 1.

The component of the disturbing acceleration R lies in the direction of r; the component S lies in the satellite plane and is perpendicular to R; and the component W is normal to both R and S. Figure 1 shows the directions of the components if they were all positive.

The expressions (4), (5), and (6) are exact and, in general, the distance $a_D$ and the angle $\gamma$ are functions of the time; however, since the Moon's orbit is nearly circular, the distance $a_D$ may be considered constant. Further, if the distance r is always small compared to $a_D$, the accelerations can be expanded in powers of $r/a_D$.

Referring to Figure 1, the distance $\rho$ may be written as

$$\rho^2 = a_D^2 + r^2 - 2\, a_D\, r \cos \phi$$

$$\frac{1}{\rho^3} = \frac{1}{a_D^3}\left(1 - \frac{2r}{a_D} \cos \phi + \frac{r^2}{a_D^2}\right)^{-3/2} = \frac{1}{a_D^3}\left(1 + 3\,\frac{r}{a_D} \cos \phi + \ldots\right)$$

or, to the first order,

$$\frac{1}{\rho^3} - \frac{1}{a_D^3} \cong 3 \frac{r}{a_D^4} \cos \phi$$

where

$$\cos \phi = \cos \gamma \cos u + \sin \gamma \sin u \cos i \tag{7}$$

Then Equation (4) will be

$$R = \mu_D \left[ - \frac{r}{a_D^3} \left( 1 + 3 \frac{r}{a_D} \cos \phi \right) + 3 \frac{r}{a_D^3} \cos^2 \phi \right]$$

or, neglecting the second-order term,

$$R = \frac{\mu_D}{a_D^3} r \left( -1 + 3 \cos^2 \phi \right)$$

or

$$R = 2K_D r \left( -1 + 3 \cos^2 \phi \right) \tag{8}$$

where

$$K_D = \frac{\mu_D}{2a_D^3}$$

Similarly,

$$S = -6K_D r \cos \phi \left( \cos \gamma \sin u - \sin \gamma \cos u \cos i \right) \tag{9}$$

and

$$W = -6K_D r \cos \phi \sin i \sin \gamma \tag{10}$$

The orbital elements which were defined earlier and which remain constant for the unperturbed motion will now vary depending upon the effects of the force components R, S, and W. These varying orbital elements will define a variable ellipse, called the osculating ellipse, which will be tangent to the actual orbit at every point and will have the same velocity as the satellite at every point. If these elements change very slowly, as is the case for weak perturbations, it is possible to calculate these changes by means of the following integral,

$$\Delta\xi = \int_A^B \frac{d\xi}{dv} dv = \int_A^B \frac{d\xi}{dt} \frac{dv}{\dot{v}}$$

or, using Equation (3),

$$\Delta\xi = \int_A^B \frac{d\xi}{dt} \frac{r^2}{h} dv \qquad (11)$$

where $\xi$ is any single orbital element.

In performing this integration, it is assumed that the orbital elements remain constant and equal to the values they have when the satellite is at point A. The integrand, then, may be considered to be a function of the true anomaly as measured along this ellipse from point A to point B. (See Figure 2.) At point B, new orbital elements ($\xi + \Delta\xi$) may be found and the process repeated.

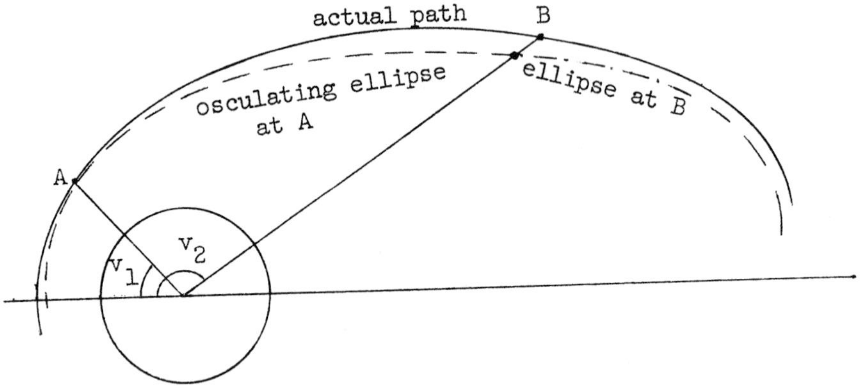


Figure 2.

In expression (11), the angular momentum, h, is considered constant and is given by Equation (3); r is given in Equation (1), and the derivatives of the elements (4), $d\xi/dt$, have been elegantly derived by M. M. Moe (5) using vector mechanics. They are

$$\frac{de}{dt} = \frac{h\,e \sin v}{r(1 + e \cos v)} R + \frac{h}{r} S \qquad (12)$$

$$\frac{dh}{dt} = rS \tag{13}$$

$$\frac{di}{dt} = \frac{r\cos(\omega + v)}{h} W \tag{14}$$

$$\frac{d\Omega}{dt} = \frac{r\sin(\omega + v)}{h} W \tag{15}$$

$$\frac{d\omega}{dt} = -\frac{r\sin(\omega + v)}{h\tan i} W - \frac{q(1+e)}{he}\cos v R$$

$$+ \frac{q(1+e)}{he}\left(1 + \frac{1}{1 + e\cos v}\right)\sin v S \tag{16}$$

where R, S, and W are given by Equations (8), (9), and (10). If a substitution of these equations is made into expression (11), the perturbations $\Delta\xi$ (with the proper expressions for R, S, W, and r also substituted) will be written in explicit integral form as a function of the true anomaly v only, except for $\gamma$ which may be considered constant within the limits of integration. For the special case where the limits are 0 and $2\pi$, the integrals have been found and applied to calculate the lifetime of 1959 Delta. (2) The perturbation expressions for these limits will be derived as a special case of the general perturbation expressions in a later section.

## Transformations

As indicated above, the perturbation expressions, (11), are too complex to integrate directly; however, with the aid of Figure 3, a transformation of the orbital elements may be found which will simplify the integrands and thus facilitate the final integrations. This set of transformations is based on the assumption that the perturbing body remains fixed in inertial space for the interval of integration considered. According to Figure 3, then, one may pass a fixed plane through the central body, the disturbing body, and the perigee of the satellite's osculating ellipse as it exists at point A, and assume this plane to be a new reference plane. Then, with respect to this plane, the ascending node of the ellipse will be at perigee (P); the inclination will be $i_P$; both $\omega_p$ and $\Omega_P$ will be zero; and $\gamma_P$ will be the angular distance between perigee and the Earth-Moon line. The other three elements, q, e, and v are independent of the reference plane used and so will remain unchanged.

This approach replaces the single difficult problem of integrating expressions (11), to that of finding the perturbations by solving two simpler problems. The first of these is

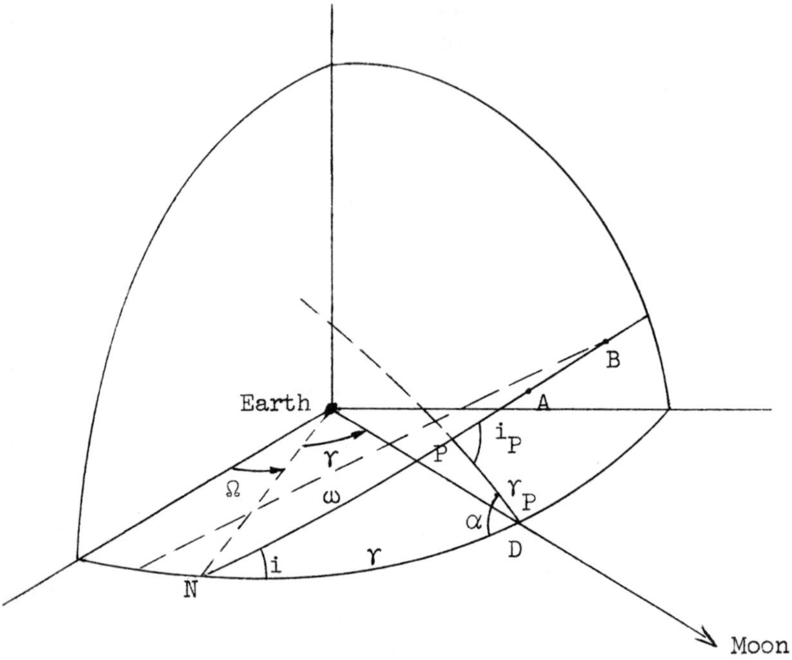


Figure 3.

to calculate the changes ($\Delta\xi_P$) in the newly defined elements, $i_P$, $\Omega_P$, $\omega_P$; and the second is to find how these changes are related to the changes ($\Delta\xi$) in the original orbital elements, $i, \Omega$, and $\omega$. The latter problem will be discussed in this section, whereas the first, concerned with the actual integrations, will be reserved for the next. It should be repeated that this entire approach is based on the assumption that the disturbing body remains fixed during the interval of integration. The problem of finding the perturbations due to a single or many revolutions of the disturbing body may be solved by repeating the above process many times and will be discussed in a later section.

Referring to Figure 3, it is seen that the spherical triangle NDP relates some of the orbital elements as written in the two reference systems. When the satellite is at point A, the elements $i, \Omega, \omega$, and the angle $\gamma$ are known, and the remaining angles, included in triangle NDP, may be found by the relations

$$\cos \gamma_P = \cos \gamma \cos \omega + \sin \gamma \sin \omega \cos i \qquad (17)$$

$$\sin \alpha = \frac{\sin \omega \sin i}{\sin \gamma_P} \tag{18}$$

and

$$\sin i_p = \frac{\sin \gamma \sin i}{\sin \gamma_P} \tag{19}$$

During the integration, the angle $\alpha$ will remain fixed since this is the angle that the reference plane makes with the Earth-Moon plane. Variations in $\gamma_P$ and $i_P$, then, will determine the variations in the angles $i$ and $\Omega$. Specifically,

$$\Delta i = \frac{\partial i}{\partial i_P} \Delta i_P + \frac{\partial i}{\partial \gamma_P} \Delta \gamma_P \tag{20}$$

and

$$\Delta\Omega = -\Delta\gamma = -\frac{\partial \gamma}{\partial i_P} \Delta i_P - \frac{\partial \gamma}{\partial \gamma_P} \Delta \gamma_P \tag{21}$$

where

$$\Delta\gamma_P = -\Delta\Omega_P$$

where the partial derivatives may be found from relations given by triangle NDP in Figure 3. Specifically,

$$\cos i = \cos \alpha \cos i_P + \sin \alpha \sin i_P \cos \gamma_P \tag{22}$$

and

$$\sin \gamma = \frac{\sin i_P \sin \gamma_P}{\sin i} \tag{23}$$

Then

$$\frac{\partial i}{\partial i_P} = \frac{\cos \alpha \sin i_P - \sin \alpha \cos i_P \cos \gamma_P}{\sin i} \tag{24}$$

$$\frac{\partial i}{\partial \gamma_P} = \frac{\sin \alpha \sin i_P \sin \gamma_P}{\sin i} \tag{25}$$

and

$$\frac{\partial \gamma}{\partial i_P} = \frac{\cos i_P \sin \gamma_P}{\cos \gamma \sin i} - \frac{\sin i_P \sin \gamma_P \cos i}{\cos \gamma \sin^2 i} \frac{\partial i}{\partial i_P} \tag{26}$$

$$\frac{\partial \gamma}{\partial \gamma_P} = \frac{\sin i_P \cos \gamma_P}{\cos \gamma \sin i} - \frac{\sin i_P \sin \gamma_P \cos i}{\cos \gamma \sin^2 i} \frac{\partial i}{\partial \gamma_P} \quad (27)$$

Substitution of Equations (24) through (27) into Equations (20) and (21) will give the changes in i and $\Omega$ once the changes in $i_P$ and $\gamma_P$ are known. The variation in $\omega$, on the other hand, is not given only by the variation in the side NP (which is $\omega'$ in Figure 4 of the triangle NDP) since the position of perigee, as the satellite moves from point A to point B, may move off of the arc DP. In fact, since by definition, $\omega_P$ is zero when the satellite is at point A, $\Delta\omega_P$ measures the angular displacement of the new perigee location, Q, along the osculating ellipse that exists when the satellite is at point B.

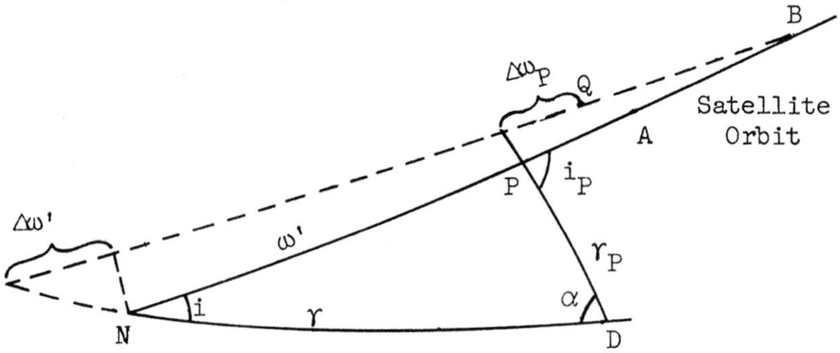


Figure 4

This angle is shown in Figure 4. The change in $\omega$, then, as shown in the figure, will be the sum of the changes in the angle $\omega'$ and $\omega_P$, or

$$\Delta\omega = \Delta\omega' + \Delta\omega_P \quad (28)$$

The variation $\Delta\omega_P$ will be found in the next section by the integration method presented there. The variation $\Delta\omega'$ can be found from the spherical triangle of Figure 4, or

$$\sin \omega' = \frac{\sin \alpha \sin \gamma_P}{\sin i} \quad (29)$$

Then

$$\Delta \omega' = \frac{\partial \omega'}{\partial \gamma_P} \Delta\gamma_P + \frac{\partial \omega'}{\partial i_P} \Delta i_P \tag{30}$$

where from (29)

$$\frac{\partial \omega'}{\partial \gamma_P} = \frac{\sin a \cos \gamma_P}{\cos \omega' \sin i} - \frac{\sin a \sin \gamma_P \cos i}{\cos \omega' \sin^2 i} \frac{\partial i}{\partial \gamma_P} \tag{31}$$

and

$$\frac{\partial \omega'}{\partial i_P} = \frac{\sin a \sin \gamma_P \cos i}{\cos \omega' \sin^2 i} \frac{\partial i}{\partial i_P} \tag{32}$$

Equations (24) and (25) give the required partial derivatives of i which will enable the evaluation of these partials. As mentioned in the previous section, the variations of the intrinsic elements q and e are independent of the coordinate system used. Thus

$$\Delta q = \Delta q_P \tag{33}$$

and

$$\Delta e = \Delta e_P \tag{34}$$

## Integrations

To summarize what has been done thus far, expressions (17) through (34) relate the changes in the orbital elements as written in two reference systems. The problem remains to find the changes with respect to the simpler, or "P" system. Here, the orbital elements are $i_P$, $\Omega_P$, $\omega_P$, $Q_P$, $e_P$, and $v_P$, where $\Omega_P = \omega_P = 0$ and $q_P = q$, $e_P = e$, and $v_P = v$. Expression (11) which gives the change in any one of the elements can be written as

$$\Delta\xi_P = \int_A^B \frac{d\,\xi_P}{dt} \frac{r^2}{h} dv \tag{35}$$

where the time derivatives, Equations (12) through (16), for this reference system are given by

$$\frac{de}{dt} = \frac{h\, e \sin v}{r(1 + e \cos v)} R + \frac{h}{r} S \tag{36}$$

$$\frac{dh}{dt} = rS \tag{37}$$

$$\frac{d i_P}{dt} = \frac{r \cos v}{h} W \tag{38}$$

$$\frac{d \gamma_P}{dt} = - \frac{d \Omega_P}{dt} = - \frac{r \sin v}{h} W \tag{39}$$

$$\frac{d \omega_P}{dt} = - \frac{r \sin v}{h \tan i_P} W - \frac{q(1 + e)}{h e} (\cos v) R$$

$$+ \frac{q(1 + e)}{h e} \left(1 + \frac{1}{1 + e \cos v}\right) (\sin v) S \tag{40}$$

The disturbing acceleration components (8), (9), and (10) must also be written in terms of the "P" reference system, or

$$R = 2K_D r(-1 + 3 \cos^2 \phi) \tag{41}$$

$$S = -6K_D r \cos \phi (\cos \gamma_P \sin v - \sin \gamma_P \cos v \cos i_P) \tag{42}$$

and

$$W = -6K_D r \cos \phi \sin i_P \sin \gamma_P \tag{43}$$

where

$$u_P = v + \omega_P = v \tag{44}$$

The $\cos \phi$ given in expression (7) will be given by

$$\cos \phi = \cos \gamma_P \cos v + \sin \gamma_P \sin v \cos i_P \tag{45}$$

In Equations (36) and (37), the derivatives of the energy and the angular momentum are given and explicit expressions for the change in these elements will be found. The variations of all other intrinsic elements are related to these two. For example, by Equations (2) and (3),

$$h^2 = \mu q (1 + e) = - \frac{\mu (1 - e) \mu}{2\epsilon} (1 + e)$$

or

$$h^2 = - \frac{\mu^2}{2\epsilon} (1 - e^2)$$

Then

$$e^2 = 1 + \frac{2h^2 \epsilon}{\mu^2} \tag{46}$$

and

$$\frac{de}{dt} = \frac{h}{e\mu^2}\left(h \frac{d\epsilon}{dt} + 2\epsilon \frac{dh}{dt}\right) \tag{47}$$

If this expression is substituted into Equation (35), then

$$\Delta e = \int_A^B \frac{de}{dt} \frac{h}{r^2} dv = \int_A^B \frac{h}{e\mu^2}\left(h \frac{d\epsilon}{dt} + 2\epsilon \frac{dh}{dt}\right)\frac{h}{r^2} dv$$

or

$$\Delta e = \frac{h}{e\mu^2}(h \,\Delta\epsilon + 2\epsilon\, \Delta h) \tag{48}$$

which gives the change in the eccentricity of the osculating ellipse. In a similar manner, it can be shown that the change in the major axis is given by

$$\Delta a = \frac{\mu}{2\epsilon^2} \Delta \epsilon \tag{49}$$

the change in perigee height is

$$\Delta q = \frac{1}{e\mu}(h\, \Delta h - q^2 \Delta \epsilon) \tag{50}$$

and the change in the period will be

$$\Delta T = \frac{3\pi}{\sqrt{-2\epsilon}} \Delta a = \frac{3\pi \mu}{2\epsilon^2 \sqrt{-2\epsilon}} \Delta \epsilon \tag{51}$$

Returning to expression (35) and substituting the derivative as given in Equation (38), the variation in the inclination is given by

$$\Delta i_P = \int \frac{r \cos v}{h} W \frac{r^2}{h} dv \tag{52}$$

The integral has been left indefinite since the limits used will depend largely on the application chosen. Now, if the expression (43) for W is placed into this integral, then

$$\Delta i_P = -\frac{6K_D \sin i_P \sin \gamma_P}{h^2} \int r^4 \cos \phi \cos v \, dv$$

Finally, if expressions (1), (3), and (45) for r, h, and cos $\phi$, respectively, are substituted into this integral,

$$\Delta i_P = -\frac{6K_D q^3 (1 + e)^3 \sin i_P \sin \gamma_P \cos \gamma_P}{\mu} \int \frac{\cos^2 v \, dv}{(1 + e \cos v)^4}$$

$$- \frac{6K_D q^2 (1 + e)^3 \sin i_P \cos i_P \sin^2 \gamma_P}{\mu} \int \frac{\sin v \cos v \, dv}{(1 + e \cos v)^4} \qquad (53)$$

If the coefficients of the two integrals are represented by $K_{i1}$ and $K_{i2}$ respectively (without the negative signs), and if the substitution of variables

$$\rho = 1 + e \cos v$$

is made, then

$$\Delta i_P = \frac{K_{i1}}{e^2} \int \left( \frac{1}{\rho^2} - \frac{2}{\rho^3} + \frac{1}{\rho^4} \right) \frac{d\rho}{\sqrt{e^2 - (\rho - 1)^2}} + \frac{K_{i2}}{e^2} \int \left( \frac{1}{\rho^3} - \frac{1}{\rho^4} \right) d\rho \qquad (54)$$

These integrals are of a standard form and may be found in numerous integral tables; however, since these same integrals, and only these integrals, appear in the calculation of all of the orbital elements and since their form depends upon the value of the eccentricity, it seems worth while to include them in Appendix A.

Integration of Equation (54) and transformation back to the variable v yields

$$\Delta i_P = \frac{K_D q^3 \sin \gamma_P \cos \gamma_P \sin i_P \sin v}{\mu (1 - e)^3 (1 + e \cos v)^3} F_i(v)$$

$$- \frac{K_D q^3 (1 + e)^3 \sin^2 \gamma_P \text{ ain } i_P \cos i_P (1 + 3e \cos v)}{\mu e^2 (1 + e \cos v)^3}$$

$$- \frac{3K_D q^3 (1 + 4e^2) \sin \gamma_P \cos \gamma_P \sin i_P}{\mu (1 - e)^3 \sqrt{\left[1 - e^2\right]}} E + C_i \qquad (55)$$

where

$$F_i(v) = (13 + 2e^2)e - 3(1 - 9e^2 - 2e^4)\cos v - e(1 - 6e^4)\cos^2 v$$

and E is defined in Appendix A. The quantity $C_i$ is the constant of integration.

In a similar manner, the variations in the other elements are found to be

$$\Delta\Omega_P = \frac{K_D q^3 (1 + e)\sin^2 \gamma_P \cos i_P \sin v}{\mu(1 - e)^2 (1 + e\cos v)} F_\Omega(v)$$

$$- \frac{K_D q^3 (1 + e)^3 \sin\gamma_P \cos\gamma_P (1 + 3e\cos v)}{\mu e^2 (1 + e\cos v)^3}$$

$$- \frac{3K_D q^3 (1 + e)\sin^2 \gamma_P \cos i_P}{\mu(1 - e)^2 \sqrt{[1 - e^2]}} E + C_\Omega \qquad (56)$$

where

$$F_\Omega(v) = 3e + 3(1 + e^2)\cos v + e(1 + 2e^2)\cos^2 v$$

and

$$\Delta\omega_P = -\cos i_P \Delta\Omega_P + \frac{K_D q^3 (1 + e)^3 \sin 2\gamma_P \cos i_P}{2\mu e^4 (1 + e\cos v)^3} F_{\omega 1}(v)$$

$$+ \frac{K_D q^3 (1 + e)\sin v}{\mu e^3 (1 - e)^2 (1 + e\cos v)^3}\left[M F_{\omega 2}(v) + e^2 N F_{\omega 3}(v)\right]$$

$$+ \frac{3K_D q^3 (1 + e)(4\cos^2 \gamma_P - \sin^2 \gamma_P \cos^2 i_P - 1)}{\mu(1 - e)^2 \sqrt{[1 - e^2]}} E + C_\omega \qquad (57)$$

where

$$F_{\omega 1}(v) = 4 - 5e^2 + 3e(4 - e^2)\cos v + 12e^2\cos^2 v$$

$$F_{\omega 2}(v) = (6 - 44e^2 + 13e^4 - 2e^6) + 3e(4 - 25e^2 + 3e^4)\cos v + e^2(8 - 37e^2 + 2e^4)\cos^2 v$$

$$F_{\omega 3}(v) = (2 + e^2) + 3e(1 + e^2)\cos v + e^2(1 + 2e^2)\cos^2 v$$

$$M = \cos^2 \gamma_P - \sin^2 \gamma_P \cos^2 i_P$$

$$N = 1 - 3\sin^2 \gamma_P \cos^2 i_P$$

The change in energy

$$\Delta \epsilon = \frac{K_D q^2 (1+e)^2}{e^2 (1 + e\cos v)^2}\Big[3e^2 \sin 2\gamma_P \cos i_P \sin v \cos v - 6e(\cos^2\gamma_P - \sin^2\gamma_P \cos^2 i_P)\cos v - 3\cos^2\gamma_P + 3(1+e^2)\sin^2\gamma_P \cos^2 i_P - e^2\Big] + C_\epsilon \quad (58)$$

and the change in the angular momentum

$$\Delta h = \frac{K_D h q^3 \sin 2\gamma_P \cos i_P \sin v}{2\mu (1-e)^3 (1 + e\cos v)^3} F_h(v) + \frac{K_D h q^3 (1+e)^3 (\cos^2\gamma_P - \sin^2\gamma_P \cos^2 i_P)(1 + 3e\cos v)}{\mu e^2 (1 + e\cos v)^3} + \frac{15 K_D h q^3 e^2 \sin 2\gamma_P \cos i_P}{2\mu (1-e)^3 \sqrt{[1 - e^2]}} E + C_H \quad (59)$$

where

$$F_h(v) = e(2e^4 - 9e^2 - 8) + 3(2 - 9e^2 - 3e^4)\cos v + e(2 - 9e^2 - 8e^4)\cos^2 v$$

## Applications

All previous discussion has been confined to the derivation of the perturbation expressions representing the effect of a third distant body on the motion of a satellite in the vicinity of a central force field. The application used in the derivation, i.e., the effects of the Moon on an Earth satellite, has been singled out for the purpose of simplifying the discussion of the theory; however, as pointed out in the introduction, the results apply to all possible motion about the central body and not only elliptic motion. Also, of course, the two finite bodies need not be the Earth and the Moon. They may be, for example, Venus and the Sun where the perturbations on a Venus satellite due to the Sun is desired.

To recapitulate, two approximating assumptions are made in the derivations. The first is the assumption that the ratio of the satellite distance to the perturbing body distance, both measured from the central body, be small. The second is the assumption that the perturbing body remain fixed in space for the interval of integration chosen. Both of these assumptions are closely related to the integration interval required and the accuracies obtainable, and these relations are greatly dependent on the masses of the two finite bodies.

Some indication of why this is so may be obtained by considering the special case where the satellite and the perturbing body move at fixed distances from the central body, i.e., in circular orbits. If their radii are a and $a_D$ respectively, then the ratio of their angular rates, or the angles through which they travel in a given time interval, is given by

$$\frac{\theta}{\theta_D} = \frac{T_D}{T} = \left(\frac{a_D}{a}\right)^{3/2} \Big/ \sqrt{1 + \frac{\mu_D}{\mu}}$$

where T and $T_D$ are the respective periods of the satellite and the disturbing body. For an Earth satellite with the Moon as the disturbing body, $\mu_D/\mu = 1/81.45$, or

$$\left(\frac{\theta}{\theta_D}\right)_E = 0.994\left(\frac{a_D}{a}\right)^{3/2}$$

where the subscript E indicates that the Earth is the central body. On the other hand, for a Moon satellite with the Earth as the disturbing body, $\mu_D/\mu = 81.45$, and

$$\left(\frac{\theta}{\theta_D}\right)_M = 0.109\left(\frac{a_D}{a}\right)^{3/2}$$

Thus, for example, if the restriction is made that the disturbing body must not move through more than 10 degrees for the interval of integration (or $\theta_D = 10^\circ$), and $a/a_D$ is taken to be 0.1 (approximately a 24-hour Earth satellite orbit), then solving for the integration interval, $\theta$,

$$\theta_E = 310^\circ$$

and

$$\theta_M = 35^\circ$$

## Earth Satellite Orbits

The above results indicate that generally for an Earth satellite whose period is 24 hours or less the integration interval may be taken to be a full revolution, or 0 to $2\pi$. No further analysis need be made concerning the integration interval of an Earth satellite, then, for it is very likely that the error induced by the first assumption (the distance assumption) will overshadow any error caused by the motion of the Moon. As for the magnitude of this distance error, some indication may be had by considering a few examples and making a direct comparison of these approximate results with the exact results obtainable by using the n-body computer program.

Appendix B gives the reduced forms of the perturbation expressions for the limits 0 and $2\pi$, and Appendix C for the special case of circular orbits.

## Lunar Satellite Orbits

The principal distinction between Earth satellite orbits and Moon satellite orbits has already been given, i.e., for fixed angular motion of the disturbing body ($\theta_D = 10^\circ$ in the case above), and for a fixed ratio of the distance $a/a_D$, the integration interval of a lunar satellite should be about one-tenth that of an Earth satellite. This implies, as calculated previously, that for lunar satellites whose radial distance is about 20,000 nautical miles, an integration interval of about 36 degrees is required. Closer satellites, of course, may have larger integration intervals.

It is interesting to compare the relative magnitudes of the perturbations of a Moon satellite with those of an Earth satellite. Glancing at the perturbation expressions (55) through (59), and assuming that the initial satellite orbit conditions are exactly the same for an Earth satellite as for a Moon satellite, then for the elements, i, $\Omega$, and $\omega$, the perturbations may be written as

$$\Delta\xi_E = \frac{K_{DE}}{\mu_E} f_\xi(e, q, \lambda, i, \Omega, \omega, v)$$

and

$$\Delta\xi_M = \frac{K_{DM}}{\mu_M} f_\xi(e, q, \lambda, i, \Omega, \omega, v)$$

where $\xi$ may stand for any one of the above angular orbital elements. Also,

$$K_{DE} = \frac{\mu_M}{2a_D^3} \quad \text{and} \quad K_{DM} = \frac{\mu_E}{2a_D^3}$$

Then, if the ratio is taken, where $a_D$ and $f\xi$ are the same in both instances,

$$\frac{\Delta\xi_M}{\Delta\xi_E} = \frac{\mu_E^2}{\mu_M} = 6630$$

Thus for identical orbital conditions, the perturbations of the Earth on a Moon satellite will be greater than the perturbations of the Moon on an Earth satellite by this factor. Obviously, this will also be the factor involved insofar as the absolute errors are concerned. The size of this factor leads one to the conclusion that the application of these perturbation expressions to Moon satellites should be restricted to either tight satellites where accuracy is required and obtainable, or to loose satellites, up to 20,000 nautical miles, where only qualitative or orbit shape information is desired.

## Hyperbolic and Parabolic Orbits

Application of the derived perturbation expressions to hyperbolic orbits are limited by the assumption that the distance of the vehicle to the central body be small compared to the distance of the perturbing body to the central body. This places a definite restriction on the application of these expressions since the extent of escape trajectories from the central body is infinite.

This restriction, however, is consistent with the approach taken by many investigators in analyzing interplanetary and lunar trajectories. In interplanetary trajectories (7), for example, the vehicle, if escaping from the Earth, is assumed to be influenced only by the Earth until it travels beyond a predetermined distance from the Earth. At this point, the Earth's gravitation is neglected, and the vehicle is assumed to be affected only by the Sun. When the vehicle approaches sufficiently near the terminal planet, the influence of all other bodies but this planet is neglected. In two of these three phases, where the vehicle is near the initial and terminal planets, refinements of the trajectory may be obtained by using the perturbation expressions to determine the influence of Sun on these portions of the trajectory.

In the case of lunar trajectories, it is again possible to break up the trajectory into two or more parts. As suggested by Egorov (6), the Moon can be enclosed in a "sphere of action" (about 20,000-nautical-mile radius) such that only the Moon's gravitational field is considered within this sphere and only the Earth's field outside of it. Egorov analyzes a multitude of trajectories in this manner including circumlunar trajectories. Since the perturbations are so much larger near the Moon, as indicated in the paragraph on lunar satellite orbits, the vehicle's trajectory near the Moon may be refined significantly by using the perturbation expressions given here.

As for the expressions themselves, (55) through (59), these have been derived in such a manner that they are directly applicable to hyperbolic orbits. This is accomplished by using the parameter q in place of a, which becomes infinite for escape orbits. The quantity E which is the eccentric anomaly in elliptic orbits has no physical meaning here and is defined mathematically in Appendix A.

For the special case of parabolic orbits, $e = 1$, the perturbation expressions become infinite at each endpoint resulting in indeterminate forms. However, as in the case of circular orbits, this problem may be resolved by either of the two methods mentioned in Appendix C. The resulting expressions, applicable to parabolic orbits, are presented in Appendix D.

## Appendix A
## Integral Forms

Evaluation of the integrals shown in expression (54) may be obtained from the general form

$$\int \frac{d\rho}{\rho^n \sqrt{a\rho^2 + b\rho + c}} = F_n(\rho) + B_n \int \frac{d\rho}{\rho \sqrt{y}}$$

where $a = -1$, $b = 2$, $c = e^2 - 1$, and $y = a\rho^2 + b\rho + c$.

Then

$$\int \frac{d\rho}{\rho^2 \sqrt{y}} = \frac{\sqrt{y}}{(1 - e^2)\rho} + \frac{1}{1 - e^2} \int \frac{d\rho}{\rho\sqrt{y}}$$

$$\int \frac{d\rho}{\rho^3 \sqrt{y}} = \frac{\sqrt{y}}{2(1 - e^2)\rho^2} + \frac{3\sqrt{y}}{2\left(1 - e^2\right)^2 \rho} + \frac{2 + e^2}{2\left(1 - e^2\right)^2} \int \frac{d\rho}{\rho\sqrt{y}}$$

and

$$\int \frac{d\rho}{\rho^4 \sqrt{y}} = \frac{\sqrt{y}}{3(1 - e^2)\rho^3} + \frac{5\sqrt{y}}{6\left(1 - e^2\right)^2 \rho^2} - \frac{2\sqrt{y}}{3\left(1 - e^2\right)^2 \rho} + \frac{5\sqrt{y}}{2\left(1 - e^2\right)^3 \rho}$$

$$+ \frac{2 + 3e^2}{2\left(1 - e^2\right)^3} \int \frac{d\rho}{\rho\sqrt{y}}$$

where integration of the remaining integral may be done directly, or

$$\int \frac{d\rho}{\rho\sqrt{y}} = -\int \frac{dv}{1 + e \cos v}$$

$$= -\frac{1}{\sqrt{1 - e^2}} \tan^{-1} \frac{\sqrt{1 - e^2} \sin v}{e + \sin v} + C_1 \; (0 \leqslant e < 1)$$

$$\int \frac{d\rho}{\rho\sqrt{y}} = \frac{1}{\sqrt{1 - e^2}} \cos^{-1}\left(\frac{e + \cos v}{1 + e \cos v}\right) + C_1 \; (0 \leqslant e < 1)$$

Similarly,

$$\int \frac{d\rho}{\rho\sqrt{y}} = -\frac{1}{\sqrt{e^2 - 1}} \cosh^{-1}\left(\frac{e + \cos v}{1 + e \cos v}\right) + C_2 \; (e > 1)$$

Now, if the variable E is defined as

$$E = \begin{cases} \cos^{-1}\left(\dfrac{e + \cos v}{1 + e \cos v}\right) & \text{for } (0 \leqslant e < 1) \\ \cosh^{-1}\left(\dfrac{e + \cos v}{1 + e \cos v}\right) & \text{for } (e > 1) \end{cases}$$

then

$$\int \frac{d\rho}{\rho\sqrt{y}} = -\frac{E}{\sqrt{1 - e^2}} + C \quad (e \neq 1)$$

It should be noted that for $e < 1$, or the elliptic case, the quantity $E$ is the familiar eccentric anomaly. For the parabolic case, where $e = 1$, this and the above integrals must be evaluated in another manner. Specifically,

$$\int \frac{d\rho}{\rho^m \sqrt{2\rho - \rho^2}} = -\frac{\sqrt{2\rho - \rho^2}}{(2m - 1)\rho^m} + \frac{m - 1}{2m - 1} \int \frac{d\rho}{\rho^{m-1}\sqrt{2\rho - \rho^2}}$$

and

$$\int \frac{d\rho}{\rho\sqrt{2\rho - \rho^2}} = \frac{2\rho - \rho^2}{\rho} + C$$

## Appendix B
## Perturbation Expressions for the Limits 0 and $2\pi$

For the application of Earth satellites and tight lunar satellites, it is possible to integrate the perturbation expressions over a single revolution of the satellite orbit. If this is done, the expressions (55) through (59) will reduce to very simple forms. The change in the inclination $i_P$, for example, will contain only a contribution by the eccentric anomaly term (E term), and this will give

$$\Delta i_P = -\frac{6\pi K_D q^3 (1 + 4e^2) \sin \gamma_P \cos \gamma_P \sin i_P}{\mu (1 - e)^3 \sqrt{|1 - e^2|}}$$

where the limits on the eccentric anomaly are identical to the limits on the true anomaly. Similarly, the expression for $\Delta\Omega_P$ reduces to

$$\Delta\Omega_P = -\frac{6\pi K_D q^3 (1 + e) \sin^2 \gamma_P \cos i_P}{\mu (1 - e)^2 \sqrt{|1 - e^2|}}$$

and that for $\Delta\omega_P$ to

$$\Delta\omega_P = -\frac{6\pi K_D q^3 (1 + e)\left(1 - 4\cos^2 \gamma_P\right)}{\mu (1 - e)^2 \sqrt{|1 - e^2|}}$$

The energy expression does not contain an eccentric anomaly term, and since each term is either even or contains a sin v, then

$$\Delta \epsilon = 0$$

The expression for the change in the angular momentum, on the other hand, reduces to

$$\Delta h = \frac{15\pi K_D h q^3 e^2 \sin 2\gamma_P \cos i_P}{\mu (1 - e)^3 \sqrt{|1 - e^2|}}$$

## Appendix C
## Perturbation Expressions for Circular Orbits

In this case, substitution of e = 0 (circular orbit) will cause the perturbation expressions to become infinite at each limit causing the final expressions to be indeterminate. This difficulty may be resolved by either of the following two methods. First, the reduction to the circular case may be made before the integration process, resulting in integrals of a much simpler form compared to the general integrals. The second method is to determine the limits of the general perturbation expressions and thus arrive at the case for circular orbits. This may be done by rearranging the infinite terms before setting the eccentricity equal to zero. The results in either case will be, where a is the radius of the circular orbit,

$$\Delta i_P = -\frac{3K_D a^3 \sin\gamma_P \sin i_P}{\mu}(v \cos\gamma_P + \cos\gamma_P \sin v \cos v$$

$$- \sin\gamma_P \cos i_P \cos^2 v) + C_i$$

$$\Delta\Omega_P = -\frac{3K_D a^3 \sin\gamma_P}{\mu}(v \sin\gamma_P \cos i_P - \sin\gamma_P \cos i_P \sin v \cos v$$

$$- \cos\gamma_P \cos^2 v) + C_\Omega$$

and

$$\Delta\epsilon = 3K_D a^2 (\sin 2\gamma_P \cos i \sin v \cos v + \cos^2\gamma_P \cos^2 v$$

$$- \sin^2\gamma_P \cos^2 i_P \cos^2 v) + C_\epsilon$$

The change in the angular momentum is seen to be related to $\Delta\epsilon$ when e is set equal to zero in Equation (48). Then

$$\Delta h = -\frac{h}{2\epsilon}\Delta\epsilon$$

where, by Equations (2) and (3),

$$\Delta h = a\sqrt{\frac{a}{\mu}}\Delta\epsilon$$

It should be noted that the true anomaly, v, may be chosen arbitrarily since a circular orbit has no perigee. Also, since this is the case, it is not possible to write an expression for the argument of perigee or its change. If after the integration the perturbations cause the orbit to be no longer circular, then, the newly formed argument of perigee must be found in another manner. For example, if from Figure 3 the symbol $\omega_A$ defines the angle from the ascending mode (P) to the lower limit of integration (point A), and the true anomaly v is taken as zero at point A, then the argument of perigee for the osculating ellipse at point B will be

$$\omega_P = \omega_A + v_{AB} - v_B$$

where $v_{AB}$ is the angle from A to B and $v_B$ is the true anomaly at point B. This angle is given from Equation (1), or

$$\cos v_B = \frac{1}{\Delta e}\left[\frac{(a + \Delta a)}{r_B}(1 - \Delta^2 e) - 1\right]$$

which, to the first order, reduces to

$$\cos v_B = \frac{1}{\Delta e}\left(\frac{a + \Delta a}{r_B} - 1\right)$$

The distance $r_B$ is not easy to find since the orientation of the ellipse is not known; however, with the two equations

$$r_B V_B \cos\theta_B = h_B$$

and

$$\frac{V_B^2}{2} - \frac{\mu}{r_B} = \epsilon_B$$

and the expression [(5), page 14]

$$\theta_B = \frac{K_D a^4}{h^2} v (3 \cos^2 \gamma_P + 3 \sin^2 \gamma_P \cos^2 i_P - 2)$$

$$+ \frac{3K_D a^4}{h^2}\left(\cos^2 \gamma_P - \sin^2 \gamma_P \cos^2 i_P\right) \sin v \cos v$$

$$+ \frac{6K_D a^4}{h^2} \sin \gamma_P \cos \gamma_P \cos i_P \sin^2 v$$

the value of $r_B$ may be solved for. The quantity $V_B$ is the velocity of the satellite at point B and $\theta_B$ is the flight path angle at point B.

## Appendix D
## Perturbation Expressions for Parabolic Trajectories

As in the case of circular orbits the perturbation expressions (55) through (59), except for the energy change, become infinite for a parabolic trajectory or $e = 1$. The general derivation remains applicable up to the point where the final integrals in terms of the parameter $\rho$ are obtained. Here, as indicated in Appendix A, the integral forms will differ. Applying the correct integral forms, the perturbation expressions are

$$\Delta i_P = - \frac{16K_D q^3 \sin \gamma_P \cos \gamma_P \sin i_P \sin v}{35\mu (1 + \cos v)^4}$$

$$(8 + 32 \cos v + 52 \cos^2 v + 13 \cos^3 v)$$

$$- \frac{8K_D q^3 \sin^2 \gamma_P \sin i_P \cos i_P}{\mu (1 + \cos v)^3}(1 + 3 \cos v) + C_i$$

$$\Delta \Omega_P = - \frac{16K_D q^3 \sin^2 \gamma_P \cos i_P \sin v}{5\mu (1 + \cos v)^3}(4 - 3 \cos v - \cos^2 v)$$

$$- \frac{8K_D q^3 \sin \gamma_P \cos \gamma_P}{\mu (1 + \cos v)^3}(1 + 3 \cos v) + C_\Omega$$

$$\Delta\omega = -\cos i_P \Delta\Omega_P - \frac{4K_D q^3 \cos i_P \sin 2\gamma_P}{\mu(1+\cos v)^3}(1 - 9\cos v - 12\cos^2 v)$$

$$- \frac{16K_D q^3 \left(\cos^2\gamma_P - \sin^2\gamma_P \cos^2 i_P\right)\sin v}{5\mu(1+\cos v)^3}$$

$$(4 + 12\cos v - \cos^2 v)$$

$$+ \frac{16K_D q^3 \left(1 - 3\sin^2\gamma_P \cos^2 i_P\right)\sin v}{5\mu(1+\cos v)^3}(1 + 3\cos v + \cos^2 v) + C_\omega$$

The change in the energy

$$\Delta\epsilon = \frac{4K_D q^2}{(1+\cos v)^2}\Big[3\sin 2\gamma_P \cos i_P \sin v \cos v$$

$$- 6\left(\cos^2\gamma_P - \sin^2\gamma_P \cos^2 i_P\right)\cos v - 3\cos^2\gamma_P$$

$$+ 6\sin^2\gamma_P \cos^2 i_P - 1\Big] + C_\epsilon$$

and, finally, the change in the angular momentum

$$\Delta h = - \frac{16K_D q^4 \sin 2\gamma_P \cos i_P \sin v}{7h(1+\cos v)^4}(4 - 5\cos v - 16\cos^2 v - 4\cos^3 v)$$

$$- \frac{16K_D q^4 \left(\cos^2\gamma_P - \sin^2\gamma_P \cos^2 i_P\right)}{h(1+\cos v)^3}(1 + 3\cos v) + C_h$$

## References

1. Kozai, Y., "Research in Space Science - Special Report No. 30," Smithsonian Institution Astrophysical Observatory, November 12, 1959.

2. Moe, M. M., "Lunar-Solar Perturbations of the Orbit of an Earth Satellite," Space Technology Laboratories, Inc., Report TR-59-0000-00871, September 29, 1959. (Also condensed and presented in the May 1960 issue, ARS Journal.)

3. Moulton, F.R., "An Introduction to Celestial Mechanics," Second Revised Edition, The MacMillan Company, p. 340.

4. ibid, p. 421.

5. Moe, M.M., "The Rates of Change of Satellite Orbital Elements Caused by a Perturbation Force," Space Technology Laboratories, Inc., Report TR-59-0000-09893, October 22, 1959.

6. Egorov, V.A., "Certain Problems of Moon Flight Dynamics," Russian Literature of Satellites, Part I, International Physical Index, Inc., 1958.

7. Mickelwait, A.B., E.H. Tompkins, and R.A. Park, "Three-Dimensional Interplanetary Ballistic Trajectories," Institute of Radio Engineers, Transactions on Military Electronics, Vol. MIL-3, No. 4, October 1959.

# GRAVITATIONAL LIBRATIONS OF A SATELLITE AND THE INFLUENCE ON CONTROL SYSTEM DESIGN

Robert R. Wolfe and Bernard Arrow
The Martin Company - Denver Division
Denver, Colorado

## Abstract

A preliminary design analysis of attitude and stabilization requirements is presented to emphasize the importance of the gravitational gradient existing on a satellite. Special attention is given to unstable orientations, indicating the tumbling motion that develops. The inherent stability boundaries are defined as a function of the orbit eccentricity. The characteristic motions of the body are illustrated by the use of phase plane techniques. Undamped sinusoidal oscillations are associated with stable orientations. Hyperbolic, divergent motions characterize the unstable orientations. A firm understanding of these conditions is necessary before attempting the design of a satellite attitude control system. A nonlinear control system is anticipated for the unstable orientations.

The equations of motion are defined in a general manner, for an elastic body in an inverse square, central force field. The equations are then simplified to rigid body motions possessing five degrees of freedom. The equations are applicable to trajectory motion, but the principal value is in control system analysis.

## Introduction

Over the past few years considerable interest has been shown in librations of satellites resulting from a gravitational gradient existing on the distributed mass of the system. The majority of published works have dealt with some unique aspect of the problem that is analyzed by the use of an integrable differential equation. However the control systems engineer, except for an intuitive feel for the problem, is left without a tool which he can use in a design study. The thought behind the present paper is to provide this tool for design and establish guidelines for the systems engineer in establishing attitude stabilization requirements. The non-linear differential equations are easily coupled with other disturbing influences to provide a complete system simulation.

## Derivation of the Equations of Motion

Previous works have been investigated concerning the gravitational gradient acting on a body orbiting the earth (1-5). In a majority of cases these works are inadequate for a comprehensive detail control system design study. Restricting the shape of the body or its orbit have been the principal means by which solutions to the differential equations of motion are obtained. These limitations provide only an intuitive feel for the problems in control system design. In order to provide a complete analysis it is necessary to use highly non-linear, complex equations of motion. Although the torque producing gradient is extremely small it is continuously acting on the body to cause angular motion. Integration of this moment over long limit cycle operations can lead to large angular displacements which cannot be neglected in a stability analysis. Overlooking the effect of a gravitational gradient will lead to a control system design that is inadequate or at best far from optimum.

The equations of motion of a body under the influence of a gravitational gradient are derived by using vector analysis (6,7). The body motion is broken into components of translation and rotation about its center of mass. This permits the application of Newton's Laws to a system of mass points. Expressions are derived for linear and angular momentum of the body as it rotates about its own axes and revolves around the earth. One convenience of a vector approach is the ability to compare the mathematical results directly with the physical interpretation of the body motions.

Three coordinate systems are used in this derivation. These systems and the basic nomenclature are presented in figure 1. The inertial system (X,Y,Z) has the center of the earth as its origin. The orbiting system (x,y,z) also has the center of earth as its origin. The center of mass of the satellite is at a distance $\bar{R}_y$ along the y direction of the orbiting axis, and the body revolves around the earth with an angular velocity $\bar{W}_I$.

The third system considered is the body coordinate system ($\xi, \eta, \zeta$). Its origin is at the satellite's center of mass. The body is allowed to rotate freely about its origin. This motion is broken into rotations about each of the three body axes. These are the final equations utilized in the stability analysis in the next section.

The general equations which follow were developed assuming elastic body conditions. A complete derivation and list of nomenclature are presented in the appendix.

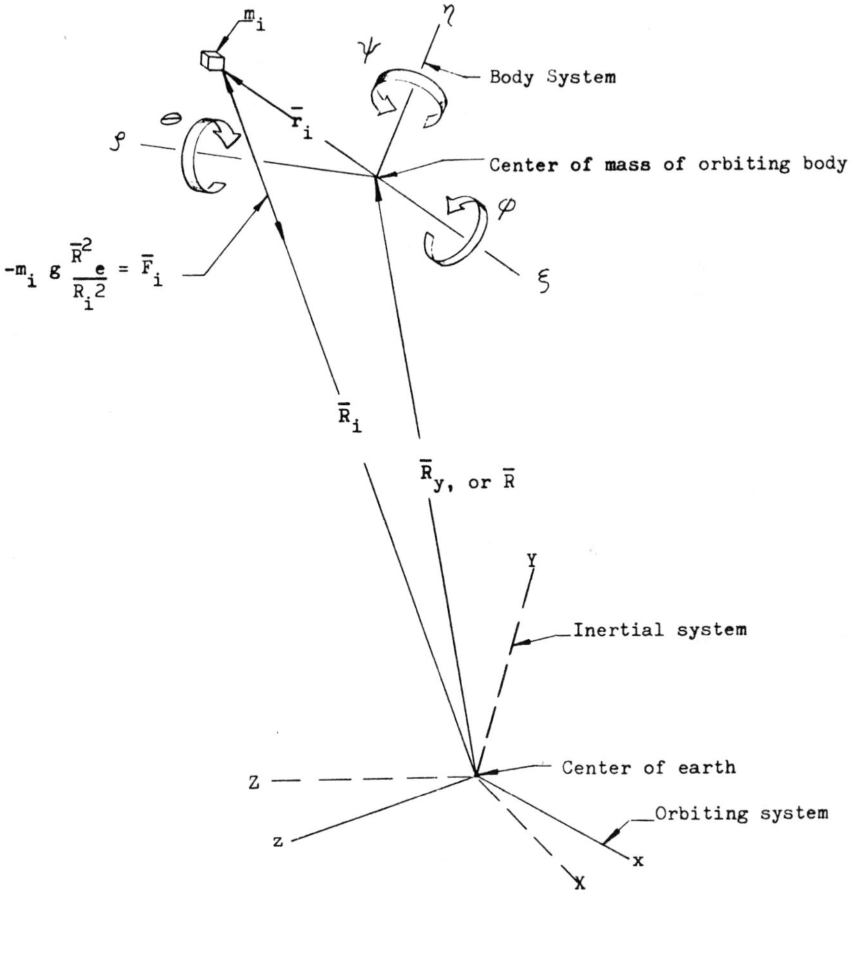


Fig. 1. Illustration of Reference Systems.

Momentum equation

$$\sum m_i \left\{ \frac{d^2R}{dt^2} + \frac{d^2\bar{r}_i}{dt^2} + (\dot{\bar{w}}_o \times \bar{r}_i) + 2(\bar{w}_o + \bar{w}_I) \times \frac{d\bar{r}_i}{dt} \right.$$

$$+ 2\,\bar{w}_I \times \frac{d\bar{R}}{dt} + (2\bar{w}_I + \bar{w}_o) \times (\bar{w}_o \times \bar{r}_i) + \dot{\bar{w}}_I \times (\bar{R} + \bar{r}_i)$$

$$\left. + \bar{w}_I \times \left[ \bar{w}_I \times (\bar{R} + \bar{r}_i) \right] \right\} = -g \sum m_i \frac{\bar{R}_e^{\,2}}{(\bar{R} + \bar{r}_i)^2} \qquad (1)$$

Angular momentum

$$\left[\frac{dH}{dt}\right]_I = \sum m_i \bar{r}_i \times \left[ \frac{d^2\bar{r}_i}{dt^2} + (\dot{\bar{w}}_o + \dot{\bar{w}}_I) \times \bar{r}_i + (\bar{w}_o + \bar{w}_I) \times \frac{d\bar{r}_i}{dt} \right.$$

$$\left. + (\bar{w}_o + \bar{w}_I) \times \left\{ \frac{d\bar{r}_i}{dt} + (\bar{w}_o + \bar{w}_I) \times \bar{r}_i \right\} \right] = -g \sum m_i \frac{\bar{r}_i \times \bar{R}_e^{\,2}}{(\bar{R} + \bar{r}_i)^2} \qquad (2)$$

The above equations are now modified by the following assumptions for the ease of reduction to component form:

a) Only rigid body motions will be considered.

$$\frac{d^2\bar{r}_i}{dt^2} = 0, \quad \frac{d\bar{r}_i}{dt} = 0$$

b) Only planar motion of the body's center of mass is allowed.

The first assumption results in general vector equations for a body possessing seven degrees of freedom. These are:

1) Three rigid body rotations about its own axes ($\xi, \eta, \zeta$).
2) Three orbiting system rotations and a translational degree of freedom directed along the $\bar{R}_y$ coordinate.

The second assumption eliminates two of the seven degrees of freedom resulting in a system possessing only five degrees of freedom. Additional degrees of freedom may be taken into account by considering the flexibility of the satellite structure. The z axis of the orbiting system will then be assumed to coincide with the Z axis of the inertial reference at all times. As a result, orbiting rotation will occur only about this axis ($W_{I_z}$).

The five resulting equations of motion are then expressed as components in the direction of and about the orbiting axes. To facilitate the solution, a transformation is made that allows the expression of orbiting coordinates in terms of body coordinates, thus allowing the mass properties of the body to be expressed independent of the motions of the system.

Several assumptions are made to facilitate expanding the vertorial equations into their components. These assumptions are considered realistic and reasonable for all practical purposes.

a) $\phi$ is small

b) $\psi$ is small

c) Choice of principal axis for the body coordinate system

d) Neglect second order terms of angles ($\phi\psi$; $\phi^2$, etc)

Assumptions a) and b) limit the satellite to small perturbations about the $\xi$ and $\eta$ axes. Thus large rotations are permitted about the $\zeta$ axis. The choice of principal axes, assumption c), will eliminate products of inertias, thereby simplifying calculations greatly. Assumption d) is feasible for most design studies. In the event these assumptions do not satisfy a particular design case in question, Eqs. (1) and (2) may again be expanded to suit the particular situation. The final equations of motion based on the above assumptions are given in the appendix as Eqs. (29) through (33). Examination of the nonlinear differential equations indicates that numerical integration by digital computation is the more propitious means of solution.

## Application of the Equations of Motion

It is now desirable to examine the general form of solution to the differential equations of motion. Eqs. (29) through (33) of the appendix are simplified to include only those terms significant to the examples that follow. The equations are written as follows:

Orbital central angle

$$\dot{w}_{I_z} = \frac{-2\dot{R}_y}{R_y} w_{I_z} + \frac{3 g R_e^2}{R_y^5 M_t} (I_{\xi\xi} - I_{\eta\eta}) \sin\theta \cos\theta \tag{3}$$

Radius vector

$$\ddot{R}_y = R_y w_{I_z}^2 - \frac{gR_e^2}{R_y^2} - \frac{1}{R_y^4 M_t} \left\{ \frac{3}{2} gR_e^2 \left[ I_{\xi\xi} - 2I_{\eta\eta} - I_{\zeta\zeta} \right] \sin\theta \right.$$

$$\left. - \frac{9}{2} gR_e^2 \left[ I_{\xi\xi} - I_{\eta\eta} \right] \sin^2\theta \right\} \tag{4}$$

Angular acceleration about $\zeta$ axis

$$\ddot{\theta} = -\dot{w}_{I_z} - \frac{3gR_e^2}{R_y^3} \left( \frac{I_{\xi\xi} - I_{\eta\eta}}{I_{\zeta\zeta}} \right) \sin\theta \cos\theta \tag{5}$$

Angular acceleration about $\xi$ axis

$$\ddot{\phi} = -w_{I_z}\left(\frac{I_{\eta\eta} - I_{\zeta\zeta}}{I_{\xi\xi}}\right)\dot{\psi} - w_{I_z}^{2}\left(\frac{I_{\eta\eta} - I_{\zeta\zeta}}{I_{\xi\xi}}\right)\phi$$

$$+ \frac{3gR_e^{2}}{R_y^{2}}\left[\frac{I_{\xi\xi}^{2} - I_{\eta\eta}\left(I_{\xi\xi} + I_{\zeta\zeta}\right) - I_{\zeta\zeta}^{2}}{I_{\xi\xi}\, I_{\zeta\zeta}}\right] X \sin\theta\cos\theta\,\psi$$

$$- \frac{3gR_e^{2}}{R_y^{2}}\left(\frac{I_{\eta\eta} - I_{\zeta\zeta}}{I_{\xi\xi}}\right)\cos^{2}\theta\,\phi \qquad (6)$$

Angular acceleration about $\eta$ axis $\ddot{\psi} = -w_{I_z}\left(\frac{I_{\xi\xi} - I_{\zeta\zeta}}{I_{\eta\eta}}\right)\dot{\phi}$

$$+ w_{I_z}^{2}\left(\frac{I_{\xi\xi} - I_{\zeta\zeta}}{I_{\eta\eta}}\right)\psi + \frac{3gR_e^{2}}{R_y^{3}}\left(\frac{I_{\xi\xi} - I_{\zeta\zeta}}{I_{\eta\eta}}\right)\sin^{2}\theta\,\psi +$$

$$\frac{3gR_e^{2}}{R_y^{3}}\left(\frac{I_{\zeta\zeta}^{2} + I_{\xi\xi}\left(I_{\eta\eta} - I_{\zeta\zeta}\right) - I_{\eta\eta}^{2}}{I_{\eta\eta}\, I_{\xi\xi}}\right)\sin\theta\cos\theta\,\phi \qquad (7)$$

The equations are easily separated into standard trajectory motion and perturbations about that trajectory. The equations are not restricted to orbital motion, but apply to re-entry and escape trajectories equally well. Independent of the trajectory, it is seen that the gravitational gradient causes a sinusoidal oscillation in the radius vector and central angle of orbital motion. However, the control system engineer is interested primarily in angular accelerations about the principal axes of inertia.

## Circular Orbits

Restricting Eqs. (5), (6), and (7) to circular orbits results in the same equations found in reference (1). Solving the pitch, ($\ddot{\theta}$), equation provides a family of curves representing the perturbed motion of the satellite as a function of its initial conditions. Reference (2) points up the influence of initial attitude rate on the inherent stability of the system but fails to show the effects of an initial displacement at the same time. This is highly important and is easily interpreted by using the phase plane analogy, (8,9) figure 2. From the derived equations, the stability boundary can be established. The stability margin for any stable oscillation is related to the energy required to force the trajectory outside the stability boundary. The stable orientation is defined as having the axis of minimum inertia aligned along the local vertical, and the axis of maximum inertia normal to the orbit plane. The phase plane analogy can be extended to a phase space analogy, as

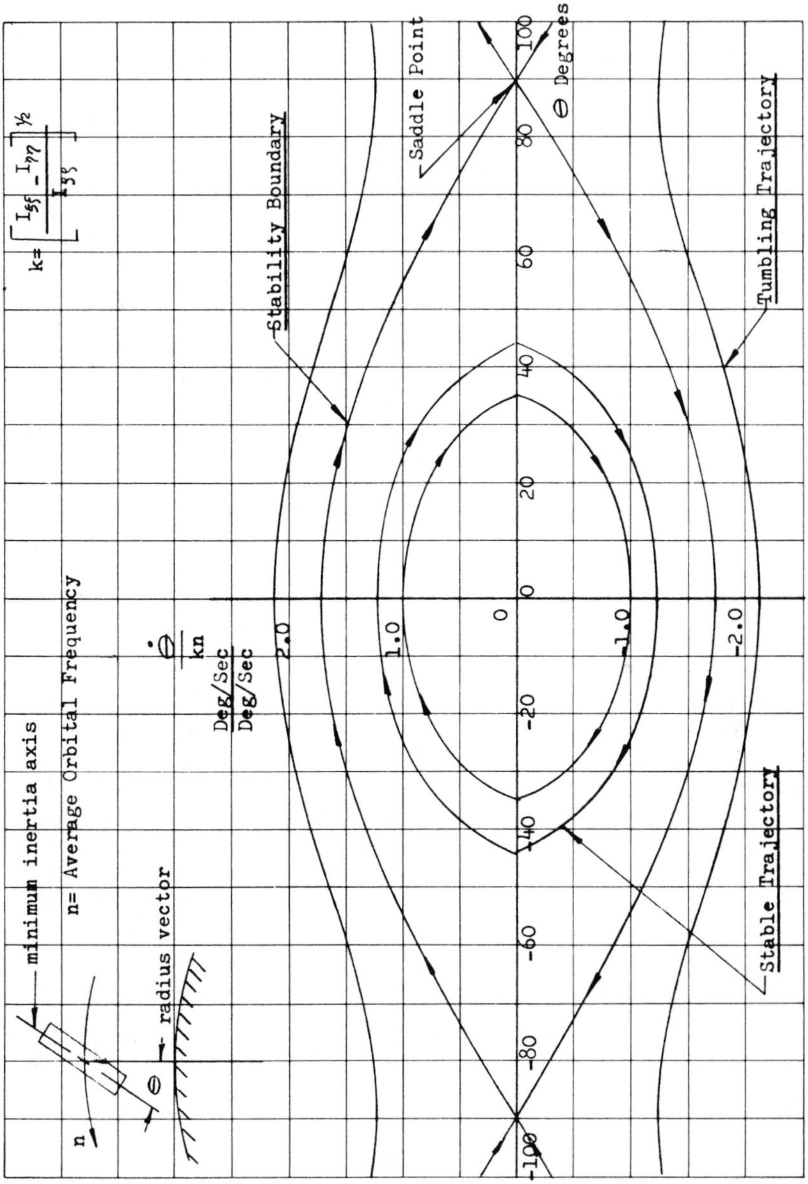


Fig. 2. Phase Plane Trajectories for Circular Orbits

shown in figure 3. This provides a better understanding of the tumbling motion that results if the satellite is forced outside the stable boundary.

Examination of figure 2 indicates that orientation of the satellite can greatly influence the demands placed upon the control system. Since the gravitational torque acting on low altitude satellites is in general several orders of magnitude greater than aerodynamic, radiation pressure, and mass movement effects, it behooves the controls engineer to take advantage of the inherent stability associated with orientation of the satellite when possible. With the stable orientation any constant torque inputs (i.e. aerodynamic) merely bias the system to oscillate off center.

Consider orientating the satellite at a saddle point as in figure 4. This would be the situation where it is desirable to have one side of the satellite always facing earth (i.e. for communication purposes). All motion about this point is divergent and the only way the trajectory can cross a separatrix is by some energy input. Time histories about this point are obtained by integrating Eq. (5). Let Eq. (5) be defined as

$$\ddot{\theta} = \alpha^2 \theta - \beta \tag{8}$$

where $\theta$ is restricted to small angles

$$\alpha = \pm \left[ 3 \, w_{I_z}^{\,2} \left( \frac{I_{\xi\xi} - I_{\eta\eta}}{I_{\zeta\zeta}} \right) \right]^{1/2}$$

and $\beta$ = Control Acceleration (constant)

then
$$\dot{\theta}(t) = \frac{(\theta(o)\alpha^2 - \beta) \sinh \alpha t + \dot{\theta}(o) \alpha \cosh \alpha t}{\alpha} \tag{9}$$

$$\theta(t) = \frac{\beta + (\theta(o) \alpha^2 - \beta) \cosh \alpha t + \dot{\theta}(o) \alpha \sinh \alpha t}{\alpha^2} \tag{10}$$

When the corrective torque is zero the time required for the system to drift from any initial conditions to a given limit is defined by

$$t_{drift} = \frac{1}{\alpha} \ln \left[ \frac{\theta_{limit} \pm \sqrt{\theta^2_{limit} - \theta^2(o) + (\dot{\theta}(o)/\alpha)^2}}{\theta(o) + (\dot{\theta}(o)/\alpha)} \right] \tag{11}$$

The sign associated with the radical is chosen to make the bracketed quantity always positive.

The motion will be restrained to lie between the attitude limits by an "on-off" reaction jet control system. The minimum impulse required to alter the angular rate from positive to negative is the energy necessary to pass from one separatrix to another at the attitude limit. The separatrices represent trajectory motion requiring an infinite time to translate some

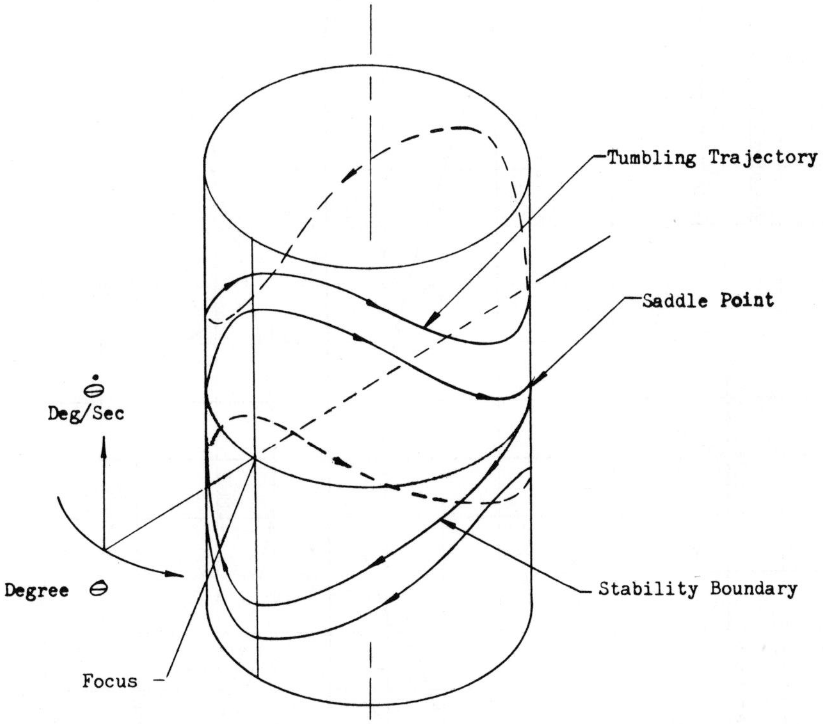


Fig. 3. Phase Space Trajectories for Circular Orbits.

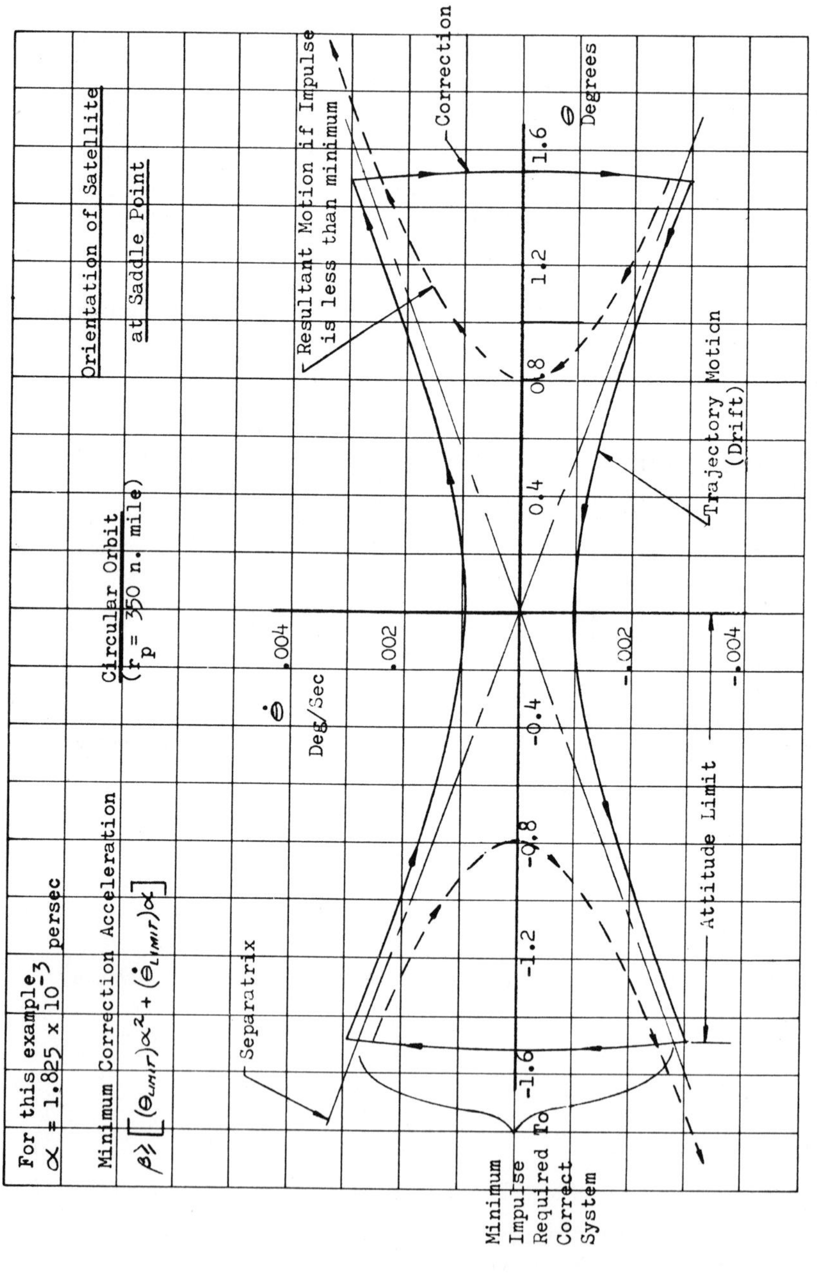


Fig. 4. Phase Plane Trajectories about a Saddle Point; Circular Orbits

finite distance. Therefore, it is desirable to have the limit cycle oscillation approach these asymptotes to achieve a maximum cycle period. At the same time it minimizes fuel consumption. It is imperative, however, that some lead be built into the system to provide damping in the light of other disturbances.

Limit cycle periods about the saddle point for a typical small manned space station placed in a 350 n. mile circular orbit are approximately 4000 seconds. The impulse required would be approximately 4.0 pounds-seconds per cycle. If the gas used to produce the corrective force were nitrogen ($I_{sp}$=70) the fuel consumption would be approximately 546 pounds per year for one axis stabilization. In the event a higher energy propellant were used the fuel consumption would be reduced by the ratio of the specific impulses. Had a stable orientation been chosen the fuel consumption **should be reduced** by at least a factor of seven to one.

## Elliptical Orbits

The analysis above can be extended to elliptical orbits by integration of Eq. (5), treating orbital angular motion as the forcing function. This was performed by numerical methods to obtain the results shown in figures 5, 6, and 7 for three different eccentricities. The angular rate is non-dimensionalized to make the curves applicable to any orbital altitude and realistic configuration. The stability boundaries are seen to deteriorate as the eccentricity increases. This is clarified by combining these results with figure 2 to obtain a volume envelope for stable orientations, shown schematically in figure 8. It is necessary to establish some fixed parameter of the orbits, (i.e. perigee radius) for the development of the envelope. This results from the fact that the average orbital frequency approaches zero as the eccentricity approaches one, hence the envelope cannot be non-dimensionalized. Highly eccentric orbits will probably never be achieved in practice. However, the lack of stability for escape trajectories is apparent from the envelope and must be considered in the control system design. Figure 9 supplements figure 8, providing a more accurate representation of the stability boundaries.

Reference (3) brings out the point that satellite librations for eccentric orbits lead the orbital motion as the satellite travels from perigee to apogee and lags orbital motion for the return path. The frequency of oscillation resulting from the orbital forcing function varies as the satellite revolves through an orbit period. This is imposed upon the natural frequency of oscillation due to the gravitational gradient, which also varies as the radius vector changes. The total angular acceleration acting on the satellite during a limit cycle operation will then depend upon the phase relationship of the two motions. Also, the

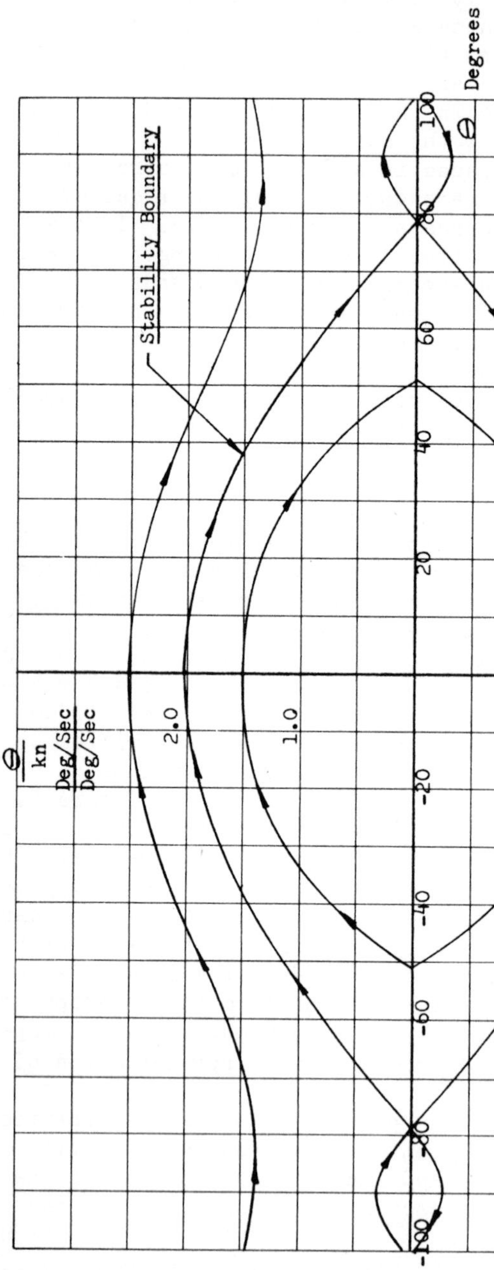

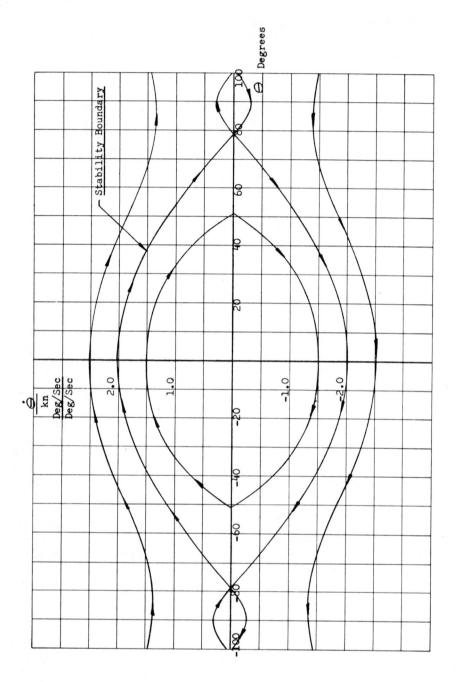

Fig. 5. Phase Plane Trajectories for an Eccentricity of 0.20

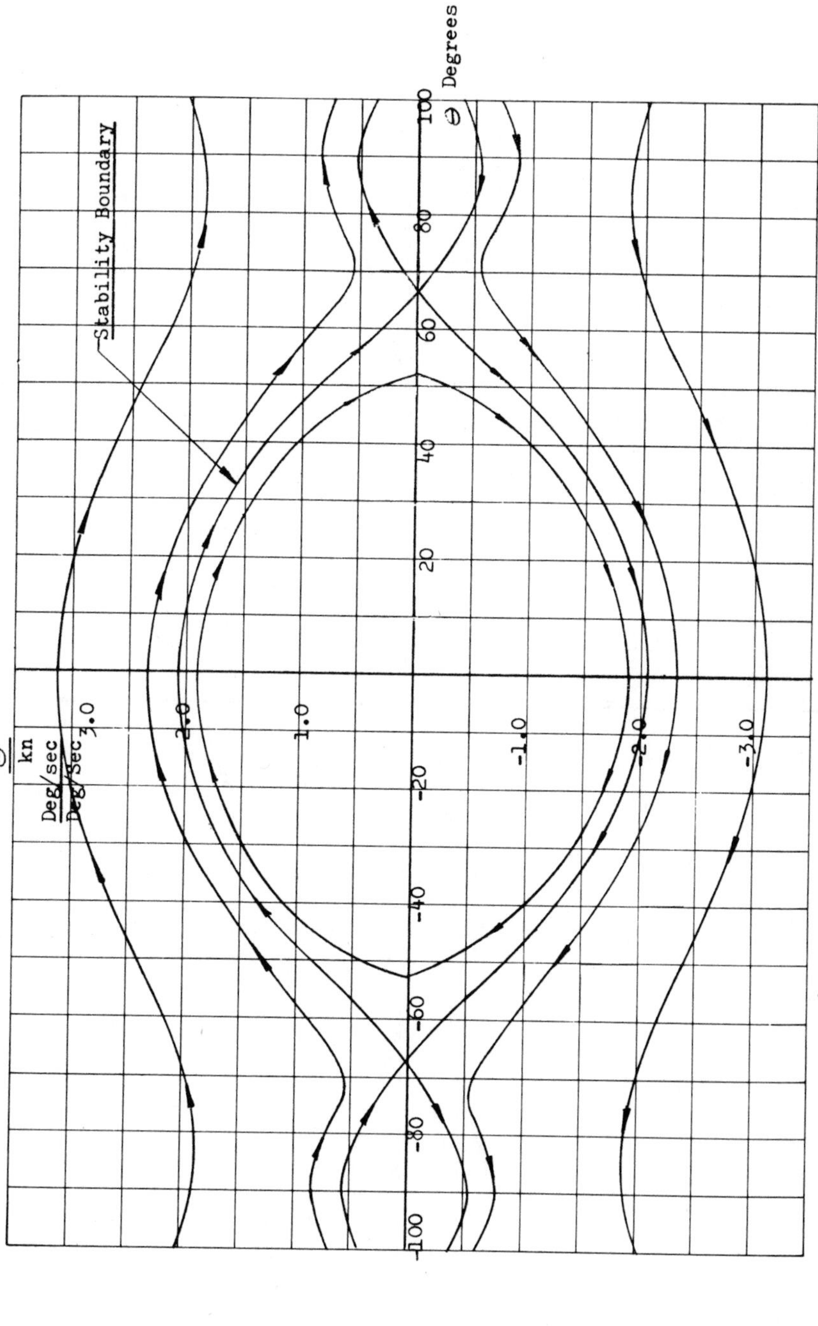


Fig. 6. Phase Plane Trajectories for an Eccentricity of 0.40

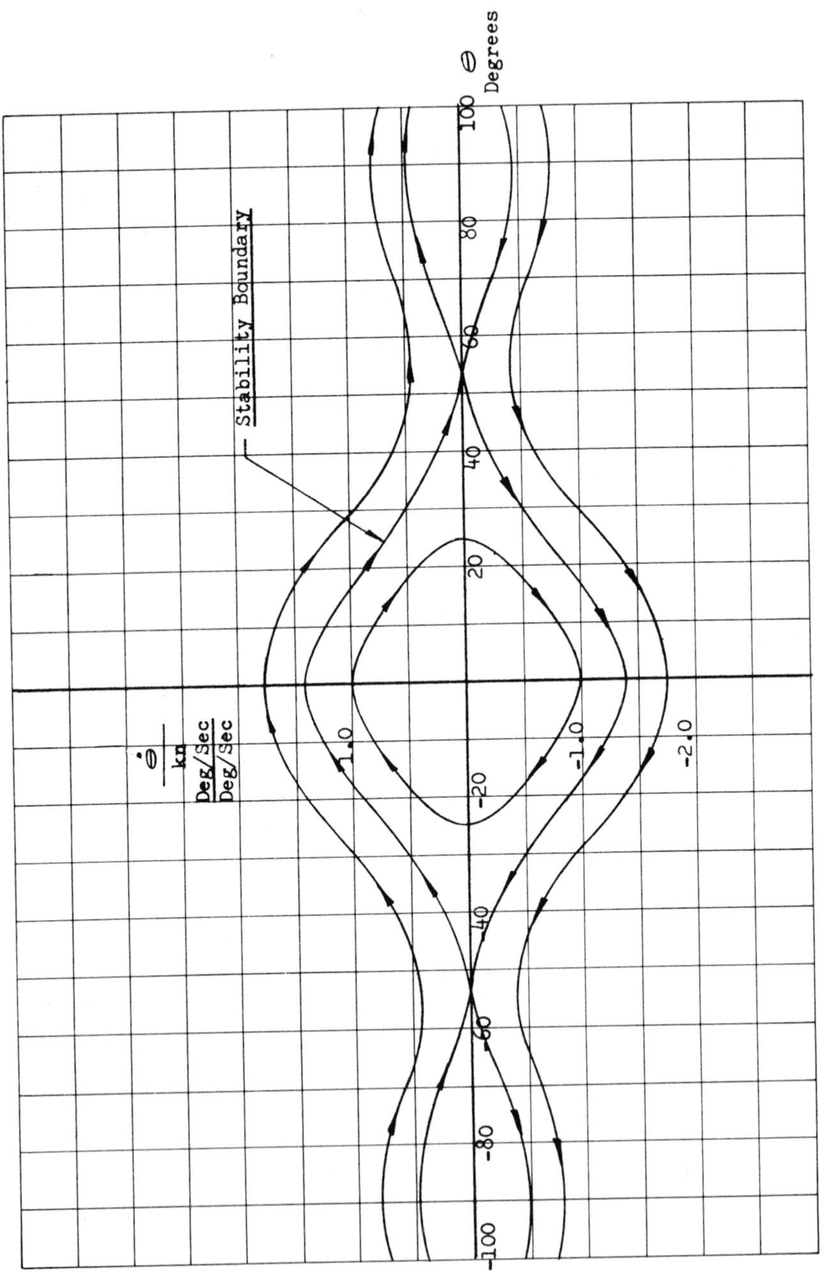


Fig. 7. Phase Plane Trajectories for an Eccentricity of 0.60

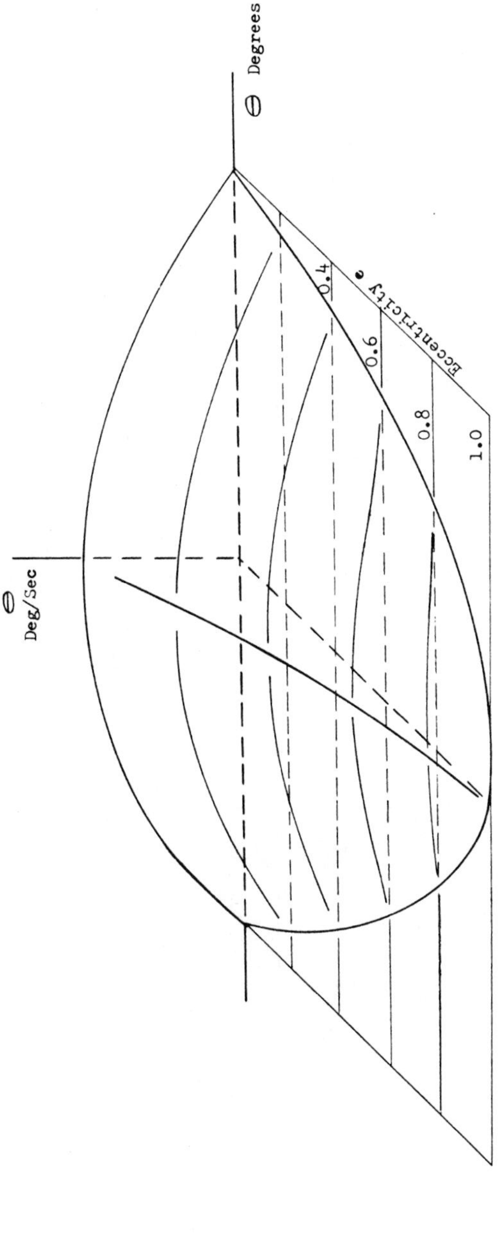


Fig. 8. Stability Envelope as a Function of Eccentricity

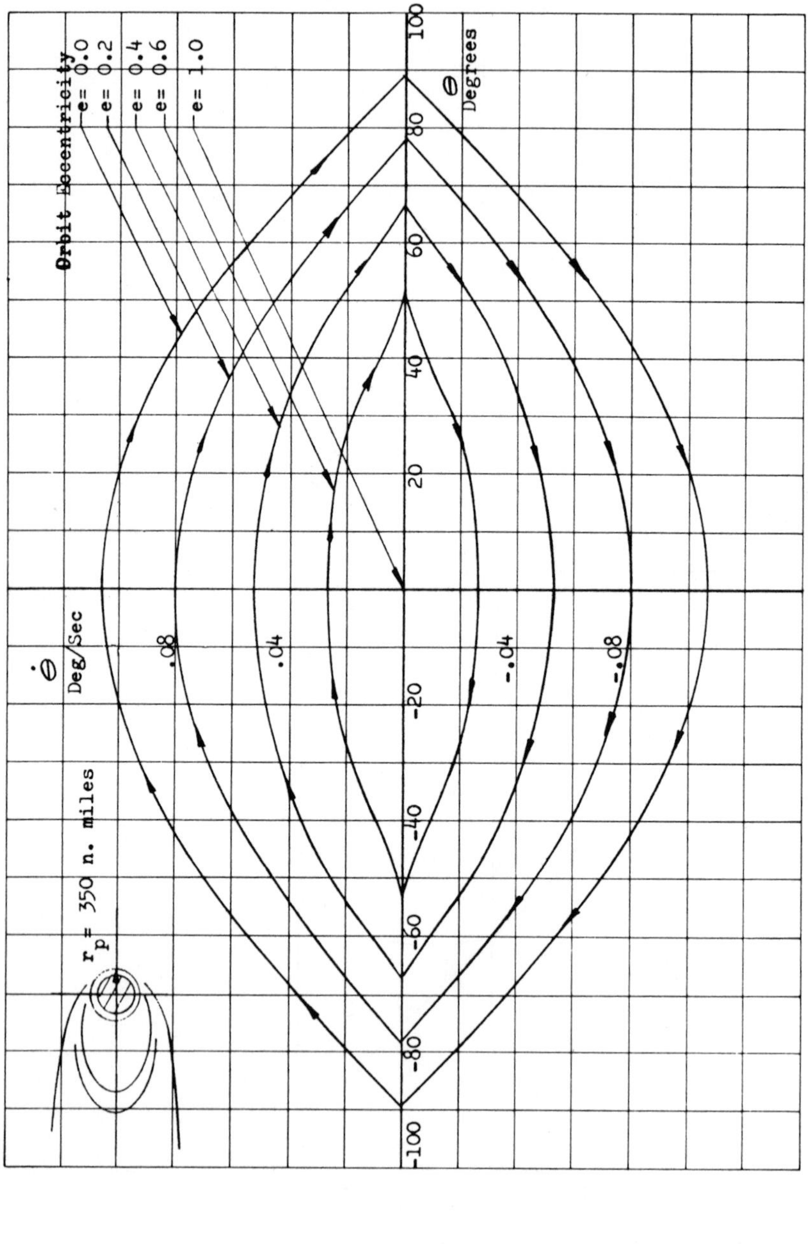


Fig. 9. Natural Stability Boundaries

impulse required is a direct function of the angular rate at the attitude limit, as well as the rate to which the system must correct in order to rotate to the opposing attitude limit. The phase relationship continually changes as the satellite revolves in orbit. In light of this, optimization of the control system to provide only the minimum impulse required complicates the system design over that required for circular orbits.

If a satellite is oriented to a fixed position relative to inertial space as it revolves in orbit, it will pass out of the stable envelope for a portion of the orbit cycle, independent of its eccentricity. Within the stable envelope the gravity gradient acts to reorient the system along the local vertical. Outside the envelope the satellite will tumble. If the satellite natural frequency of oscillation were equal to the orbital frequency the integrated effects would cancel over a given orbit period. However, in pitch this is highly improbable because of the inertia relationship that would be required. Consequently, to hold this orientation the fuel consumption and torque requirements will increase substantially over that required for orientation along the local vertical. A high fuel consumption will also be realized if the satellite is always oriented along the velocity vector.

There is one area that is not fully understood. This is that the saddle point for circular orbits, figure 2, reverts to a focus for an eccentricity greater than zero, figure 8. This leads to the conclusion that there is a certain eccentricity beyond which it is more advantageous to orient 90 degrees away from the local vertical. It is felt that this reorientation of the stability boundaries results from the phase relationship of the orbital motion forcing effects. There is a possibility that altering the orientation of the satellite from one focus to another may improve energy requirements for stabilization by improving the stability margin. Again, phasing of the control system is necessary to take advantage of this. In this region it is felt that considerable more work will be necessary before a clear understanding of stabilization requirements is reached.

## Conclusions

Attitude stabilization and orientation of an unsymmetrical satellite represent severe design problems for the control engineer. In order to provide himself with an adequate understanding of the problem it is necessary to have as complete as possible the differential equations of dynamic motion. The principal objective of this paper has been to present those equations, with derivations, which are the first step in establishing control system design requirements. In the differential form, as they are presented, it is now possible to include additional perturbations, such as aerodynamic and solar radiation, without undue labor. The gravitational gradient is, in general, several orders of magnitude greater than any other torque acting on the system.

The phase plane and phase space techniques were found to be very useful for preliminary design in defining and interpreting the stability boundaries that exist. Degradation of stability due to orbit eccentricity must be analyzed when considering highly eccentric orbits or escape trajectories. A system designed for low eccentricities will probably not be adequate for orbits of high eccentricity. Phasing of the control torques becomes more important for highly eccentric orbits because of the forcing function that exists due to orbital motion. This effect continually alters the frequency of oscillation.

In general, limit cycle operations on the order of one hour are about the maximum that can be expected for low altitude orbits. Cycle time may be increased by orientation at a saddle point, but fuel consumption rises. Expanding attitude limits beyond a few degrees for unstable orientations has little effect on cycle time because of the hyperbolic nature of the motion. This is in general not true for stable orientations, but the stability margins suffer.

The orientation of the satellite relative to the local vertical is highly significant. The margins that exist for stable orientations in many cases will be adequate to stabilize outside disturbances. Damping must still be applied to the system to bring it into specified attitude limits after a disturbance. Relatively constant torque inputs (i.e. aerodynamic torques) merely act as a small bias, tending to displace the origin about which the the system oscillates. To take advantage of these stabilizing effects the axis of minimum inertia should be aligned with the local vertical. The axis of maximum inertia should be aligned normal to the orbit plane.

## Appendix

### Derivation of the Equations of Motion

The equations of motion will now be derived using vector algebra and the concepts of moving axes and relative motion. First, consider the momentum of the body. The total change in the momentum vector $\bar{U}$ may be expressed as

$$\left[\frac{d\bar{U}}{dt}\right]_I = \frac{d\bar{U}}{dt} + \bar{w}_1 \times \bar{U} \qquad (1)$$

The distance vector $\bar{R}_i$ (with respect to the orbiting axes) to mass $m_i$ is (see figure 1)

$$\bar{R}_i = \bar{R} + \bar{r}_i \tag{2}$$

and, with respect to the inertial axes, is

$$\bar{R}_i = \bar{R}_{I_i} \tag{3}$$

Now,

$$\frac{d\bar{R}_{I_i}}{dt} = \frac{d\bar{R}_i}{dt} + \bar{w}_I \times \bar{R}_i \tag{4}$$

$$\bar{U} = \sum m_i \frac{d\bar{R}_{I_i}}{dt} = \sum m_i \left[\frac{d\bar{R}_i}{dt} + \bar{w}_I \times \bar{R}_i\right] \tag{5}$$

Therefore,

$$\frac{d\bar{U}}{dt} = \sum m_i \left[\frac{d^2\bar{R}_i}{dt^2} + \dot{\bar{w}}_I \times \bar{R}_i + \bar{w}_I \times \frac{d\bar{R}_i}{dt}\right] \tag{6}$$

Substituting Eqs. (6) into (1),

$$\left[\frac{d\bar{U}}{dt}\right]_I = \sum m_i \left[\frac{d^2\bar{R}_i}{dt^2} + 2\bar{w}_I \times \frac{d\bar{R}_i}{dt} + \dot{\bar{w}}_I \times \bar{R}_i + \bar{w}_I \times (w_I \times \bar{R}_i)\right] \tag{7}$$

We shall now introduce the body coordinate system into Eq. (7) referring to Eq. (2)

$$\frac{d\bar{R}_i}{dt} = \frac{d\bar{R}}{dt} + \frac{d\bar{r}_i}{dt} + \bar{w}_c \times \bar{r}_i \tag{8}$$

$$\frac{d^2\bar{R}_i}{dt^2} = \frac{d^2\bar{R}}{dt^2} + \frac{d^2\bar{r}_i}{dt^2} + \dot{\bar{w}}_o \times \bar{r}_i + 2\bar{w}_o \times \frac{d\bar{r}_i}{dt} + \bar{w}_o \times (\bar{w}_o \times \bar{r}_i) \tag{9}$$

Substituting Eqs. (8) and (9) into (7),

$$\begin{aligned}\left[\frac{d\bar{U}}{dt}\right]_I = \sum m_i \Bigg\{ & \frac{d^2\bar{R}}{dt^2} + \frac{d^2\bar{r}_i}{dt^2} + \dot{\bar{w}}_o \times \bar{r}_i + 2\bar{w}_o \times \frac{d\bar{r}_i}{dt} + \bar{w}_o \times (\bar{w}_o \times \bar{r}_i) \\ & + 2\bar{w}_I \times \left[\frac{d\bar{R}}{dt} + \frac{d\bar{r}_i}{dt} + \bar{w}_o \times \bar{r}_i\right] + \dot{\bar{w}}_I \times (\bar{R} + \bar{r}_i) \\ & + \bar{w}_I \times \left[\bar{w}_I \times (\bar{R} + \bar{r}_i)\right]\end{aligned} \tag{10}$$

or

$$\begin{aligned}\left[\frac{d\bar{U}}{dt}\right]_I = \sum m_i \Bigg\{ & \frac{d^2\bar{R}}{dt^2} + \frac{d^2\bar{r}_i}{dt^2} + \dot{\bar{w}}_o \times \bar{r}_i + 2(\bar{w}_o + \bar{w}_I) \times \frac{d\bar{r}_i}{dt} \\ & + 2\bar{w}_I \times \frac{d\bar{R}}{dt} + (2\bar{w}_I + \bar{w}_o) \times (\bar{w}_o \times \bar{r}_i) + \dot{\bar{w}} \times (\bar{R} + \bar{r}_i) \\ & + \bar{w}_I \times \left[\bar{w}_I \times (\bar{R} + \bar{r}_i)\right]\Bigg\}\end{aligned} \tag{11}$$

Also,

$$\left[\frac{d\bar{U}}{dt}\right]_I = \bar{F} \tag{12}$$

and

$$\bar{F} = -\sum m_i\, g \frac{\bar{R}_e^{\,2}}{\bar{R}_i^{\,2}} \tag{13}$$

Substituting Eqs. (11) and (13) into (12) will express the desired equation in vector notation:

$$\sum m_i \left\{ \frac{d^2\bar{R}}{dt^2} + \frac{d^2\bar{r}_i}{dt^2} + (\dot{\bar{w}}_o \times \bar{r}_i) + 2(\bar{w}_o + \bar{w}_I) \times \frac{d\bar{r}_i}{dt} + 2\,\bar{w}_I \times \frac{d\bar{R}}{dt} \right.$$
$$+ (2\bar{w}_I + \bar{w}_o) \times (\bar{w}_o \times \bar{r}_i) + \dot{\bar{w}}_I \times (\bar{R} + \bar{r}_i)$$
$$\left. + \bar{w}_i \times \left[\bar{w}_I \times (\bar{R} + \bar{r}_i)\right] \right\} = -g \sum m_i \frac{\bar{R}_e^{\,2}}{(\bar{R} + \bar{r}_i)^2} \tag{14}$$

The vector equation representing the total moment of momentu of the system must now be considered. For a body possessing appreciable physical dimensions, the center of force cannot be assumed to coincide with the center of mass. The forces may be transferred to the center of mass if the corresponding overturning moment about the center of mass is applied there also.

The total angular momentum will now be found about the center of mass, with respect to an inertial reference. The center of mass of the satellite may be considered to be the origin of the reference system without affecting the magnitude of the moment. This will facilitate the solution.

The angular momentum about the center of mass with respect to inertial space is

$$\left[H\right]_I = \sum m_i \left[\bar{r}_i \times \bar{v}_i\right]_I \tag{15}$$

$$\left[\bar{v}_i\right]_I = \left[\frac{d\bar{r}_i}{dt}\right]_I = \frac{d\bar{r}_i}{dt} + (\bar{w}_o + \bar{w}_I) \times \bar{r}_i \tag{16}$$

$$\left[\frac{d\bar{v}_i}{dt}\right]_I = \left[\frac{d^2\bar{r}_i}{dt^2}\right]_I = \frac{d\bar{v}_i}{dt} + (\bar{w}_o + \bar{w}_I) \times \bar{v}_i = \frac{d^2\bar{r}_i}{dt^2}$$
$$+ (\bar{w}_o + \bar{w}_I) \times \frac{d\bar{r}_i}{dt} + (\dot{\bar{w}}_o + \dot{\bar{w}}_I) \times \bar{r}_i$$
$$+ (\bar{w}_o + \bar{w}_I) \times \left[\frac{d\bar{r}_i}{dt} + (\bar{w}_o + \bar{w}_I) \times \bar{r}_i\right] \tag{17}$$

Also,

$$\left[\frac{d\bar{H}}{dt}\right]_I = \sum m_i \left[\bar{r}_i \times \frac{d^2\bar{r}_i}{dt^2}\right]_I \tag{18}$$

Substituting Eq. (17) into (18),

$$\left[\frac{d\bar{H}}{dt}\right]_I = \sum m_i \, \bar{r}_i \; X \left\{ \left[\frac{d^2\bar{r}_i}{dt^2}\right] + (\dot{\bar{w}}_o + \dot{\bar{w}}_I) \; X \; \bar{r}_i + (\bar{w}_o + \bar{w}_I) \; X \; \frac{d\bar{r}_i}{dt} + (\bar{w}_o + \bar{w}_I) \; X \left[\frac{d\bar{r}_i}{dt} + (\bar{w}_o + \bar{w}_I) \; X \; \bar{r}_i\right]\right\} \quad (19)$$

Now,

$$\left[\frac{d\bar{H}}{dt}\right]_I = \sum m_i \, (\bar{r}_i \; X \; \bar{F}_i) = -g \sum m_i \, \bar{r}_i \; X \; \frac{\bar{R}_e^{\,2}}{\bar{R}_i^{\,2}} = -g \sum m_i \, \bar{r}_i \; X \; \frac{\bar{R}_e^{\,2}}{(\bar{R} + \bar{r}_i)^2} \quad (20)$$

Therefore,

$$\left[\frac{d\bar{H}}{dt}\right]_I = \sum m_i \, \bar{r}_i \; X \left[\frac{d^2\bar{r}}{dt^2} + (\dot{\bar{w}}_o + \dot{\bar{w}}_I) \; X \; \bar{r}_i + (\bar{w}_o + \bar{w}_I) \; X \; \frac{d\bar{r}_i}{dt} + (\bar{w}_o + \bar{w}_I) \; X \left\{\frac{d\bar{r}_i}{dt} + (\bar{w}_o + \bar{w}_I) \; X \; \bar{r}_i\right\}\right] = -g \sum m_i \, \bar{r}_i \; X \; \frac{\bar{R}_e^{\,2}}{(\bar{R} + \bar{r}_i)^2} \quad (21)$$

Equations (14) and (21) present the equations of motion of the satellite in vector form.

Assuming rigid body conditions ($\frac{d\bar{r}_i}{dt} = 0$, $\frac{d^2\bar{r}_i}{dt^2} = 0$),

Eqs.(14) and (21) reduce, respectively, to

$$\sum m_i \left\{ \frac{d^2\bar{R}}{dt^2} + \dot{\bar{w}}_o \; X \; \bar{r}_i + 2\bar{w}_I \; X \; \frac{d\bar{R}}{dt} + (2\bar{w}_I + \bar{w}_o) \; X \; (\bar{w}_o X \; \bar{r}_i) + \dot{\bar{w}}_I \; X \; (\bar{R} + \bar{r}_i) + \bar{w}_I \; X \left[\bar{w}_I \; X \; (\bar{R} + \bar{r}_i)\right]\right\} = -g \, R_e^{\,2} \sum m_i \frac{\bar{1}}{(\bar{R} + \bar{r}_i)^2} \quad (22)$$

And,

$$\sum m_i \, \bar{r}_i \; X \left\{ (\dot{\bar{w}}_o + \dot{\bar{w}}_i) X \; \bar{r}_i + (\bar{w}_o + \bar{w}_I) \; X \left[(\bar{w}_o + \bar{w}_I) \; X \; \bar{r}_i\right]\right\} = -g \, R_e^{\,2} \sum m_i \, \bar{r}_i \; X \; \frac{\bar{1}}{(\bar{R} \; X \; \bar{r}_i)^2} \quad (23)$$

These two vector equations may be written in component forms, i.e., they may be broken into their components along the orbiting axes. Because of the assumption of planar motion of the center of mass, five equations result. They appear below.

$$\sum m_i \Big[ z\,\dot{w}_y - y\,(\dot{w}_z + \dot{w}_{Iz}) - x\,(w_y^2 + w_z^2 + w_{Iz}^2) + y\,w_x w_y + z\,w_x w_z + 2w_{Iz}\,(z\,w_x - x\,w_z) - 2w_{Iz}\,\dot{R}_y - \dot{w}_{Iz}\,R_y \Big] = K'x \tag{24}$$

$$\sum m_i \Big[ -z\,\dot{w}_x + x(\dot{w}_z + \dot{w}_{Iz}) - y(w_x^2 + w_z^2) - (R_y + y)\,w_{Iz}^2 + w_y\,(xw_x + zw_z) \pm 2w_{Iz}\,(z\,w_y - y\,w_z) + \ddot{R}_y \Big] = K'\,(R_y + y) \tag{25}$$

$$\sum m_i \Big[ \dot{w}_x(y^2 + z^2) - xy\,\dot{w}_y - xz\,(\dot{w}_z + \dot{w}_{Iz}) + yz\,(-w_y^2 + w_z^2 + w_{Iz}^2) - xz\,w_x w_y + xy\,w_x\,(w_z + w_{Iz}) + w_y\,(y^2 - z^2)(w_z + w_{Iz}) + 2yz\,w_z w_{Iz} \Big] = K'\,z\,R_y \tag{26}$$

$$\sum m_i \Big[ -xy\,\dot{w}_x + \dot{w}_y\,(x^2 + z^2) - yz\,(\dot{w}_z + \dot{w}_{Iz}) + xz\,(w_x^2 - w_z^2 - w_{Iz}^2) + yz\,w_x w_y + w_x(z^2 - x^2)(w_z + w_{Iz}) - xy\,w_y\,(w_z + w_{Iz}) - 2xz\,w_z w_{Iz} \Big] = 0 \tag{27}$$

$$\sum m_i \Big[ -xz\,\dot{w}_x - yz\,\dot{w}_y + (x^2 + y^2)(\dot{w}_z + \dot{w}_{Iz}) - xy\,(w_x^2 - w_y^2) + w_x w_y\,(x^2 - y^2) - yz\,w_x(w_z + w_{Iz}) + xz\,w_y(w_z + W_{Iz}) \Big] = K'\,x\,R_y \tag{28}$$

where

$$K' = -g\,R_e^2 \sum m_i \frac{1}{\left[R_y^2 + x^2 + y^2 + z^2 + 2y\,R_y\right]^{3/2}}$$

NOTE: x,y,z = Coordinates in the orbiting reference system of the individual mass particles.

The five equations have been expressed in terms of orbiting coordinates. By use of a transformation matrix, these equations may be expressed in body coordinates. This transformation matrix, shown below, simply accounts for the rotations of the body about its 3 cartesian axes. The body coordinates are $\xi$, $\eta$, and $\zeta$; the orbiting coordinates are x, y, z; and the rotations about the corresponding body axes are $\dot{\phi}$, $\dot{\psi}$, and $\dot{\theta}$. Rotations are assumed to occur in the order of $\theta$, $\psi$, and then $\phi$. The final form of the matrix is:

$$\begin{bmatrix} x \\ y \\ z \end{bmatrix} = \begin{bmatrix} a_1 & a_2 & a_3 \\ a_4 & a_5 & a_6 \\ a_7 & a_8 & a_9 \end{bmatrix} \begin{bmatrix} \xi \\ \eta \\ \zeta \end{bmatrix}$$

where the direction cosines $a_i$ are defined as:

$$a_1 = \cos\psi \cos\theta$$

$$a_2 = -\cos\phi \sin\theta + \sin\phi \sin\psi \cos\theta$$

$$a_3 = \sin\phi \sin\theta + \cos\phi \sin\psi \cos\theta$$

$$a_4 = \cos\psi \sin\theta$$

$$a_5 = \cos\phi \cos\theta + \sin\phi \sin\psi \sin\theta$$

$$a_6 = -\sin\phi \cos\theta + \cos\phi \sin\psi \sin\theta$$

$$a_7 = -\sin\psi$$

$$a_8 = \sin\phi \cos\psi$$

$$a_9 = \cos\phi \cos\psi$$

Similarly,

$$\begin{bmatrix} w_x \\ w_y \\ w_z \end{bmatrix} = \begin{bmatrix} 1 & 0 & -\sin\psi \\ 0 & \cos\phi & (\sin\phi \cos\psi) \\ 0 & -\sin\phi & (\cos\phi \cos\psi) \end{bmatrix} \begin{bmatrix} \dot{\phi} \\ \dot{\psi} \\ \dot{\theta} \end{bmatrix}$$

The final equations after performing the transformation are simplified by the assumptions given earlier in the text. In expressing the right hand sides of the equations (external forces and moments), the unwieldly expressions were simplified and approximated by the binomial expansion theorem. The coefficients of the various products of the five variables ($K_1$ through $K_{113}$) are functions of body properties, such as mass and mass moments of inertia, as well as combinations of the constant term "$gR_e^2$."

The resulting equations are long and cumbersome and are derived only after tedious algebraic and trigonometric computations. They do, however, represent the five complete rigid body equations of motion, written in terms of body coordinates. Constants for equations 29 through 33 are listed below:

Let:

$$A = I_{\xi\xi} = \sum m(\eta^2 + \zeta^2) \qquad D = A - B \qquad H = A + B - C$$

$$B = I_{\eta\eta} = \sum m(\xi^2 + \zeta^2) \qquad E = A - C \qquad I = A - B - C$$

$$C = I_{\zeta\zeta} = \sum m(\xi^2 + \eta^2) \qquad F = B - C \qquad J = A - B + C$$

$$P = 3g\,R_e^{\,2} \qquad M_T = \sum m_i$$

$$r_i = (\xi^2 + \eta^2 + \zeta^2) \qquad M_{111} = \sum m_i \xi\xi\xi$$

$$r_1 = \sum m_i r_i \xi \qquad M_{112} = \sum m_i \xi\xi\eta$$

$$r_2 = \sum m_i r_i \eta \qquad M_{113} = \sum m_i \xi\xi\zeta$$

$$r_3 = \sum m_i r_i \zeta \qquad M_{122} = \sum m_i \xi\eta\eta$$

$$r_{11} = \sum m_i r_i \xi\xi \qquad M_{123} = \sum m_i \xi\eta\zeta$$

$$r_{12} = \sum m_i r_i \xi\eta \qquad M_{133} = \sum m_i \xi\zeta\zeta$$

$$r_{13} = \sum m_i r_i \xi\zeta \qquad M_{222} = \sum m_i \eta\eta\eta$$

$$r_{22} = \sum m_i r_i \eta\eta \qquad M_{223} = \sum m_i \eta\eta\zeta$$

$$r_{23} = \sum m_i r_i \eta\zeta \qquad M_{233} = \sum m_i \eta\zeta\zeta$$

$$r_{33} = \sum m_i r_i \zeta\zeta \qquad M_{333} = \sum m_i \zeta\zeta\zeta$$

Using the above definitions,

$C_1 = 1/M_T$ $\qquad C_5 = -M_T$ $\qquad C_9 = 2Pr_1$

$C_2 = -2M_T$ $\qquad C_6 = PM_T$ $\qquad C_{10} = 2Pr_2$

$C_3 = PD$ $\qquad C_7 = 0.5P(D-F)$ $\qquad C_{11} = -2Pr_3$

$C_4 = -1/M_T$ $\qquad C_8 = -1.5\ PD$ $\qquad C_{12} = 2Pr_3$

$C_{13} = 2.5\ PM_{111}$ $\qquad C_{39} = 2.5\ BP(2M_{122} - M_{112})$ $\qquad C_{65} = 2.5P(AM_{111} - 2EM_{122} - 2CM_{133})$

$C_{14} = 2.5\ PM_{222}$ $\qquad C_{40} = 2.5\ BP(M_{222} - 2M_{112})$ $\qquad C_{66} = -2.5\ EPM_{112}$

$C_{15} = -7.5\ PM_{223}$ $\qquad C_{41} = 5BP\ (M_{223} - M_{113})$ $\qquad C_{67} = 5P(AM_{112} - 0.5\ EM_{222} - CM_{233})$

$C_{16} = 7.5\ PM_{113}$ $\qquad C_{42} = -5BPM_{123}$ $\qquad C_{68} = 2.5\ APM_{122}$

$C_{17} = 7.5\ PM_{112}$ $\qquad C_{43} = -5PM_{123}\ (B + C)$ $\qquad C_{69} = 0.5CP\ r_2$

$C_{18} = -7.5\ PM_{113}$ $\qquad C_{44} = 2.5P(2BM_{113} - (2B+C)\ M_{223})$ $\qquad C_{70} = 0.5CP\ r_3$

$C_{19} = 15\ PM_{123}$

$C_{20} = -15\ PM_{123}$

$C_{21} = 7.5\ PM_{122}$

$C_{22} = 7.5\ PM_{223}$

$C_{23} = 1/BC$

$C_{24} = -BI$

$C_{25} = FI$

$C_{26} = BJ$

$C_{27} = -BD$

$C_{28} = FI$

$C_{29} = -BC$

$C_{30} = -BDP$

$C_{31} = 0.5BPr_1$

$C_{32} = -0.5BPr_2$

$C_{33} = 0.5\ CPr_3$

$C_{34} = 2.5\ BPM_{112}$

$C_{35} = -2.5\ BPM_{122}$

$C_{36} = -2.5\ CPM_{113}$

$C_{37} = 5BPM_{123}$

$C_{38} = 5BPM_{123}$

$C_{45} = 2.5BP\ (r_{22}-r_{11})$

$C_{46} = -5BP\ r_{12}$

$C_{47} = 2.5BP\ r_{12}$

$C_{48} = -2{,}5BP\ r_{13}$

$C_{49} = -2.5P\ r_{23}(B+C)$

$C_{50} = -2.5CP\ r_{13}$

$C_{51} = 2.5\ BP\ r_{13}$

$C_{52} = 2.5\ BP\ r_{23}$

$C_{53} = 1/AC$

$C_{54} = -AJ$

$C_{55} = -CH$

$C_{56} = -CF$

$C_{57} = CF$

$C_{58} = -2CF$

$C_{59} = -CF$

$C_{60} = -CF$

$C_{61} = EJP$

$C_{62} = -CFP$

$C_{63} = -0.5AP\ r_1$

$C_{64} = 0.5\ EP\ r_2$

$C_{71} = -2.5CPM_{112}$

$C_{72} = -2.5CPM_{113}$

$C_{73} = 2.5CP(2M_{233} - M_{222})$

$C_{74} = -2.5CPM_{223}$

$C_{75} = 5CP\ (M_{133}-M_{122})$

$C_{76} = -5CPM_{123}$

$C_{77} = 2.5P\ (Ar_{11}-Er_{22} - Cr_{33})$

$C_{78} = 2.5AP\ r_{12}$

$C_{79} = -2.5\ EP\ r_{12}$

$C_{80} = 2.5CP(r_{33}-r_{22})$

$C_{81} = -2.5CP\ r_{12}$

$C_{82} = -2.5\ CP\ r_{13}$

$C_{83} = -2.5CP\ r_{23}$

$C_{84} = 1/BC$

$C_{85} = -FI$

$C_{86} = -CH$

$C_{87} = CE$

$C_{88} = -CE$

$C_{89} = 2CE$

$C_{90} = CE$

$C_{91} = CEP$

$C_{92} = FIP$

$C_{93} = -0.5\ CP\ r_1$

$C_{94} = 0.5\ BP\ r_2$

$C_{95} = -0.5\ FP\ r_1$

$C_{96} = 0{,}5\ CP\ r_3$

$C_{97} = 2.5\ CP\ (M_{111} - 2M_{133})$

$C_{98} = -2.5\ BPM_{112}$

$C_{99} = -2.5\ CPM_{113}$

$C_{100} = 2.5\ CPM_{122}$

$C_{101} = 2.5P\ (2FM_{112} - AM_{222} + 2CM_{233})$

$C_{102} = -2.5\ CPM_{223}$

$C_{103} = 5CP\ (M_{112} - M_{233})$

$C_{104} = 5P\ (0.5FM_{111} - AM_{122} + CM_{133})$

$C_{105} = -5CPM_{123}$

$C_{106} = 2.5\ FPM_{122}$

$C_{107} = 2.5\ CP(r_{11} - r_{33})$

$C_{108} = 2.5\ P(Fr_{11} - Ar_{22} + Cr_{33})$

$C_{109} = -2.5\ APr_{12}$

$C_{110} = 2.5\ CPr_{12}$

$C_{111} = -2.5CPr_{13}$

$C_{112} = -2.5\ C\ Pr_{23}$

$C_{113} = 2.5\ FPr_{12}$

$$\dot{w}_{I_z} = C_1\left[\dot{R}_y R_y^{-1} w_{I_z} C_2 + R_y^{-5} \sin\theta \cos\theta\, C_3\right] \tag{29}$$

$$\ddot{R}_y = C_4\Big[R_y w_{I_z}^2 C_5 + \frac{R_y^{-2} C_6}{3} + R_y^{-4} (C_7 \sin\theta + \sin^2\theta\, C_8) + R_y^{-5} (\sin\theta\, C_9 + \cos\theta\, C_{10} + \phi \cos\theta\, C_{11} + \psi \sin\theta\, C_{12} + \sin^3\theta\, C_{13} + \cos^3\theta\, C_{14} + \phi \cos^3\theta\, C_{15} + \psi \sin^3\theta\, C_{16} + \sin^2\theta \cos\theta\, C_{17} + \phi \sin^2\theta \cos\theta\, C_{18} + \psi \sin^2\theta \cos\theta\, C_{19} + \phi \sin\theta \cos^2\theta\, C_{20} + \sin\theta \cos^2\theta\, C_{21} + \psi \sin\theta \cos^2\theta\, C_{22})\Big] \tag{30}$$

$$\ddot{\theta} = C_{23}\Big[\dot{\theta}\dot{\psi}\psi C_{24} + \dot{\phi}\dot{\theta}\phi C_{25} + \dot{\phi}\dot{\psi} C_{26} + w_{I_z}\dot{\psi}\psi C_{27} + w_{I_z}\dot{\phi}\phi C_{28} + \dot{w}_{I_z} C_{29} + R_y^{-3} \sin\theta \cos\theta\, C_{30} + R_y^{-4}(\cos\theta\, C_{31} + \sin\theta\, C_{32} + \phi \sin\theta\, C_{33} + \sin^3\theta\, C_{34} + \cos^3\theta\, C_{35} + \phi \sin^3\theta\, C_{36} + \psi \sin^3\theta\, C_{37} + \phi \cos^3\theta\, C_{38} + \sin^2\theta \cos\theta\, C_{39} + \sin\theta \cos^2\theta\, C_{40} + \psi \sin^2\theta \cos\theta\, C_{41} + \psi \sin\theta \cos^2\theta\, C_{42} + \phi \sin^2\theta \cos\theta\, C_{43} + \phi \sin\theta \cos^2\theta\, C_{44}) + R_y^{-5} (\sin\theta \cos\theta\, C_{45} + \cos^2\theta\, C_{46} + C_{47} + \psi \sin\theta \cos\theta\, C_{48} + \phi \sin\theta \cos\theta\, C_{49} + \phi \sin^2\theta\, C_{50} + \phi \cos^2\theta\, C_{51} + \psi \sin^2\theta\, C_{52})\Big] \tag{31}$$

$$
\begin{aligned}
\ddot{\phi} = C_{53}\Big[ & \dot{\phi}\dot{\psi}\psi\, C_{54} + \dot{\theta}\dot{\psi} C_{55} + \dot{\theta}^2 \phi\, C_{56} + \dot{\psi}^2 \phi\, C_{57} + w_{I_z} \dot{\theta}\, \phi C_{58} \\
& + w_{I_z} \dot{\psi}\, C_{59} + w_{I_z}^{\;2}\, \phi\, C_{60} + R_y^{-3} (\psi \sin\theta \cos\theta\, C_{61} + \phi \cos^2 \\
& \theta\, C_{62}) + R_y^{-4} (\psi \cos\theta\, C_{63} + \psi \sin\theta\, C_{64} + \psi \sin^2\theta \cos\theta\, C_{65} \\
& + \psi \sin^3\theta\, C_{66} + \psi \sin\theta \cos^2\theta\, C_{67} + \psi \cos^3\theta\, C_{68} \\
& + \phi \cos\theta\, C_{69} + \cos\theta\, C_{70} + \phi \sin^2\theta \cos\theta\, C_{71} + \sin^2\theta \cos\theta C_{72} \\
& + \phi \cos^3\theta\, C_{73} + \cos^3\theta\, C_{74} + \phi \sin\theta \cos^2\theta\, C_{75} + \sin\theta \cos^2\theta \\
& C_{76}) + R_y^{-5} (\psi \sin\theta \cos\theta\, C_{77} + \psi \cos^2\theta\, C_{78} + \psi \sin^2\theta\, C_{79} \\
& + \phi \cos^2\theta\, C_{80} + \phi \sin\theta \cos\theta\, C_{81} + \sin\theta \cos\theta\, C_{82} \\
& + \cos^2\theta\, C_{83})\Big]
\end{aligned}
\tag{32}
$$

$$
\begin{aligned}
\ddot{\psi} = C_{84}\Big[ & \dot{\phi}\dot{\psi}\phi\, C_{85} + \dot{\phi}\dot{\theta}\, C_{86} + \dot{\theta}^2 \psi\, C_{87} + w_{I_z} \dot{\phi}\, C_{88} \\
& + w_{I_z} \dot{\theta}\psi\, C_{89} + w_{I_z}^{\;2} \psi\, C_{90} + R_y^{-3}(\psi \sin^2\theta\, C_{91} + \phi \sin\theta \cos\theta C_{92}) \\
& + R_y^{-4} (\psi \sin\theta\, C_{93} + \phi \sin\theta\, C_{94} + \phi \cos\theta\, C_{95} + \sin\theta\, C_{96} \\
& + \psi \sin^3\theta\, C_{97} + \phi \sin^3\theta\, C_{98} + \sin^3\theta\, C_{99} + \psi \sin\theta \cos^2\theta\, C_{100} \\
& + \phi \sin\theta \cos^2\theta\, C_{101} + \sin\theta \cos^2\theta\, C_{102} + \psi \sin^2\theta \cos\theta\, C_{103} \\
& + \phi \sin^2\theta \cos\theta\, C_{104} + \sin^2\theta \cos\theta\, C_{105} + \phi \cos^3\theta\, C_{106}) \\
& + R_y^{-5} (\psi \sin^2\theta\, C_{107} + \phi \sin\theta \cos\theta\, C_{108} + \phi \sin^2\theta\, C_{109} \\
& + \psi \sin\theta \cos\theta\, C_{110} + \sin^2\theta\, C_{111} + \sin\theta \cos\theta\, C_{112} \\
& + \phi \cos^2\theta\, C_{113})\Big]
\end{aligned}
\tag{33}
$$


## Acknowledgements

The authors wish to extend credit to Ron Johnston for the tedious task he performed in expanding and reducing the vector equations of motion. Also, without the assistance of Floyd Oslund in the digital solution of the non-linear pitch equation, a large portion of the work would necessarily be omitted.

## References

1. Frye, W.E. and Stearns, V.B., "Stabilization and Attitude Control of Satellite Vehicles," ARS Journal, vol 29, no. 12, December 1959, p 927-931.

2. Klemperer, W.B., "Satellite Librations of Large Amplitude," ARS Journal, vol 30, no. 1, January 1960, p 123-24.

3. Baker, R.M. Jr., "Librations on a Slightly Eccentric Orbit," ARS Journal, vol 20, no. 1, January 1960, p 124-26.

4. Baker, R.M. Jr., "Plane Libration of a Prolate Ellipsoidal Shell," ARS Journal, vol 20, no. 1, January 1960, p 126-28.

5. Nidey, Russell A., "Gravitation Torque on a Satellite of Arbitrary Shape." ARS Journal, vol. 30 no. 2, February 1960, p 203-04.

6. Arrow, B. and Johnson, R., "Dynamics of Orbiting Bodies: Development of Equations of Motion," The Martin Company-Denver Division, November, 1959.

7. Goldstein, Herbert, "Classical Mechanics," Addiston-Wesley Press, Inc., 1951.

8. Chaikin, Andronow, "Theory of Oscillation," Chapter VIII, 1949.

9. Cosgriff, R. L., "Non-linear Control Systems," Chapter 6. McGraw-Hill Series in Controls Systems Engineering, 1958.

# THE MOTION OF AN EQUATORIAL SATELLITE OF AN OBLATE PLANET

J. L. Brenner
Stanford Research Institute
Menlo Park, California

## Abstract

In this report, the exact solution of the differential equation $U'' + U - 1 = J_1 U^2$ is expanded into a convergent Fourier series. This equation arises in the problem of the motion of an equatorial satellite of an oblate planet. The period is $2\pi / [1 - J_1 - J_1^2 (3/2 + 5/12\ e^2)]$ if the amplitude is approximately 2e. Other properties of the solution are given as functions of $J_1$. Rigorous bounds on the accuracy of various "perturbation procedures" can be calculated directly from the formulas in this report. If $J_1 < 1/4$, periodic solutions always exist. Corresponding numerical bounds for the equation $U'' + U - 1 = J_1 U^2 + (3/7) D_1 U^4$ are $(48/7) D_1 + 4J_1 < 1$. Erroneous first- and second-order solutions are constructed and discussed.

## I. Introduction

Because of its broad interest in the theory of satellite orbits, the National Aeronautics and Space Administration is sponsoring a study at this Institute of the orbit of a near satellite of an oblate planet, including the effect of a resisting medium. The goal of this study is the development of orbital equations, together with an estimate and mathematical proof of the length of time over which the equations remain valid. In this report, it is shown how to make such an estimate for a particular case.

## II. Background

The differential equations which govern the motion of a near satellite of the earth are nonlinear and are not solvable in terms of elementary functions, except in very special cases. The equations of motion are, however, close to linear; they are usually solved by a perturbation procedure. An example of such an equation is

* An index of notation appears at the end of this article.

$$\frac{d^2U}{dM^2} + U - 1 = J_1 U^2$$

in which $J_1$ is close to zero. This equation governs the motion of a satellite in an equatorial orbit if there is no drag and if only the zero-th and second harmonic terms are present in the gravitational potential of the primary. (See Notation at end of paper for definition of symbols.)

The usual perturbation procedure for solving this equation can be explained as follows. When $J_1 = 0$, the solution is

$$U = 1 - e \cos M$$

where M is the independent variable. When $J_1$ is close to zero, a first (unsuccessful) assumption could be made that U has the form

$$U = 1 - e \cos M + J_1 f_1(M) + J_1^2 f_2(M) + \ldots \qquad \text{(i)}$$

where $f_1(M)$, $f_2(M)$ are Fourier series in M. That is, the assumption is made that U can be represented as a Fourier series, expansible as a power series in the small parameter $J_1$. This is reasonable physically, and it can be proved that U is an analytic function of $J_1$, and hence expansible as a power series in $J_1$.

Although the expansion (i) is correct in a certain sense, it is hopelessly inadequate. It is valid only for small values of M and for small values of $J_1$. The second requirement may not be a serious restriction on the application of the series to observations, but the limitation that M be small destroys the value of the solution. Indeed an equation is needed which follows the motion for a large number of revolutions, and this means that M increases from 0 to a very large number.

To obtain an expansion that is valid for large as well as for small M, it is necessary to make a linear transformation of the independent variable; that is, to write

$$U = 1 - e \cos(wM - M_o) + J_1 f_1(wM - M_o) + \ldots \qquad \text{(ii)}$$

It is found in practice that Eq. (ii) represents observations well, provided the functions $f_1, \ldots$ are determined by a perturbation procedure. Hence the expansion has some validity. It is the object of this report to give the expansion (ii) not only an observational validity but also a rigorous mathematical proof.

Even in practical applications, it is not enough to know that the expansion (ii) is convergent for all sufficiently small values of $J_1$. It is necessary to have a numerical bound on the radius of convergence; this numerical bound tells how small is "sufficiently small." It is shown in this report that the series converges for $J_1 < 1/4$, and diverges for $J_1 > 1/4$. Corresponding information is given for the nonlinear differential equation

$$U'' + U - 1 = J_1 U^2 + (3/7) D_1 U^4 \qquad \text{(iii)}$$

which takes into account an additional harmonic in the formula for the gravitational potential field in which the satellite moves. Eq. (iii) has no periodic solutions if $D_1$ exceeds 63/256; that is, if the coefficient of $U^4$ exceeds 0.11. For this equation, "sufficiently small" means really rather small.

This report shows that an equatorial satellite of an oblate primary which remains in the vicinity of the primary for 5/6 of a revolution is in a stable (nonescaping) orbit. Without some analysis, it is not possible to conclude from observations alone that a satellite is in a stable orbit, no matter how many revolutions the observations cover.

The question of the validity of expansion (ii) is a two-pronged question. The first point is to decide whether, for the given value of the constant $J_1$, the expansion can be used at all. This question is answered by the assertion that it can be used if $J_1$ is less than 1/4. The second point in connection with (ii) concerns the error committed in using the finite series obtained by truncating the infinite series.

If all the terms in the infinite series are known, then one can easily compute the error committed in using only the terms up to and including the term in $J_1$ and neglecting the terms in powers of $J_1$ higher than the first power. This error is the sum of all the terms neglected. Although this sum involves an infinite number of terms, it is possible to give a realistic estimate of the error for the problem at hand.

Nevertheless, it has seemed desirable to take a different point of view. It is better not start with the assumption that all the (infinitely many) terms in (ii) are known. If the satellite is moving in an inclined rather than an equatorial orbit, infinitely many terms will not be known. The usual perturbation procedures (rotating phase of Krylov-Bogolyubov; Fourier series; power series) obtain the terms one at a time. In particular, the term in $J_1$ is first obtained. Using this term, and the differential equation which must be satisfied, the term in $J_1^2$ is computed. Sometimes it is impossible to find a term in $J_1^2$ free of infinities, unless the original term in $J_1$ is modified. The necessity for such a modification indicates that the "first-order solution" originally obtained was incorrect.

The next step is to compute the term in $J_1^3$, using the terms in $J_1$ and $J_1^2$ which have already been obtained. To get a result free of infinities, it may be necessary to modify the term in $J_1^2$, and even to revise further the modified term in $J_1$ (the corrected first-order solution).

With this point of view it seemed desirable to investigate at each stage the tentative results obtained by the usual perturbation procedures. These results are written down in this report, and shown to be correct in some cases, erroneous in others.

It is interesting to point out the connection between expansion (ii) and the well-known exact solution of the differential equation of motion in terms of elliptic functions. The two solutions are equal wherever they are both valid; but they are of different character. The solution in terms of elliptic functions [see Eq. (17)] is written in terms of the so-called elliptic parameters; these involve the roots $\xi_1$, $\xi_2$, $\xi_3$ of the third-degree polynomial

$$\frac{2}{3} J_1 U^3 - U^2 + 2U + \text{const.}$$

The dependence of the solution on $J_1$ is somewhat more indirec in this formula than it is in formula (ii). Perhaps the solution i terms of elliptic functions is also less useful in practice.

To bring out the connection between the two solutions, a Fourier series for the function $\text{sn}^2 u$ is developed, and the latter is transformed into the series (ii). This gives a proof not only of the existence of series (ii), which had been obtained by independent methods previously (4), but more than this, a proof that the series converges for $\overline{J}_1 < 1/4$, and a means for estimating the error in truncating the series. All these results are believed to be new.

The miniature theory in this report gives a complete solution of the orbit problem in the absence of drag in the special case of equatorial orbits of an oblate primary. For inclined orbits it has been conjectured (by Prof. G.E. Latta in conversation) that the general solution is an almost-periodic function of the physical coordinates. This conjecture is now proved for this special case. For an orbit of general inclination, Vinti has established the same result when the potential has a special form (5). Further extension of this result, or proof of the entire conjecture, would be most interesting.

## III. Exact Solution of the Equation of Motion

In this section, the equation of motion is derived and the exact solution is given. The expansion of the solution into a Fourier series is carried out in Appendix A. This expansion is useful for comparing the exact solution with the approximate solutions derived by a perturbation procedure in Section IV.

The gravitation potential V of an oblate planet, axially symmetric and symmetric about its equatorial plane, is given by the formula

$$V = -\frac{gR^2}{r} - \frac{JgR^4}{r^3}\left(\frac{1}{3} - \cos^2\theta\right) - \frac{DgR^6}{35r^5}(35\cos^4\theta - 30\cos^2\theta + 3) + \ldots \quad (1)$$

where g, J, D, R are constants, r is radial distance, and θ is colatitude. If the deviation from sphericity is small, J and D are close to zero. R is the equatorial radius, and $g(1 + J + 3D/7)$ is the acceleration of gravity on the equator. The values sometimes taken to describe the earth's field are (1), (2) $g = 979.82$ cm sec$^{-2}$, $J = (1.6245 \pm 0.0003)\,10^{-3}$, $D = (6 \pm 1)\,10^{-6}$, $R = (6.378388 \pm 0.000018)\,10^8$ cm.

Relation (1) may be thought of as an infinite series, with the first three terms explicitly given. The full series may be written

$$V = -\Sigma_n A_{2n} r^{-2n-1} P_{2n}(\cos\theta) \quad (2)$$

where

$$P_o \equiv 1, \quad P_2 \equiv \frac{1}{2}(3z^2 - 1), \quad P_4 \equiv \frac{1}{8}(35z^4 - 30z^2 + 3), \ldots$$

$$P_n(z) = \sum_{r=o}^{[n/2]} (-1)^r \frac{(2n - 2r)!}{2^n r!\,(n - r)!\,(n - 2r)!} z^{n-2r}$$

For $P_2$, Jeffreys (2) has replaced $(3z^2-1)/2$ by $1/3 - z^2$, since the latter decreases by 1 from equator ($z = 1$) to pole. He recommends a corresponding replacement for $P_4$.

The kinetic energy of a satellite of mass 1 is

$$T = \frac{1}{2}(\dot{x}^2 + \dot{y}^2 + \dot{z}^2) = \frac{1}{2}(\dot{r}^2 + r^2\dot{\theta}^2 + r^2\sin^2\theta\,\dot{\phi}^2)$$

where x, y, z, r, θ, φ are the usual cartesian and spherical coordinates. For an equatorial orbit, it is necessary to set $\cos\theta = 0$, $\sin\theta = 1$, $\dot{\theta} = 0$. The equations of motion of a small satellite moving in the plane of the equator are

$$\frac{d}{dt}\frac{\partial(T - V)}{\partial\dot{q}_i} - \frac{\partial(T - V)}{\partial q_i} = 0, \quad q_i = r, \phi \quad (3)$$

These equations neglect all force-fields except the gravitational potential (1). Eqs. (3) are indeed

$$\ddot{r} - r\dot{\phi}^2 = -\frac{\partial V}{\partial r} \tag{4}$$

$$r^2\dot{\phi} = p = \text{const.} \tag{5}$$

where p is a constant of the motion (constant of integration).

Eqs. (3) have an ("energy"-) integral $T + V$ = constant. The proof of this fact is sketched in Appendix B. For this problem, $T + V$ is equal to $\left[(\dot{r}^2 + r^2\dot{\phi}^2)/2\right] - (gR^2/r) + O(J, D, \ldots)$. Thus $r\dot{\phi}$ is bounded. Moreover, r is bounded from zero unless $\dot{\phi}$ can become infinite.

As long as r is positive, the relation

$$\frac{d}{dt} = \frac{p}{r^2}\frac{d}{d\phi}$$

derived from Eq. (5) can be used to rewrite Eq. (4) so that $\phi$ is the independent variable. The result is more convenient if the dependent variable is taken as

$$U = \frac{1}{rL}, \quad L = \frac{gR^2}{p^2}$$

These substitutions lead to the equation

$$U'' + U = \frac{r^2}{p^2 L}\frac{\partial V}{\partial r} \tag{6}$$

which can be written in either of the forms (7), (8):

$$U'' + U - 1 = J_1 U^2 + \frac{3}{7} D_1 U^4 + \ldots \tag{7}$$

$$J_1 = JL^2R^2, \quad D_1 = DL^4R^4$$

$$U'' + U = \Sigma C_{2n} U^{2n} \tag{8}$$

$$C_{2n} = p^{-2} L^{2n-1} (2n + 1) P_{2n}(0) A_{2n}$$

Eq. (7) is the equation under study. The independent variable is called M (instead of $\phi$) henceforth.

Theorem 1. For small values of the parameters $J_1$, $D_1$, Eq. (7) has bounded, periodic solutions; and every bounded solution of (7) is periodic.

To prove Theorem 1, multiply both sides of the equation by $2U'$ and integrate:

$$U'^2 = U^2 - 2U + \frac{2}{3} J_1 U^3 + \frac{6}{35} D_1 U^5 + \ldots + c \qquad (9)$$

Every solution of (7) must satisfy (9) for some value of the constant of integration $c$.

In case $J_1 = D_1 = 0$, call the constant of integration* $c = e^2 - 1$, $0 \leqq e < 1$. The locus (9) plotted in the $(U, U')$-plane is a circle with center at $(1, 0)$ and radius $e$ (Fig. 1). The motion $U = f(M)$, $U' = f'(M)$ must follow this circle. When $U'$ is positive, $U$ is increasing; when $U'$ is negative, $U$ is decreasing. When $M$ increases, the representative point $P$ must traverse the upper and lower semicircles as shown. Unless $e = 0$, neither of the values $U = \xi_1$, $U = \xi_2$ which correspond to $U' = 0$ is an equilibrium point, as is shown by the equation $U'' + U - 1 = 0$. Hence the representative point $P$ traverses the full circle in Fig. 1, and the motion is periodic. If $J_1$, $D_1$ are not zero, there is a value of the

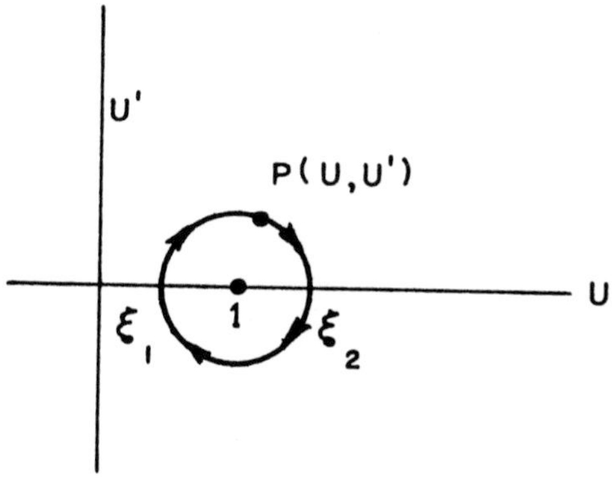


Fig. 1. Simple Harmonic Motion in the Phase Plane.

constant of integration $c$ such that two roots $\xi_1$, $\xi_2$ of the polynomial

$$- U^2 + 2U + \frac{2}{3} J_1 U^3 + \frac{6}{35} D_1 U^5 + \ldots + c$$

are close to $1 - e$, $1 + e$ when $J_1$, $D_1$ are small. The locus of this polynomial is that of Fig. 2. Hence, one possible

*If $e \geqq 1$, even the orbit "periodic in the $(U, U')$-plane" represents an escape.

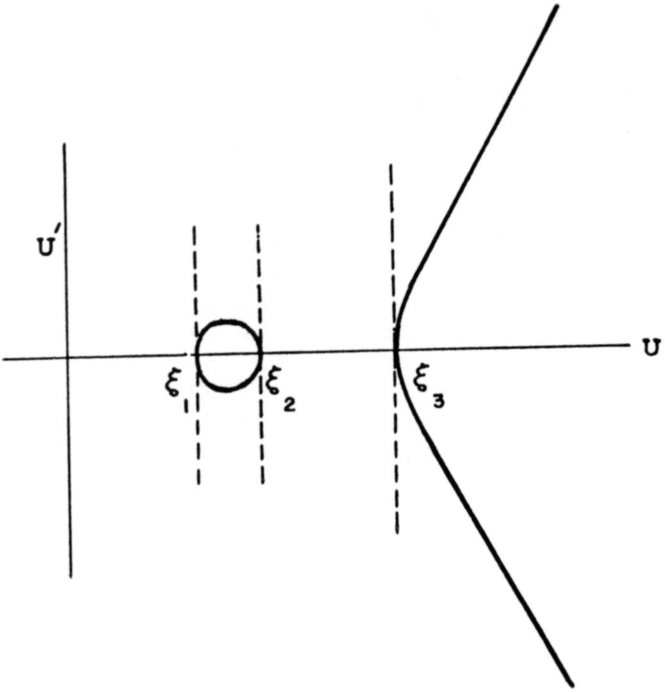


Fig. 2. Motions in the Phase Plane Described by an Elliptic Integral.

motion is periodic, with U increasing from $\xi_1$ to $\xi_2$ and returning.

The graph of the relation $y^2 = p(x)$, where p is a polynomial, contains closed and open branches. Every bounded branch is closed (see Fig. 3). Hence, every bounded motion satisfying (9) is periodic. This proves the theorem.

It is necessary to make precise the term "provided $J_1$, $D_1$ are small." As an example, suppose $D_1 = \ldots = 0, J_1 \neq 0$. It is permissible to choose $\xi_1 = 1 - e$. If $0 \leqq e < 1$, the following lemma holds.

Lemma 1. The differential equation

$$U'' + U - 1 = J_1 U^2$$

has nonconstant periodic (everywhere positive) solutions if $J_1 < 1/4$, constant real solutions if $J_1 \leqq 1/4$, and no periodic solutions if $J_1 < 1/4$.

Proof. The existence or nonexistence of constant solutions is trivial, since $U'' = 0$ for a constant solution.

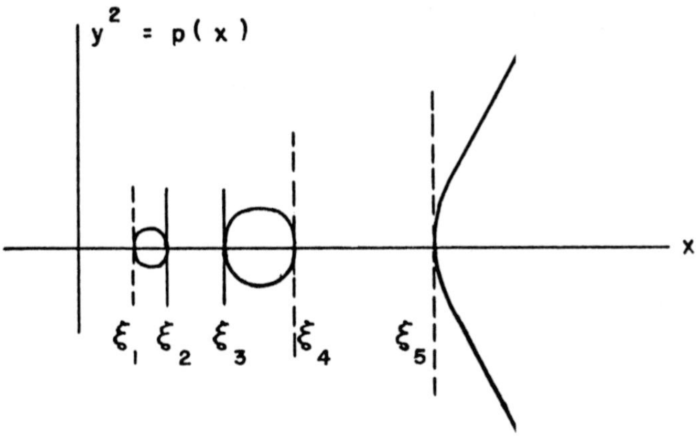


Fig. 3. Graph of the Relation $y^2 = p(x)$, where p is a Polynomial.

The other assertions are conveniently proved from the first integral

$$U'^2 = \frac{2}{3} J_1 U^3 - U^2 + 2U + \text{const.}$$

The polynomial

$$P(U) = \frac{2}{3} J_1 U^3 - U^2 + 2U + \text{const.} \tag{10}$$

can have three positive roots only if the derivative of P(U) has two positive roots. Since the derivative of P(U) is

$$P'(U) = \left(J_1 - \frac{1}{4}\right) U^2 + \left(\frac{1}{2} U - 1\right)^2$$

the condition $J_1 \leqq 1/4$ is necessary for the existence of three positive roots. But there can be no (everywhere positive) periodic motion unless P(U) has three positive roots, because P(U) is positive only when U exceeds the largest root of P(U), or when U lies between the two smallest roots (when there are three roots). Hence, the condition $J_1 \leqq 1/4$ is a necessary condition for the existence of everywhere positive periodic motion.

This condition $J_1 \leqq 1/4$ is also sufficient. For if this condition is satisfied, the polynomial P(U) has extrema for two positive values of U; and by adjusting the constant term in P(U), it can be arranged that P(U) has three positive roots, so that there is periodic motion with U everywhere positive. When $J_1 = 1/4$, however, the only periodic motion is U = constant.

Lemma 2. The differential equation

$$U'' + U - 1 = J_1 U^2 + \frac{3}{7} D_1 U^4 \qquad (11)$$

has nonconstant periodic (everywhere positive) solutions provided the relation

$$\frac{48}{7} D_1 + 4 J_1 \leqq 1 \qquad (12)$$

holds.

Remark. This inequality is valid at every point in the cross-hatched region R in the $(J_1, D_1)$-plane.

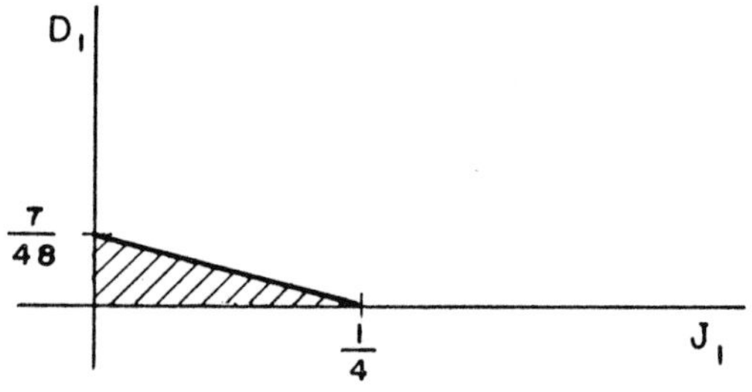


Fig. 3a. The Region R.

The proof of lemma 2 is similar to the proof of lemma 1. If the polynomial

$$Q(U) = \frac{6}{35} D_1 U^5 + \frac{2}{3} J_1 U^3 - U^2 + 2U + \text{const.}$$

has three real and positive roots, the differential Eq. (11) has periodic, everywhere positive solutions. A sufficient condition for this is that Q(U) have two positive extrema. Since

$$Q'(U) = 2\left(\frac{3}{7} D_1 U^4 + J_1 U^2 - U + 1\right)$$

is positive for $U = 0$ and $U = \infty$, and is negative for $U = 2$ provided the inequality of the lemma is satisfied, the truth of the lemma follows.

Lemma 2 gives a sufficient, but not a necessary condition for the existence of a periodic solution of (11). The necessary and sufficient condition is somewhat complicated, and corresponds to a larger region than that shown in Fig. 3a.

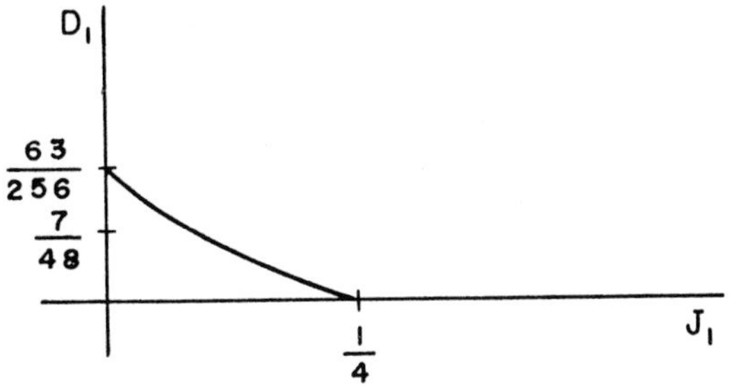


Fig. 3b. The Region $R_1$.

The region $R_1$ is bounded by a curve C which has parametric equations

$$\begin{cases} J_1 = \dfrac{3t - 4}{2t^2} \\ D_1 = \dfrac{7(2 - t)}{6t^4}, \quad \dfrac{4}{3} \leqq t \leqq 2 \end{cases}$$

The proof of this fact is given in Appendix C.

The differential equation

$$U'' + U - 1 = \sum_{n-1}^{\infty} A_{2n} U^{2n}$$

has periodic solutions if the coefficients $A_{2n}$ are suitably restricted. This problem will be discussed in a later report, and it will be shown there that the proofs can be made independent of the existence of a first integral.

Computations for an equatorial satellite of the earth give the following results. Let g be the acceleration of gravity, R the equatorial radius of the earth;

$$J \approx 1.7 \cdot 10^{-3}, \quad D \approx 10^{-5}$$

values suggested in (2). The conditions $D_1 < 1/4$, $J_1 < 1/4$ are necessary for the existence of a stable orbit. Since $J_1 = JR^2 L^2$, $D_1 = DR^4 L^4$, $L = gR^2/p^2$, these conditions are

$$p^4 > 4Jg^2 R^6$$

$$p^4 > (4D)^{1/2} g^2 R^6$$

where p is the angular momentum. It is interesting that these two inequalities come to about the same condition on p.

It is remarkable that the tiny coefficient D of the quadripole term in the potential seems to be as important as the value of the coefficient J of the dipole term in determining the possibility of periodic motion. No observational test of this conclusion seems feasible.

The same bounds are valid when the minimum value $\xi_1$ of U is $1 - e + mJ_1$ instead of $1 - e$, where m is a small number such as $1 + (1/3)e^2$, or $1 + (1/3)e^2 + (1/6)e^2 J_1$. All that is necessary for this extension of the lemmata to hold is that $\xi_1$ and $2 - \xi_1$ both be positive. This is always the case if $\xi_1$ and e are both positive, provided $mJ_1 < 1 + e$.

In almost all that follows, $D_1$ is taken as zero. In this paragraph, it is assumed that $J_1$ is small enough so that there is a periodic motion. Lemma 1 gives numerical bounds on $J_1$ which guarantee that periodic motion can exist.

The differential equation

$$U'' + U - 1 = J_1 U^2 \quad \left( ' \equiv \frac{d}{dM} \equiv \frac{d}{d\phi} \right) \tag{13}$$

has a first integral

$$U'^2 = \frac{2}{3} J_1 U^3 - U^2 + 2U + c \tag{14}$$

as shown above. If $0 < J_1 < 1/4$, and if the smallest root $\xi_1$ of the polynomial $(2/3)J_1U^3 - U^2 + 2U + c$ is between 0 and 1, the polynomial has 3 positive roots $\xi_1, \xi_2, \xi_3$, $0 < \xi_1 < \xi_2 < 1/2\,J_i < \xi_3$, and has the factorization

$$\frac{2}{3} J_1 U^3 - U^2 + 2U + c = \frac{2}{3} J_1 (U - \xi_1)(\xi_2 - U)(\xi_3 - U) \tag{15}$$

Periodic motion occurs if the initial conditions are $U_o = \xi_1$, $U_o' = 0$. The definite integral which represents this motion is

$$\int_{\xi_1}^{U} \frac{dU}{\sqrt{\frac{2}{3} J_1 (U - \xi_1)(\xi_2 - U)(\xi_3 - U)}} = M \tag{16}$$

Strictly speaking, this formula is valid only during the first passage along the upper branch of the closed curve in Fig. 2. Formula (17) below, which is given (No. 547) in Peirce's tables for (16), can be shown to be universally valid. It describes the motion for all time.

$$U = \xi_1 + (\xi_2 - \xi_1)\, \mathrm{sn}^2(\Phi, k) \tag{17}$$

$$k^2 = \frac{\xi_2 - \xi_1}{\xi_3 - \xi_1}, \quad \Phi = \frac{M}{2}\sqrt{\frac{2}{3} J_1 (\xi_3 - \xi_1)}$$

Here, $\mathrm{sn}\,\Phi$ is the Jacobian elliptic function, connected with the Jacobian F-function

$$F(\psi, k) = \int_0^{\psi} \frac{dt}{\sqrt{(1 - t^2)(1 - k^2 t^2)}}$$

by the relation $x = \mathrm{sn}\,F(\sin^{-1} x, k)$. The function $\mathrm{sn}\,\Phi$ is tabulated in Ref. 3.

The function $\mathrm{sn}^2\,\Phi$ can be approximated in various ways. A Fourier series for this function is derived in Appendix A. By substituting this expansion into (17), one obtains the relation

$$U = \xi_1 + (\xi_2 - \xi_1) \frac{4\pi^2}{K^2 k^2} \sum_{n=1}^{\infty} \frac{nq^n}{1 - q^{2n}} \sin^2 \frac{n \Phi \pi}{2K} \tag{18}$$

where $\Phi, k$ are given above; $k'^2 = 1 - k^2$;

$$K = K(k) = \int_0^1 \frac{dt}{\sqrt{(1 - t^2)(1 - k^2 t^2)}}$$

is the complete elliptic integral of the first kind;

$$K' = K(k'); \quad q = \exp \frac{-\pi K'}{K}$$

Eq. (18) expresses an even function of $\Phi$ as an absolutely convergent sum of even functions.

## IV. Approximate Formulas Derivable from the Exact Solution

The formula (18), above, represents that solution of the differential equation

$$U'' + U - 1 = J_1 U^2$$

for which

$$U_o = \xi_1, \quad U_o' = 0$$

The same formula can be written in a more convenient form. In this section, the parameters $\xi_1$, $\xi_2$, K, k, q, $\Phi$ are written in terms of $J_1$ and a single additional parameter, e. This reworking of Eq. (18) makes possible an intuitive comparison of the exact formula and various approximations to it.

A (zero-th order) approximation to (18) is obtained by setting J = 0. Then

$$J_1 = 0, \quad \xi_3 = \infty, \quad k = 0, \quad sn^2 u = \sin^2 u, \quad K = \frac{\pi}{2},$$

$$\Phi = \frac{M}{2}, \quad \xi_1 + \xi_2 = 2$$

Set

$$\xi_1 = 1 - e, \quad \xi_2 = 1 + e$$

then the approximation in question reads

$$U = 1 - e + 2e \sin^2 \frac{M}{2} \tag{19}$$

which differs only in notation from the familiar

$$U = 1 - e \cos M$$

the equation of a Keplerian ellipse.

A "first-order" approximation to (18) is obtained by writing

$$\xi_1 = 1 - e + mJ_1 \tag{20}$$

Then $\xi_2$, $\xi_3$ must be determined so that $0 < \xi_1 < \xi_2 < \xi_3$, and $\xi_1$, $\xi_2$, $\xi_3$ are all zeros of the polynomial

$$\frac{2}{3} J_1 U^3 - U^2 + 2U + c \tag{21}$$

for some constant c. To within terms of order $J_1^2$, it is found that

$$c = e^2 - 1 + J_1 \left[ - \frac{2}{3} (1 - e)^3 - 2em \right]$$

$$\xi_2 = 1 + e + J_1 \left(2 + \frac{2}{3} e^2 - m\right)$$

$$\frac{2}{3} J_1 \xi_3 = 1 - \frac{4}{3} J_1$$

The formula for $k^2$ is $(\xi_2 - \xi_1)/(\xi_3 - \xi_1)$, thus

$$k^2 = \frac{4}{3} J_1 e, \qquad q = \frac{1}{12} J_1 e, \qquad \frac{2K}{\pi} = 1 + \frac{1}{3} J_1 e,$$

$$\sqrt{\frac{2}{3} J_1 (\xi_3 - \xi_1)} = 1 + J_1\left(-1 + \frac{1}{3} e\right)$$

These results follow from the relations $16q \approx k^2$, $2K/\pi \approx 1 + (1/4)k^2 + (9/64)k^4$. The number $w$ is defined by the formula

$$w = \frac{\pi}{2K} \sqrt{\frac{2}{3} J_1 (\xi_3 - \xi_1)}$$

so that

$$\frac{wM}{2} = \frac{\pi \Phi}{2K}$$

An approximation to $w$ is $w = 1 - J_1$.

The first-order approximation to (18) neglects all terms of order $J_1^2$, and retains (parts of) only two terms beyond the constant term. The complete formula is

$$U = 1 - e + mJ_1 + \left[2e + J_1\left(2 + \frac{2}{3} e^2 - 2m\right)\right] \sin^2 \frac{wM}{2}$$

$$+ \frac{1}{3} J_1 e^2 \sin^2 \frac{2wM}{2}, \qquad w = 1 - J_1 \tag{22}$$

The approximate period [the exact period for Eq. (22)] is $2\pi/(1 - J_1)$, which is independent of the amplitude. This isochronism is not maintained in the second-order solution, which does depend on the amplitude $\xi_2 - \xi_1$.

The second-order solution is obtained by commencing with the relation

$$\xi_1 = 1 - e + m_1 J_1 + m_2 J_1^2$$

and "neglecting all terms in $J_1^3$." It reads

$$U = 1 - e + m_1 J_1 + m_2 J_1^2$$
$$+ \sin^2 \frac{wM}{2} \left[2e + J_1\left(-2m_1 + 2 + \frac{2}{3} e^2\right)\right.$$
$$\left. + J_1^2\left(-2m_2 + 4 - \frac{4}{3} e - \frac{4}{3} m_1 e + \frac{20}{9} e^2 + \frac{29}{72} e^3\right)\right]$$
$$+ \sin^2 \frac{2wM}{2} \left[\frac{1}{3} J_1 e^2 + J_1^2\left(\frac{2}{3} e - \frac{2}{3} m_1 e - \frac{2}{9} e^2 + \frac{2}{9} e^3\right)\right]$$
$$+ \sin^2 \frac{3wM}{2} \left(-\frac{1}{24} J_1^2 e^3\right)$$

$$w = 1 - J_1 - J_1^2 \left(\frac{3}{2} + \frac{5}{12} e^2\right)$$

The period $2\pi/w$ is extraordinarily insensitive to the amplitude. For a near-earth satellite, $J_1$ is about $1.7 \cdot 10^{-3}$. Therefore, if the equatorial orbit of a near-earth satellite changed suddenly from one with perigee and apogee at 250 and 750 miles respectively from the earth's surface to a nearby circular orbit at the same average distance (same angular momentum), the synodic period, from perigee to perigee, would change by less than 4 parts in $10^9$.

## V. Solution by the First Perturbation Procedure

In this section, a special form of solution is prescribed, and the arbitrary functions and constants in that special form are found by solving linear finite and differential equations. When $J_1 = 0$, the equation

$$U'' + U - 1 = J_1 U^2 \tag{23}$$

with initial conditions $U_o = 1 - e$, $U_o' = 0$, has the solution

$$U = 1 - e \cos M$$

### A. First-Order Solution

A reasonable perturbation of this formula to try is

$$U = 1 - e \cos wM + J_1 u_1$$

where $e$, $w$, $u_1$ are functions of $M$ to be determined. It add nothing to the generality to replace 1 by a function of $M$; and if $w$ is assumed to be 1, even the best choice for $e$ and $u_1$ doe not match the differential equation very well.

It turns out that e and w can be taken as constants. Assuming that e and w vary merely complicates the formulas without improving their flexibility. The initial conditions are taken as $U_o = 1 - e + mJ_1$, $U_o' = 0$; in particular, m, which is preassigned, may be 0. The computations

$$J_1 U^2 = J_1\left(1 + \frac{1}{2} e^2 - 2e \cos wM + \frac{1}{2} e^2 \cos 2 wM\right) + O(J_1^2)$$

$$U'' + U - 1 = e(w^2 - 1) + J_1 (u_1'' + u_1) = O(J_1^2)$$

show that Eq. (23) can be satisfied either by setting

$$w = 1,$$

$$u_1'' + u_1 = 1 + \frac{1}{2} e^2 - 2e \cos wM + \frac{1}{2} e^2 \cos 2 wM \qquad (24)$$

or by setting

$$w^2 - 1 = 2J_1$$

$$u_1'' + u_1 = 1 + \frac{1}{2} e^2 + \frac{1}{2} e^2 \cos 2 wM \qquad (25)$$

But assumption (24) would force $u_1$ to be unbounded, and contradict the requirement that $J_1 u_1$ be small. Therefore (25) is the correct assumption. It leads to the results

$$w = 1 - J_1 + O(J_1^2)$$

$$u_1 = 1 + \frac{1}{2} e^2 - \frac{e^2}{6} \cos 2 wM + \left(m - 1 - \frac{1}{3} e^2\right) \cos wM \qquad (26)$$

$$U = 1 - e \cos wM + J_1 \left[m + \left(- 2m + 2 + \frac{2}{3} e^2\right) \sin^2 \frac{wM}{2} + \frac{1}{3} e^2 \sin^2 wM\right]$$

$$U = 1 - e + mJ_1 + \left[2e + J_1 \left(-2m + 2 + \frac{2}{3} e^2\right)\right] \sin^2 \frac{wM}{2} + \frac{1}{3} e^2 J_1 \sin^2 \frac{2 wM}{2}$$

$$w = 1 - J_1 \qquad (27)$$

This formula is identical with formula (22).

Formula (26) is an approximate solution for Eq. (25). Without the context of the present discussion, an equally valid solution for Eq. (25) would be

$$\bar{u}_1 = 1 + \frac{1}{2} e^2 - \frac{1}{6} e^2 \cos 2\, wM + \left(m - 1 - \frac{1}{3} e^2\right) \cos M \tag{28}$$

The formula $U = 1 - e \cos wM + J_1 \bar{u}_1$ differs from (27) by the bounded quantity

$$\eta = J_1 \left(2m - 2 - \frac{2}{3} e^2\right) \sin M \sin \frac{1}{2} J_1 M \tag{29}$$

The average value of the error $\eta$ during the first revolution is approximately zero; but the graph of $\eta$ has the peculiar form given in Fig. 4. If m is precisely $1 + (1/3) e^2$, $\eta$ is identically zero.

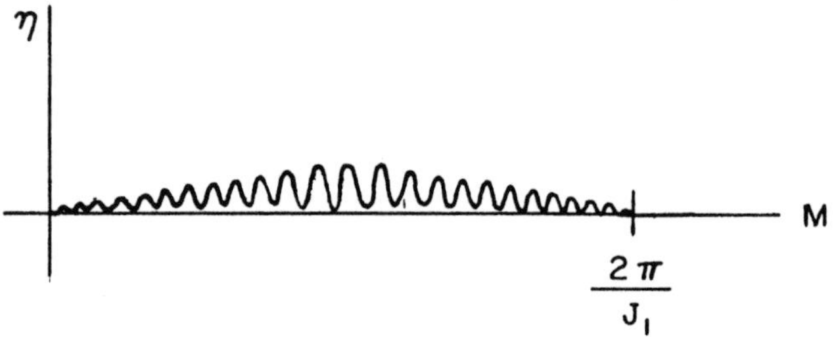


Fig. 4. Error $\eta$ of the Erroneous Solution.

It is interesting that the period of $\eta$ is the same as the period of the apses, i.e., the pattern of $\eta$ repeats over the length of time required for perigee to precess 360 degrees. The averag value

$$\frac{1}{2\pi} \int_{k\pi}^{(k+2)\pi} \eta\, dM = \bar{\eta}$$

of $\eta$ during the $k^{th}$ revolution is approximately

$$J_1^2 \left(2m - 2 - \frac{2}{3} e^2\right) \sin \left[J_1 (k + 1) \pi\right]$$

Within the present context, Eq. (26) is preferred to Eq. (28) since it is known that the motion is periodic with period $2\pi/\omega$. In some problems which are customarily attacked by a perturbation procedure, a priori knowledge of periodicities is lacking, and an intrinsic test is desirable. An intrinsic method of comparing (26) with (28) and choosing (26) is given later in this section. The basis of this test is a priori knowledge of the fact that U is bounded.

Without some a priori knowledge concerning the solution of a differential equation, no (mechanical) perturbation procedure can yield unequivocal information concerning the solution. It is important to remember this, even in the hurly-burly practical press to obtain "results." It is not denied that properties of the solution of $U'' + U - 1 = \epsilon f(U_1, U_1', M)$ can be obtained asymptotic for $\epsilon \to 0$. In practical problems, information of this kind is seldom useful, since $\epsilon$ is a given finite number as a rule.

## B. Second-Order Solution

A second-order approximation to U is taken to have the form

$$U = 1 - e \cos wM + J_1 u_1 + J_1^2 u_2$$

$$w = 1 - J_1 + J_1^2 w_2$$

with $u_1$ given by Eq. (26). Initial conditions are

$$U_o = 1 - e + m_1 J_1 + m_2 J_1^2$$

$$U_o' = 0$$

In particular $m_1$, $m_2$, which are preassigned, may be zero. The details are exactly parallel to those involved in computing the first-order solution, only more tedious. The result is

$$\begin{aligned} U = {} & 1 - e + m_1 J_1 + m_2 J_1^2 \\ & + \sin^2 \frac{wM}{2} \left[ 2e + J_1 \left( -2m_1 + 2 + \frac{2}{3} e^2 \right) \right. \\ & \qquad \left. + J_1^2 \left( -2m_2 + 4 - \frac{4}{3} e - \frac{4}{3} m_1 e + \frac{20}{9} e^2 + \frac{29}{72} e^3 \right) \right] \\ & + \sin^2 \frac{2wM}{2} \left[ \frac{1}{3} J_1 e^2 + J_1^2 \left( \frac{2}{3} e - \frac{2}{3} m_1 e - \frac{2}{9} e^2 + \frac{2}{9} e^3 \right) \right] \\ & + \sin^2 \frac{3wM}{2} \left( -\frac{1}{24} J_1^2 e^3 \right) \end{aligned} \qquad (30)$$

$$w = 1 - J_1 - J_1^2 \left(\frac{3}{2} + \frac{5}{12} e^2\right)$$

For the more general Eq. (7), the value of $w$ is

$$w = 1 - J_1 - D_1\left(2 + \frac{3}{2} e^2\right) - J_1^2\left(\frac{3}{2} + \frac{5}{12} e^2\right)$$

The k-th order solution will contain the term $\sin^2 (wf_k M/2)$ where $f_k$ is the (k-1)-st term in the Fibonacci series 1, 2, 3, 5, 8, ... .

It has been explained above how an erroneous function in a first-order solution could be obtained during the analysis of the perturbation procedure. There is a corresponding possibility in the work of finding a second-order solution. The error in this case will also return to zero after a complete precession of the apses, and the maximum value of the error will be $J_1^2$ times a bounded quantity.

It is instructive to see how the erroneous first-order solution

$$U = 1 - e \cos wM + J_1 \bar{u}_1$$

reveals itself to be faulty. To find a second-order solution, it is reasonable to attempt to determine $\bar{u}_2$ so that

$$U = 1 - e \cos wM + J_1 \bar{u}_1 + J_1^2 \bar{u}_2$$

is a solution of $U'' + U - 1 = J_1 U^2$. This attempt leads to a differential equation for $\bar{u}_2$ which has a true resonance; every solution of the differential equation $[m - 1 - (1/3)\, e^2 \neq 0]$

$$\bar{u}_2'' + \bar{u}_2 = 2\left(m - 1 - \frac{1}{3} e^2\right)\cos M + \ldots \tag{31}$$

is unbounded as $M \rightarrow \infty$.

A first-order solution is not useful unless it is a truncated asymptotic or convergent solution. Eq. (28) is not a useful formula.

For a more complicated equation than

$$U'' + U - 1 = J_1 U^2$$

it is not always easy to test for resonances. The point is that it must be proved of a first-order solution not only that it leads to a bounded second-order solution, but also that bounded solutions of all orders are available, starting with the given first-order solution. The finding of a complete (infinite) asymptotic formula has eluded analysts in most cases.

## VI. Solution by the Second Perturbation Procedure

In this section, $J_1$ is a small parameter; the differential equation

$$U'' + U - 1 = J_1 U^2$$

is solved approximately by the method of Krylov and Bogoliubov. The first- and second-order solutions found conform to the solutions of the same equation found in Sections III and IV.

The method in question is also called the "method of rotating phase." The solution of

$$U'' + U - 1 = J_1 U^2, \qquad U_o = 1 - e + mJ_1, \qquad U_o' = 0$$

is assumed to have the form

$$U = 1 - \alpha \cos (wM + v) + aJ_1$$

where

$$\alpha = e + O(J_1)$$

Here, all parameters are variables instead of constants. It is allowable in the case of this equation to take $\alpha$, w, a as constants, so that U, M, v are the only variables. The computations needed are

$$U'' + U - 1 = \sin (wM + v)(\alpha v'')$$

$$+ \cos (wM + v) \left[ e(w^2 - 1) + 2e\, wv' + v'^2 \right] + aJ_1 \qquad (32)$$

$$J_1 U^2 = J_1 \left[ 1 - 2e \cos (wM + v) + e^2 \cos^2 (wM + v) \right] \qquad (33)$$

Expressions (32) and (33) are equal if the coefficients of $aJ_1$, $\sin (wM + v)$, and $\cos (wM + v)$ in these expressions are equal. But $\sin^2 (wM + v) + \cos^2 (wM + v) = 1$. Hence

$$w^2 - 1 = -2J_1$$

$$\alpha v'' = (1 - a) \sin (wM + v) \cdot J_1$$

$$2e\, wv' + v'^2 = (1 - a + e^2) \cos (wM + v) \cdot J_1$$

A solution of these equations is

$$w = 1 - J_1$$

$$a = 1 + \frac{1}{3} e^2$$

$$av' = \frac{1}{3} J_1 e^2 \cos(wM + v)$$

$$a = e + J_1 \left(1 + \frac{1}{3} e^2 - m\right)$$

so that, finally,

$$U = 1 + J_1 \left(1 + \frac{1}{3} e^2\right) - \left[e + J_1 \left(1 + \frac{1}{3} e^2 - m\right)\right] \cos(wM + v)$$

$$v = \frac{1}{3} J_1 e \sin(wM + v) \qquad (34)$$

$$w = 1 - J_1$$

By application of the fomulas $\sin T \approx T - (T^3/6)$, $\cos T \approx 1 - (T^2/2$ it can be shown that formula (34) conforms to the first-order solution given in Sections IV and V.

To make it evident that (34) represents a periodic function, it would be correct to write, instead of

$$v = \frac{1}{3} J_1 e \sin(wM + v) \qquad (35)$$

the formula $v = (1/3) J_1 e \sin wM$, which approximates (35) to $O(J_1^2)$. The formula

$$v = \frac{1}{3} J_1 e \sin\left(wM + \frac{1}{3} J_1 e \sin wM\right)$$

while unnecessarily complicated, would also exhibit this periodicity. A second-order solution corresponding to (34) is

$$U = 1 + J_1 \left(1 + \frac{1}{3} e^2\right) + J_1^2 \left(2 + \frac{2}{3} e + \frac{2}{3} e^2 + \frac{2}{9} e^3 - 2 e m_1\right)$$

$$- \left[e + J_1 \left(1 + \frac{1}{3} e^2 - m_1\right)\right] \cos(wM + v)$$

$$- J_1^2 \left(2 + \frac{2}{3} e + \frac{2}{3} e^2 + \frac{2}{9} e^3 - 2 e m_1 - m_2\right) \cos(wM + v$$

$$v = \frac{1}{3} J_1 e \sin(wM + v) + J_1^2 \left(-\frac{1}{3} - \frac{2}{3} e - \frac{1}{9} e^2\right.$$

$$\left. + \frac{1}{3} m_1\right) \sin(wM + v) - \frac{1}{24} J_1^2 e^2 \sin(2 wM + 2v)$$

$$w = 1 - J_1 - J_1^2 \left(\frac{3}{2} + \frac{5}{12} e^2\right)$$

To see that this solution is periodic with period $2\pi/w$, write $v$ in the form

$$v = \frac{1}{3} J_1 \, e \sin\left(wM + \frac{1}{3} J_1 \, e \sin wM\right)$$

$$+ J_1^2 \left(- \frac{1}{3} - \frac{2}{3} e - \frac{1}{9} e^2 + \frac{1}{3} m_1\right) \sin (wM + v)$$

$$- \frac{1}{24} J_1^2 \, e^2 \sin (2\,wM + 2v)$$

## VII. Future Work

The remaining time and funds for this contract will be devoted as follows:

1. Numerical estimates will be made of the errors in the first- and second-order solutions obtained in this report.

2. If the second and fourth harmonics are both present in the gravitational potential of an oblate planet, the equation

$$U'' + U - 1 = J_1 U^2 + 5 D_1 U^4$$

governs the motion of an equatorial satellite. Analysis of this equation will be carried out. If it is possible to expand the solution in a Fourier series, the results should be analogous to the results of this report.

3. General theorems will be given concerning the equation

$$U'' + U - 1 = f(U)$$

where $f(U)$ is an even power series in $U$.

4. If time permits, equatorial orbits will be investigated in which there is drag. Strict bounds for variation in radial distance would be interesting to obtain in this case.

----------------

## Appendix A

### The Fourier Series for the Function $sn^2 \Phi$

The Jacobian elliptic function $sn^2(\Phi, k)$ is an even function of the real argument $\Phi$ and has period 2K. The function is moreover sufficiently regular to possess a Fourier expansion of the form

$$sn^2 \Phi = \Sigma a_n \cos \frac{n \pi \Phi}{2K}$$

In this appendix, the coefficients $a_n$ are determined by a very expeditious method due to Whittaker-Watson (Ref. 6, p. 510).

Lemma 3. The poles of $sn^2(2Kx/\pi)$ are at

$$\frac{i\pi K'}{2K}, \quad \frac{i\pi K'}{2K} \pm \pi, \quad \frac{i\pi K'}{2K} \pm 2\pi, \ \ldots$$

Lemma 4. The residue of $sn^2(2Kx/\pi) \exp inx$ at $x = i\pi K'/2k$ is $in\pi^2 q^{n/2}/4K^2 k^2$; the residue of the same function at $x = (i\pi K'/2K) - \pi$ is $(-1)^n in\pi^2 q^{n/2}/4K^2 k^2$.

Proof. In the reference cited, the relation $sn\,u = u - (1/6)(1 + k^2)u^3 + O(u^5)$ is proved. From this, there follows

$$sn(u + iK') = k^{-1}(sn\,u)^{-1} = \frac{1}{ku} + \frac{1 + k^2}{6k} u + O(u^3)$$

$$sn^2(u + iK') = \frac{1}{k^2 u^2} + \frac{1 + k^2}{3k^2} + O(u^2)$$

$$sn^2\left[\frac{2K}{\pi}\left(x + i\frac{K'\pi}{2K}\right)\right] = \frac{1}{k^2 x^2}\frac{\pi^2}{4K^2} + \frac{1 + k^2}{3k^2} + O(x^2) \qquad (36)$$

Moreover,

$$\exp inx = \exp\frac{\pi n K'}{2K} \cdot \exp\left[in\left(x + \frac{\pi i K'}{2K}\right)\right]$$

so that

$$\exp\left[in\left(x + \frac{\pi i K'}{2K}\right)\right] = \left(\exp - \frac{\pi n K'}{2K}\right)\left(1 + inx + \ldots\right) \qquad (37)$$

The first assertion of the lemma follows from (36) and (37), with $x_1 - \pi i K'/2K$ written in place of $x$. The second assertion is an obvious consequence of the first. The lemma is proved.

Scholium.

$$sn^2\frac{2Kx}{\pi} = \Sigma a_n \cos nx \qquad (38)$$

where

$$a_n = \frac{-1}{1 - q^n} q^{n/2} \frac{n\pi^2}{K^2 k^2}, \quad \text{if} \quad n = 2, 4, 6, \ldots$$

$$a_n = 0 \quad \text{if} \quad n = 1, 3, 5, \ldots \qquad (39)$$

Proof. By the general theory of Fourier series, the formula for $a_n$ is

$$2\pi a_n = \int_{-\pi}^{\pi} sn^2 \frac{2Kx}{\pi} \cos nx\,dx = \int_{-\pi}^{\pi} sn^2 \frac{2Kx}{\pi} e^{inx}\,dx \qquad (40)$$

By considering the parallelogram R (Fig. 5) in the

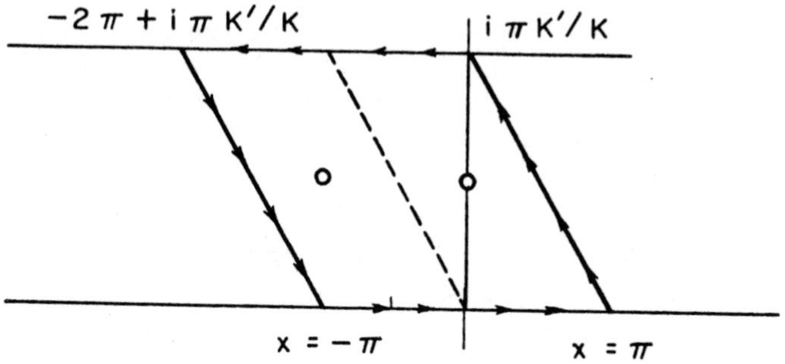


Fig. 5. The Contour R of Integration $\oint sn^2 \frac{2Kx}{\pi} \exp inx\,dx.$

complex x-plane, and using the periodicities of the functions $sn^2\,2Kx/\pi$, $e^{inx}$, the scholium will be proved. Let q equal $\exp(-\pi K'/K)$; it is convenient to start from the obvious identity

$$2\pi\left[a_n - (-1)^n q^n a_n\right] = \oint_R - \int_{\pi}^{i\pi K'/K} - \int_{i\pi K'/K}^{-2\pi+i\pi K'/K} - \int_{-2\pi+i\pi K'/K}^{-\pi} -2\pi(-1)^n q^n a_n \qquad (41)$$

each integrand being

$$sn^2 \frac{2Kx}{\pi} \exp inx\,dx$$

The contour integral $\oint$ has the value $-2\pi(\pi^2 m\,q^m/K^2 k^2)$ when $n = 2m$ is even, and has the value 0 when n is odd; this was shown in lemmas 3 and 4. The second and fourth terms (first and third line integrals) of the right member of (41) add to zero because of the periodicities of the integrand. The third term (second line integral) of the right member of

(41) can be simplified by use of the substitution $x = x' - \pi + \pi i K'/K$, if account is taken of the identities

$$\mathrm{sn}^2 \frac{2Kx}{\pi} = \mathrm{sn}^2 \left(\frac{2Kx'}{\pi} + 2K - 2iK'\right) = \mathrm{sn}^2 \frac{2Kx'}{\pi}$$

$$\exp inx = q^n (-1)^n \exp inx'$$

Eq. (40) shows that this third term annuls the last term of the right member of (41). Eqs. (38), (39) have been shown to be consequences of Eq. (41); the scholium is proved.

Since $\mathrm{sn}^2 u$ is 0 when u is 0, the constant term of the Fourier series is determined. This gives the result (since $1 - \cos 2Z = 2 \sin^2 Z$):

$$\mathrm{sn}^2 u = \frac{4\pi^2}{K^2 k^2} \Sigma \frac{m q^m}{1 - q^{2m}} \sin^2 \frac{m\pi u}{2K}$$

## Appendix B

## The Energy Integral

Suppose $q_1, q_2, q_3$ vary with time; $q_i$ are called "canonical coordinates." Let there be given a homogeneous quadratic form T of the second degree in the "velocities" $\dot{q}_1, \dot{q}_2, \dot{q}_3 \equiv (dq_i/dt)$. For example,

$$T = \frac{1}{2}(\dot{q}_1^2 + \dot{q}_2^2 + \dot{q}_3^2)$$

or again

$$T = \frac{1}{2}(\dot{r}^2 + r^2\dot{\theta}^2 + r^2 \sin^2 \theta \, \dot{\phi}^2)$$

In the second example $(q_1, q_2, q_3) = (r, \theta, \phi)$; $(\dot{q}_1, \dot{q}_2, \dot{q}_3) = (\dot{r}, \dot{\theta}, \dot{\phi})$. Let V be a function of $q_1, q_2, q_3$, independent of $\dot{q}_1, \dot{q}_2, \dot{q}_3$. If T and V have the necessary number of derivatives in each variable that occurs explicitly ($q$, $\dot{q}$ in the one; q in the other), and if $\ddot{q}$ exists, then the system of differential equations

$$\frac{d}{dt} \frac{\partial(T - V)}{\partial \dot{q}_i} - \frac{\partial(T - V)}{\partial q_i} = 0, \quad i = 1, 2, 3 \qquad (42)$$

has the following integral: T + V = constant.

To prove this, two simple facts are needed. The first is that

$$\dot{q}_1 \frac{\partial T}{\partial \dot{q}_1} + \dot{q}_2 \frac{\partial T}{\partial \dot{q}_2} + \dot{q}_3 \frac{\partial T}{\partial \dot{q}_3} = 2T$$

This is a general property of quadratic forms. The second fact is that

$$\frac{dT}{dt} = \Sigma \dot{q}_i \frac{\partial T}{\partial q_i} + \Sigma \ddot{q}_i \frac{\partial T}{\partial \dot{q}_i}$$

and

$$\frac{dV}{dt} = \Sigma \dot{q}_i \frac{\partial V}{\partial q_i}$$

The algebraic manipulation required to complete the proof reads as follows

$$\Sigma \dot{q}_i \frac{\partial V}{\partial q_i} + \Sigma \dot{q}_i \frac{d}{dt} \frac{\partial T}{\partial \dot{q}_i} - \Sigma \dot{q}_i \frac{\partial T}{\partial q_i}$$

$$= \frac{dV}{dt} + \Sigma \dot{q}_i \frac{d}{dt} \frac{\partial T}{\partial \dot{q}_i} + \Sigma \ddot{q}_i \frac{\partial T}{\partial \dot{q}_i} - \Sigma \ddot{q}_i \frac{\partial T}{\partial \dot{q}_i}$$

$$- \Sigma \dot{q}_i \frac{\partial T}{\partial q_i}$$

$$= \frac{dV}{dt} + \frac{d}{dt}\left(\Sigma \dot{q}_i \frac{\partial T}{\partial \dot{q}_i}\right) - \frac{dT}{dt}$$

$$= \frac{dV}{dt} + 2 \frac{dT}{dt} - \frac{dT}{dt}$$

$$= \frac{d}{dt} (T + V)$$

But this must be zero, since the first member of this chain of equalities is zero. Indeed, if Eqs. (42) are multiplied respectively by $\dot{q}_1$, $\dot{q}_2$, $\dot{q}_3$ and added, the result is the first member of this chain. The fact that $T + V =$ constant has been established.

## Appendix C

### Domains of Stability of Certain Nonlinear Differential Equations Involving a Parameter

Lemma 5. A necessary and sufficient condition that the differential equation

$$U'' + U - 1 = J_1 U^2 + \frac{3}{7} D_1 U^4, \qquad J_1 \geqq 0, \qquad D_1 \geqq 0 \qquad (43)$$

have periodic solutions is that the (constant) values of $J_1, D_1$ lie in the region $R_1$ (see Fig. 3b) in the $(J_1, D_1)$-plane, bounded by the curves

$$J_1 = 0$$

$$D_1 = 0 \qquad (44)$$

$$J_1 = \frac{3t - 4}{2t^2}$$

$$D_1 = \frac{7(2 - t)}{6t^4}, \qquad \frac{4}{3} \leqq t \leqq 2 \qquad (45)$$

Proof. As in lemmas 1 and 2, it is necessary and sufficient that the polynomial

$$Q(U) = \frac{6}{35} D_1 U^5 + \frac{2}{3} J_1 U^3 - U^2 + 2U + \text{constant}$$

have three positive roots. The condition for this is that the constant be properly chosen, and that the polynomial

$$Q'(U) = 2\left(\frac{3}{7} D_1 U^4 + J_1 U^2 - U + 1\right)$$

have two positive zeros.

The polynomial $Q'(U)$ is positive for $U = 0, \infty$ in any case $(J_1 \geqq 0,\ D_1 \geqq 0)$. For an arbitrary but fixed value of $U$, the condition

$$\frac{3}{7} D_1 U^4 + J_1 U^2 - U + 1 \leqq 0 \qquad (46)$$

is therefore sufficient for the existence of these two positive zeros.

The locus of (46) is a half-plane in the $(J_1, D_1)$-plane; its intercepts are

$$D_1 = \frac{7(1 - U)}{3U^4}, \qquad J_1 = \frac{1 - U}{U^2}$$

The first of these increases for $1 \leqq U \leqq 4/3$; the second increases for $1 \leqq U \leqq 2$.

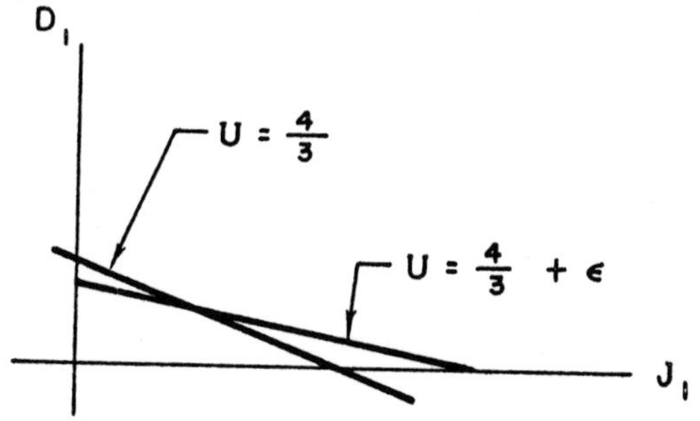


Fig. 6. The Various Loci in the $(J_1, D_1)$-Plane.

What is wanted is obviously the envelope of the inequalities (46). This envelope is obtained in parametric form if the relations

$$\frac{3}{7} D_1 t^4 - J_1 t^2 - t + 1 \leqq 0 \tag{47}$$

$$\frac{12}{7} D_1 t^3 - 2 J_1 t - 1 \leqq 0 \tag{48}$$

are satisfied simultaneously. Eliminating $D_1$ or $J_1$ from (47) and (48), one obtains (44) and (45). The lemma is proved.

## Notation

$A_{2n}$ coefficient; see Eq. (2)

$c$ constant; see Eq. (21)

$D$ oblateness constant; coefficient of fourth harmonic in the expression for the gravitational potential. For the earth, $D = (6 \pm 1)\ 10^{-6}$.

$D_1$ $DL^4 R^4$

$e$ constant of integration

$F(x, k)$ elliptic function; see Eq. (17)

$g$ constant of gravity: $g(1 + J + 3D/7)$ is the acceleration of gravity at the equator on the surface of the primary; observed acceleration differs from this by the centrifugal force. For the earth, $g \approx 979.82$ cm sec$^{-2}$.

| | |
|---|---|
| $J$ | oblateness constant; coefficient of second harmonic in the expression for the gravitational potential. For the earth, $J = (1.6245 \pm 0.0003)\, 10^{-3}$. |
| $J_1$ | $JL^2 R^2$ |
| $k$ | parameter in Jacobi elliptic function; see Eq. (17) |
| $k'^2$ | $1 - k^2$ |
| $K$ | $\mathrm{sn}^{-1}\, 1$; $\mathrm{sn}(K, k) = 1$ |
| $K'$ | $\mathrm{sn}^{-1}\, 1$; $\mathrm{sn}(K', k') = 1$ |
| $L$ | $gR^2 p^2$ |
| $m$ | arbitrary number; see Eq. (20) |
| $m_1, m_2$ | constants; see Eq. (22) |
| $M$ | longitude of satellite; i.e., measure of direction of radius vector to satellite |
| $M_o$ | constant of integration |
| $p$ | $r^2\dot{M} = r^2\, dM/dt$, angular momentum, constant of the motion |
| $P(U)$ | $(2/3)\, J_1 U^3 - U^2 + 2U +$ constant |
| $q$ | $\exp(-\pi K'/K)$ |
| $Q(U)$ | $2K_1 U^5 + (2/3)\, J_1 U^3 - U^2 + 2U +$ constant |
| $r$ | radial distance in spherical coordinates |
| $R$ | equatorial radius of the primary. For the earth, $R = (6.378388 \pm 0.000018)\, 10^8$ cm. |
| $t$ | time |
| $\mathrm{sn}\, U$ | Jacobi elliptic function |
| $u_1$ | see Eq. (24) |
| $\bar{u}_1$ | see Eq. (28) |

| | |
|---|---|
| $\bar{u}_2$ | see Eq. (31) |
| $U$ | $1/Lr$ |
| $U_o$ | constant; initial value of $U$ (when $M = 0$) |
| $U'_o$ | constant; initial value of $dU/dM$ (when $M = 0$) |
| $v$ | variable phase angle in second perturbation procedure |
| $V$ | gravitational potential |
| $w$ | frequency (of the variation of U) |
| $z$ | $\cos\theta$ |
| $\alpha$ | constant |
| $\theta$ | colatitude in spherical coordinates |
| $\xi_1, \xi_2, \xi_3$ | roots of the polynomial $P(U)$ or of $Q(U)$ |
| $\phi$ | longitude in spherical coordinates |
| $\Phi$ | $\frac{M}{2}\sqrt{(2/3)\, J_1 (\xi_3 - \xi_1)}$ |

## References


1. King-Hele, D.G. and R.H. Merson, "A New Value for the Earth's Flattening, Derived from Measurements of Satellite Orbits," Nature, vol. 183, pp. 881-882, 28 March 1959.
2. Jeffreys, H., The Earth, 4th ed., Cambridge University Press, 1959.
3. Milne-Thompson, L.M., Jacobian Elliptic Function Tables, Dover Publications, Inc., New York; Peirce, B.O., A Short Table of Integrals, Ginn, Boston, 1910.
4. Brenner, J.L., G.E. Latta, and M. Weisfeld, "A New Coordinate System for Satellite Orbit Theory," Stanford Research Institute, June 15, 1959.
5. Vinti, J.P., "A New Method of Solution for Unretarded Satellite Orbits," J. Res. National Bureau of Standards, vol. 63B, pp. 105-116, 1959.
6. Whittaker, E.T., and G.N. Watson, A Course of Modern Analysis, 4th ed., Cambridge University Press, 1952.

# INTERPLANETARY TRAJECTORY SIMULATION

D. S. Merrilees and J. C. Walker
Douglas Aircraft Company, Inc.
Missiles and Space Systems Engineering
Santa Monica, California

## Abstract

The purpose of this paper is to demonstrate that an interplanetary trajectory simulation program which obtains velocities and positions of the astronomical bodies, as well as of the vehicle, by numerical integration yields a much smaller, simpler program than one that obtains planetary information by table look up; that no loss of accuracy results due to obtaining planetary position by numerical integration rather than by table look up; that the solution is accomplished in reasonable machine time; and that this approach allows launch to impact simulation of interplanetary flight as only a minor modification to existing ballistic missile programs.

## Introduction

Developments in the field of rocket propulsion during recent years have generated the capability of launching rocket propelled vehicles from the surface of the earth at very high velocities. This capability was first employed to place artificial satellites in orbit about the Earth. This first step has been followed by probes which have impacted the Moon or escaped the Earth. The next logical step in this sequence will be to hurl an instrumented package to the neighborhood of another planet. Adequate planning for such interplanetary flight requires a study of the trajectory which such a vehicle would follow, including the problems of propulsion, guidance, aerodynamics, etc., of now familiar long-range missile simulations, and with the n-body problem added. For ballistic operation above the atmosphere, the n-body problem is the total problem. It is with this domain that this paper is concerned.

Much valuable qualitative and some quantitive information concerning interplanetary trajectories has been obtained by approximating the vehicle's orbit by the solution of three two-body problems, i.e., by assuming that the vehicle is affected first only by the Earth, then only by the Sun, and finally only by the target body. However, a numerical integration of the full n-body problem is still necessary for adequate design work (1). The actual formulation of this process for use with electronic computers can take several forms. The choice of form and the skill with which the formulation is accomplished greatly influence the capabilities and cost of operation of the resulting analysis tool. The Missiles and Space Systems Engineering Department of Douglas Aircraft Company has developed such a method. This has been programmed for the IBM 704 and 709 EDPM, and has been used for the simulation of both cislunar and interplanetary flight.

It is the intent of the present paper to show that the method used leads to a solution in a reasonable computing time, is conservative in use of machine memory, and may easily be adapted as the gravitational contribution in a total system simulation.

First, the form of Newton's law of gravitation which is used as the equation of motion will be explained. Second, methods of obtaining initial planetary positions and velocities from: (a) the elements of the orbit and Kepler's third law, and (b) by numerical differentiation of an ephemeris, will be indicated and compared for accuracy. An explanation of the integration scheme and why it was chosen will complete the discussion of the present model. Program extensions to include effect of thrust, aerodynamics and guidance will be indicated since simple extension is the main reason for this approach. Applications to lunar studies will be used to show the use of the automatic hunting procedure. The use of the program to check and extend inferential two-body methods of interplanetary trajectory studies will also be demonstrated.

## DISCUSSION OF METHOD

### Form of Gravitation Law

Programs for ballistic trajectory simulation in the solar system must use as the equation of motion of the vehicle some form of Newton's law for the gravitational attraction between two bodies of masses $m_1$ and $m_2$,

$$F = \frac{Gm_1m_2}{r^2} \qquad (1)$$

where
$F$ = force of attraction
$r$ = distance between two bodies
$G$ = gravitational constant

and Newton's second law,

$$F = ma \qquad (2)$$

where a = acceleration. For the n-body problem, equations (1) and (2) must be considered as vector equations. A common mechanization of these equations evaluates the components of these vectors in rectangular components. This may be written

$$ {}_m\ddot{X}_j = G \sum_{k=0}^{n} \frac{m_k \left({}_mX_j - {}_kX_j\right)}{d_{mk}^{\;3}} - \sum_{k=1}^{n} \frac{m_k \left({}_kX_j - {}_0X_j\right)}{d_{0k}^{\;3}}, \quad j=1,2,3 \qquad (3) $$

where n is the number of bodies whose effect on the vehicle is deemed significant, and

$m_k$ = mass of the kth body

$d_{mk}$ = the distance between the vehicle and kth body

$m_0$ = mass of the Sun

$d_{0k}$ = the distance between the Sun and kth body

$X_1$, $X_2$, $X_3$ are rectangular coordinates with origin at the center of the Sun and are rotationally fixed with respect to inertial space

${}_mX_j$ = j position coordinate of the vehicle

${}_kX_j$ = j position coordinate of kth body

${}_m\ddot{X}_j$ = jth component of vehicle acceleration.

The first term in the brackets of (3) is a solution of (1) and (2). The second term is the acceleration of the Sun due to the other bodies and is necessary because the origin of coordinates, traveling with the Sun, is not fixed in inertial space. It is assumed that the coordinates do not rotate.

## Planetary Position and Velocity

There remains the major problem of specifying the position of the n-bodies as a function of time. Since the velocity of the missile with respect to selected bodies is usually desired as an output, the velocities of these bodies with respect to the sun must also be determined. The usual method is to store tables of planetary position and to interpolate and numerically differentiate at each point, or to store polynomials of planetary position and to evaluate these and their derivatives at each point.

The approach described herein is believed to lead to a simpler and more compact program. Equation (3) is rewritten

$$ {}_{i}\ddot{X}_{j} = G \sum_{\substack{k=0 \\ k \neq i}}^{10} \frac{m_k \left( {}_{i}X_{j} - {}_{k}X_{j} \right)}{d_{ik}^{3}} - \sum_{\substack{k=0 \\ k \neq c}}^{10} \frac{m_k \left( {}_{k}X_{j} - {}_{c}X_{j} \right)}{d_{ck}^{3}} \qquad (4) $$

where $j = 1,2,3$; and $i = 1,2,\ldots 11$; $i \neq c$.

The only changes from equation (3) have been the replacing of the subscript m with i and the subscript 0 with c.

Equations(4) is the total equation of motion of 12 bodies, 36 simultaneous 2nd order differential equations. If we associate

0 with the Sun ( ☉ )
1 with the Earth ( ⊕ )
2 with Mercury ( ☿ )
3 with Venus ( ♀ )
4 with Mars ( ♂ )
5 with Jupiter ( ♃ )
6 with Saturn ( ♄ )
7 with Uranus ( ⛢ )
8 with Neptune ( ♆ )
9 with Pluto ( ♇ )
10 with the Moon ( ☾ )

and

11 with the vehicle,

then equations (4) represent the equations of motion of the principal bodies of the solar system and the one other body, the vehicle, in which we are most interested. The subscript c replacing subscript 0 indicates that the coordinate system used has its origin at body c, the closest body to the vehicle. This was done to minimize round-off error in distances that would otherwise be prohibitive with the 704-709 floating point word length. Obviously, all three components of the acceleration of the body c are zero. Thus the system is a system of order 66 (33 second order equations). Given suitable initial conditions, the future relative positions and velocities of each body can be determined by numerical integration of equations (4).

The compactness of the program need hardly be discussed. Although equations(4) represents 33 equations, by simple looping in the coding, it can be made to occupy only little more space than the 3 equations (3) which all n-body space programs must carry; in addition no tables or polynomials are required. For a typical code, equations (3), for the missile alone, require 62 instructions, whereas equations (4), for the whole solar system, require 100 instructions.

To keep the form of simulation of the gravitational contribution to system performance compact is clearly attractive, for even though machines with 32,000 word memories are available, the simulation of terrestrial missions, including guidance, controls, aerodynamics, thrust, etc., requires a very large percentage of this memory. Extra-terrestrial systems will include all of these elements plus the astronomical problems.

Since astronomical tables present only planetary positions, initial velocities must be calculated to commence the integration. These calculations are space consuming, but need not be in the memory during the simulation.

As to accuracy, note that the presently used ephemerides of the five outer planets have been obtained by numerical integration. Note also that the vehicle with its close approach to at least one, and probably two, other bodies will certainly have the most complex orbit of any of the n-bodies considered. If a trajectory program assumes, as is commonly the case, that the vehicle orbit may be accurately determined by a method of numerical integration, then the same integration method must certainly suffice for the simpler planetary orbits. Experimental verification of the accuracy will be indicated later.

The most important investigation for evaluating the feasibility of this method is that of determining the relative machine running time required for solving these many differential equations as compared to the more common practice of solving the three differential equations of motion of the vehicle and obtaining the positions and velocities of the planets by various other means.

First it will be mentioned that in no one mission is it expected that all 11 bodies will have a significant effect on the vehicle's orbit. The provisions for all these bodies were included to give the program the capability of simulating a variety of missions. In any particular case, their effect may be flagged out on the load sheets with a corresponding saving of computing time. For instance, in simulation of cislunar trajectories only the Earth and Moon, or Earth, Moon, and Sun, are normally considered; in a Mars vehicle design study, only the Earth, Mars, Sun, and Jupiter would normally be considered. On any particular run, almost no time is lost because the program was written "generally". The order of the system to be solved is then $6(r-1)$, where $r \leq 12$ is the number of bodies, including the vehicle, being considered.

Let us again examine the $3(r-1)$ equations(4). As noted previously, the second term is common to all equations and hence is evaluated only once. The calculation of $d_{ik}^3$, which involves a square root, is the largest time consumer in the evaluation. But each $d_{ik}$ is used in 6 terms (since it is independent of j and $d_{ik} = d_{ki}$). Each $Gkm/d_{ik}^3$ appears in three terms. Thus the calculation of each term consists of one subtraction, one multiplication, one-third of a division, and one-sixth of the calculation of $d_{ik}^3$. The flow chart, figure 1, shows the steps used in an evaluation of these equations, so as

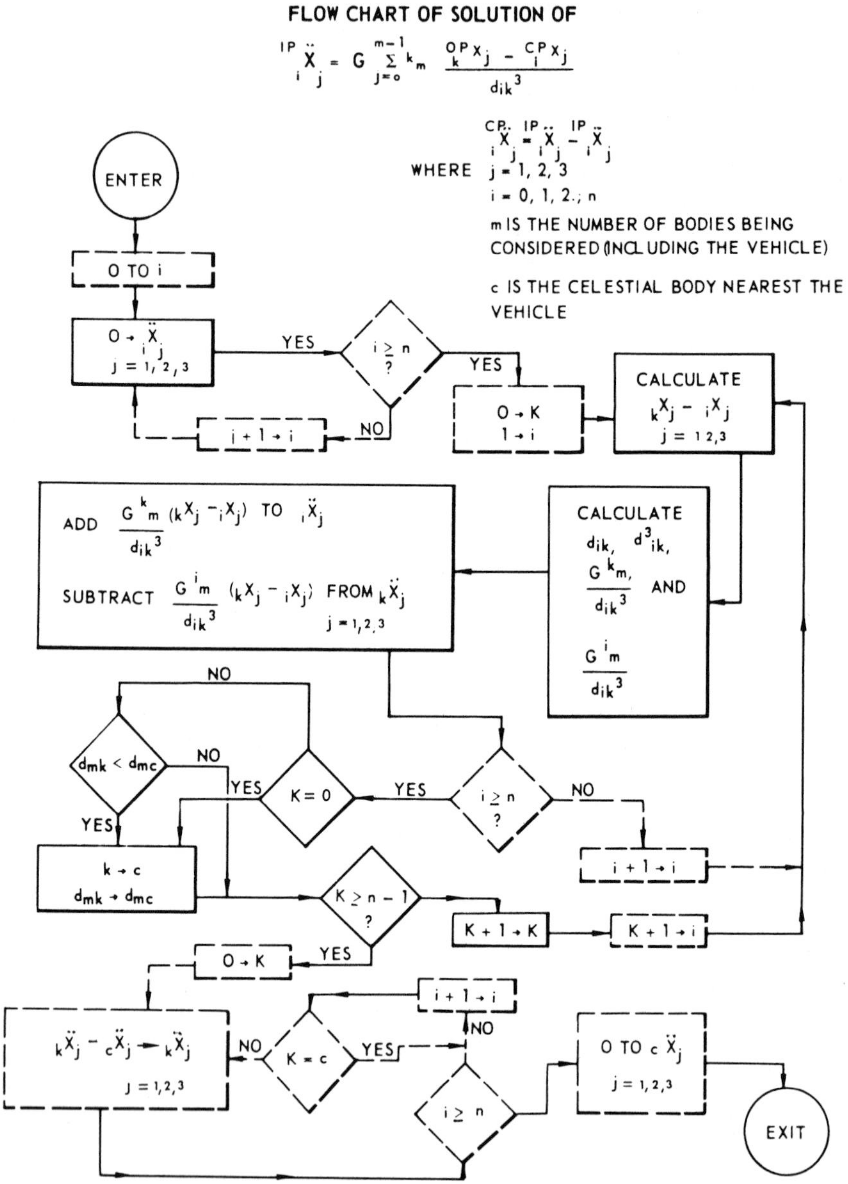
FLOW CHART OF SOLUTION OF
$${}^{IP}_{i}\ddot{X}_{j} = G \sum_{j=0}^{m-1} k_m \frac{{}^{OP}_{k}X_j - {}^{CP}_{i}X_j}{d_{ik}^3}$$
WHERE ${}^{CP}_{i}\ddot{X}_j = {}^{IP}_{i}\ddot{X}_j - {}^{IP}_{i}\ddot{X}_j$
$j = 1, 2, 3$
$i = 0, 1, 2., n$
m IS THE NUMBER OF BODIES BEING CONSIDERED (INCLUDING THE VEHICLE)
c IS THE CELESTIAL BODY NEAREST THE VEHICLE
ENTER
0 TO i
YES
NO
YES
CALCULATE
$j = 1,2,3$
ADD
TO
SUBTRACT
FROM
CALCULATE
AND
NO
NO
YES
YES
K = 0
NO
YES
k → c
$d_{mk} \to d_{mc}$
K + 1 → K
K + 1 → i
YES
0 → K
i + 1 → i
NO
NO
K = c
YES
0 TO c
EXIT

Figure 1.

to take advantage of the above facts while maintaining a compact code. (Figuratively speaking, those portions in solid boxes, or in solid portions of boxes, are necessary to solve only the vehicle's equation of motion. The dashed portions show what must be added to evaluate the equations of motion of the other bodies. Since an integration routine may be assumed to be present for integration of the vehicle's equations of motion, these dashed portions in essence replace all tables and table look up, and/or numerical differentiation, and/or polynominals and polynomial evaluation.) Care such as this has been important in attaining low running time with these equations of motion. With this technique the time for the evaluation of all equations of motion is about double that for the equations of motion of the missile alone. The time used for the numerical integration equations is almost directly proportional to the number of bodies considered, but the time to evaluate the integration formulae is only about 10% of the time required to evaluate the equations of motion.

## Integration Technique

In integrating space trajectories, it is customary to use some "no-past-history" scheme of numerical integration such as Runge-Kutta to start the trajectory and then to shift to a scheme requiring less iterations, such as Adams-Moulton, as soon as the required number of points have been calculated. However, from a user's standpoint, the choice of print times should not be limited to required calculation times. If the principal integration scheme requires equally spaced points, it would generally need restarting by some Runge-Kutta type scheme at each special print point. Further, expansions of the program will most likely require discontinuous control programs. It was thus felt that schemes of integration other than Runge-Kutta would be of value only if they could represent a major gain in running time during that portion of the flight when they were being used. The adaption of the Runge-Kutta method outlined below, which was made by O. Senda, formerly of Douglas Aircraft Company, has proved so efficient that the inclusion of any other integration scheme has not to date shown any reduction in running time or improvement of accuracy.

Scarborough (2) gives the general Runge-Kutta equations for the numerical integration of a second order system as

$$k_1 = \Delta t\ f(t_n, x_n, \dot{x}_n)$$

$$k_2 = \Delta t\ f(t_n + \frac{\Delta t}{2}, x_n + \frac{\Delta t}{2}\dot{x}_n + \frac{\Delta t}{8}k_1, \dot{x}_n + \frac{k_1}{2})$$

$$k_3 = \Delta t\ f(t_n + \frac{\Delta t}{2}, x_n + \frac{\Delta t}{2}\dot{x}_n + \frac{\Delta t}{8}k_1, \dot{x}_n + \frac{k_2}{2})$$

$$k_4 = \Delta t\ f(t_n + \Delta t, x_n + \Delta t\ \dot{x}_n + \frac{\Delta t}{2}k_3, \dot{x}_n + k_3)$$

$$\Delta x = \Delta t\left[\dot{x}_n + \frac{1}{6}(k_1 + k_2 + k_3)\right]$$

$$\Delta\dot{x} = \frac{1}{6}(k_1 + 2k_2 + 2k_3 + k_4)$$

where f indicates any of the equations of motion (4) and $\Delta t$ represents the computing interval. Scarborough also points out that if f is independent of velocity, then $k_2 = k_3$.

Because of the choice of rectangular components, which was done primarily for engineering convenience, the equations of motion are independent of velocity. For this special case, fourth order Runge-Kutta accuracy can be obtained from three, rather than the normal four, cycle computation. This leads to the interesting condition that the second order equations used are being integrated with less calculation than is generally required for first order equations. That is, the time for solution of the 6(r-1) order system is about three-fourths of what would normally be expected for a system with the same number of first order equations (a 2-1/4 (r-1) order system).

The method used to compute the time interval is a development from reference (3). In this approach a backward integration over the previous interval is made and the difference between the final and initial conditions is assumed to be twice the error in the forward integration. From the assumption that the error in fourth-order Runge-Kutta integration methods is proportional to the fifth power of the time interval and that the coefficient of this term varies slowly, the possible time interval for any allowable position error may then be calculated.

In this method, backward integration is used for only one component of one body. By methods more mesmeristic than mathematical, it has been decided that the position component having the biggest error and determining the time interval will be the one corresponding to the largest velocity component of the vehicle or the Moon, which ever has the greater acceleration at the moment.

When using this technique, very few integration steps are required for either lunar or Martian missions, as will be demonstrated in the examples below.

A self-computing time interval scheme is a necessity for efficient operation with the variations of time interval possible in an extra-terrestrial mission. This will be illustrated by example. However, the requirement that the integration error be proportional to $(\Delta t)^5$ does require that the allowable integration error be one order of magnitude larger than round off error. Nevertheless, IBM 704 single precision floating point has sufficed. As has been mentioned above, this same limit on accuracy would exist if only the vehicle orbit were integrated and planetary positions and velocities were obtained by any other means. One indication of accuracy is provided by integrating the equations of motion of the solar system for 330 days and comparing the results to the American Ephemeris and Nautical Almanac (4). As an example, the error in the position of Jupiter was 1650 nautical miles (0.7" error in arc) when the integration was performed with a fixed 6 hour integration interval and 1400 nautical miles (0.6" error in arc) when the more rapid self-computing interval was used.

Further accuracy checks are given below in the examples of typical uses of the program.

Position data of the principal objects of our solar system as a function of time are readily available, but velocities are not. Both are required as initial conditions for the numerical integration. Velocities may be derived from the elements of the orbits (i.e., inclination, semi-major axis, eccentricity, longitude of ascending node, longitude of perihelion, sidereal period, and mean longitude at epoch, see figure (2) and Kepler's law of equal areas (5). Mean elements for any future time may be calculated from simple formulas available in (6) and (7) and are shown in Table 1. For many astronautical purposes, the mean elements have been adequate and convenient. For more accurate calculations, osculating elements could be used. Unfortunately, these are not available for the whole period of astronautical interest.

Numerical differentiation of tables now available can provide extremely accurate velocities (error of less than 1 ft/sec in the case of the Earth), but is more awkward than obtaining velocities from the orbital elements.

A more detailed explanation of the mathematics involved in this program is presented in reference (5).

## Analysis of Cislunar Trajectories

Studies of Earth to Moon trajectories conducted at the Douglas Aircraft Company have been based on the interplanetary trajectory simulation, (8) and (9). This has allowed the results to include the proper gravitational effects of Earth, Moon, and Sun. The effects of other planets on cislunar trajectories were examined and found to be negligible (the effect of including Jovian gravity in the calculations is a displacement of 0.01 miles at time of impact on the Moon).

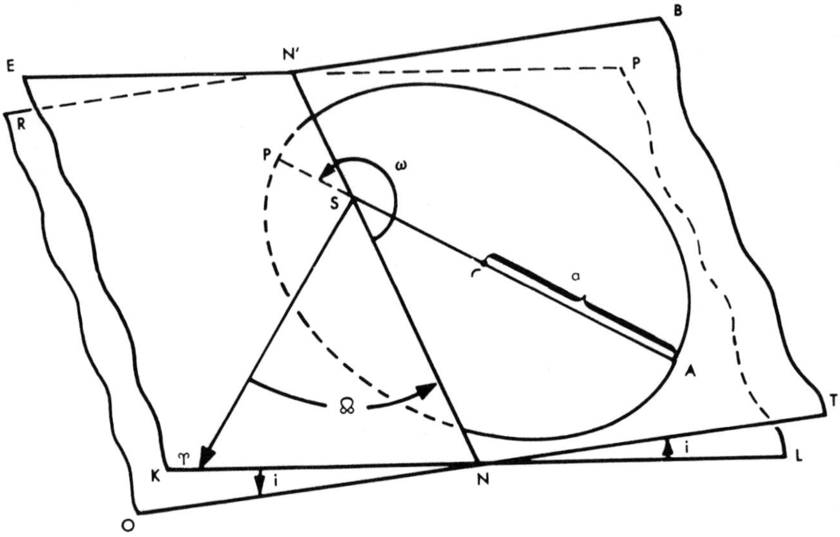


NN' LINE OF NODES
i INCLINATION
a SEMI-MAJOR AXIS
☊ LONGITUDE OF THE ASCENDING NODE
☊ + ω LONGITUDE OF PERIHELION
EKLP PLANE OF ECLIPTIC
ORBT PLANE OF PLANET'S ORBIT
S SUN
A APHELION
P PERIHELION
♈ VERNAL EQUINOX
C GEOMETRIC CENTER OF ORBIT

Figure 2. Definition of Elements.

Table 1. Elements of the Planets' Orbits.

| PLANET | MEAN DISTANCE | PERIOD | ECCENTRICITY, e | INCLINATION TO THE ECLIPTIC |
|---|---|---|---|---|
| 1. EARTH | 1.000000 | 1.00004 | 0.01675104 − 0.00004180 T | |
| 2. MERCURY | 0.387099 | 0.24085 | 0.205615 + 0.000020 T | 7° 0′ 10.6″ + 6.3″ T |
| 3. VENUS | 0.723332 | 0.61521 | 0.006818 − 0.000050 T | 3° 23′ 37.1″ + 4.5 T |
| 4. MARS | 1.523691 | 1.88089 | 0.093310 + 0.000094 T | 1° 51′ 1.1″ − 2.3″ T |
| 5. JUPITER | 5.202803 | 11.86223 | 0.048335 + 0.000164 T | 1° 18′ 31.4″ − 20.5″ T |
| 6. SATURN | 9.538843 | 29.45772 | 0.055892 − 0.000345 T | 2° 29′ 33.1″ − 14.0″ T |
| 7. URANUS | 19.181945 | 84.01308 | 0.0470 + 0.0002 T | 0° 46′ 20.9″ + 2.3″ T |
| 8. NEPTUNE | 30.057767 | 164.79405 | 0.0087 + 0.00004 T | 1° 46′ 45.3″ − 34.3″ T |
| 9. PLUTO | 39.51774 | 248.4302 | 0.247 | 17° 8′ 44.0″ − 20.0″ T |

| | MEAN LONGITUDE OF | | |
|---|---|---|---|
| | ASCENDING NODE | PERIHELION | PLANET ** |
| 1. | 0 | 101° 13′ 15″ + 6189″ T | 99° 41′ 48.08″ + 129,602,768.13″ T + 1.089″ $T^2$ |
| 2. | 47° 8′ 43″ + 4266″ T | 75° 53′ 54″ + 5596″ T | 178° 10′ 44.68″ + 538,106,654.80″ T + 1.084″ $T^2$ |
| 3. | 75° 47′ 1″ + 3260″ T | 130° 9′ 8″ + 5056″ T | 342° 46′ 1.39″ + 210,669,162.88″ T + 1.1148″ $T^2$ |
| 4. | 48° 47′ 12″ + 2786″ T | 334° 13′ 6″ + 6626″ T | 293° 44′ 51.46″ + 68,910,117.33″ T + 1.1184″ $T^2$ |
| 5. | 99° 26′ 36″ + 3638″ T | 12° 43′ 15″ + 5796″ T | 238° 2′ 57.32″ + 10,930,687.148″ T + 1.20486″ $T^2$ − 0.005936″ $T^3$ |
| 6. | 112° 47′ 25″ + 3134″ T | 91° 5′ 54″ + 7050″ T | 266° 33′ 51.76″ + 4,404,635.581″ T + 1.16835″ $T^2$ − 0.021″ $T^3$ |
| 7. | 73° 28′ 38″ + 1795″ T | 169° 3′ 0″ + 5800″ T | 244° 11′ 50.89″ + 1,547,508.265″ T + 1.13774″ $T^2$ − 0.002176″ $T^3$ |
| 8. | 130° 40′ 53″ + 3956″ T | 43° 50′ 0″ + 2400″ T | 84° 27′ 28.78″ + 791,589.291″ T + 1.15374″ $T^2$ − 0.002176″ $T^3$ |
| 9. | 108° 57′ 17″ + 4889″ T | 222° 48′ 0″ + 5000″ T | 137° 38′ 0.00″ |

$$T = \frac{\text{JULIAN DAY NO.} - 2415020.0}{36525}$$

*ASTRONOMICAL QUANTITIES BY C. W. ALLEN

**FRENCH NAUTICAL ALMANAC, CONNAISSANCE DES TEMPS

If initial conditions for a trial trajectory are chosen so that the resulting path passes within several thousand miles of the moon, these initial conditions may then be corrected to redu this miss distance by a system which is built into the program. This reduction amounts to about two-thirds of the miss distance per step, as shown in figure 3, for a typical case. The automatic system holds velocity fixed and computes correction to the flight path angle and azimuth at each step. The technique used was simply to resolve the miss distance into the planes of the initial azimuth angle and flight path angle and then to assure that the required change in input values of these angles would be the component of miss distance in their planes divided by the distance to the Moon (see figure 4). When this guess overcorrected to the other side of the center of the Moon, a linear interpolation was made for the next run. The original method was used again for the following run. The process was stopped when the miss distance was less than a specified tolerance or if any step failed to improve over the previous step by at least this same tolerance. The computer time required per trajectory is approximately 1.2 minutes. Because of the manner in which the integration interval is calculated by the program, this machine running time is essentially unaffected by moderate changes in initial velocity.

The number of computing steps required was approximately 88 including recalculation where the original estimate of the time interval proved too large. A typical calculating time interval versus flight time plot is shown in figure 5. The rapid change of time interval, shown here on a log plot, indicates the type of running time gains that are obtained by the self-computing intervals as compared to the method of using a step function based on the user's best guesses.

The final trajectory was rerun allowing double the error in each integration step. The impact position varied by one mile and the time of impact by 7.5 seconds. A check allowing 10 times the original error in the individual step indicated that total error is linear with step error, i.e., the error in the most accurate trajectory may be taken to be about 0.5 mile at impact with an impact time error of 4 seconds.

## Application to Interplanetary Problems

For simulation of interplanetary trajectories, it is necessary to make a careful choice of initial conditions. A preliminary study using inferential techniques has proved useful as a basis for the selection of initial conditions. The choice should be made so that the vehicle trajectory will pass within a few million miles of the target planet. If this is accomplished, the miss distance can be reduced by a differential correction procedure. Each component of miss distance, $\Delta X_u$, is

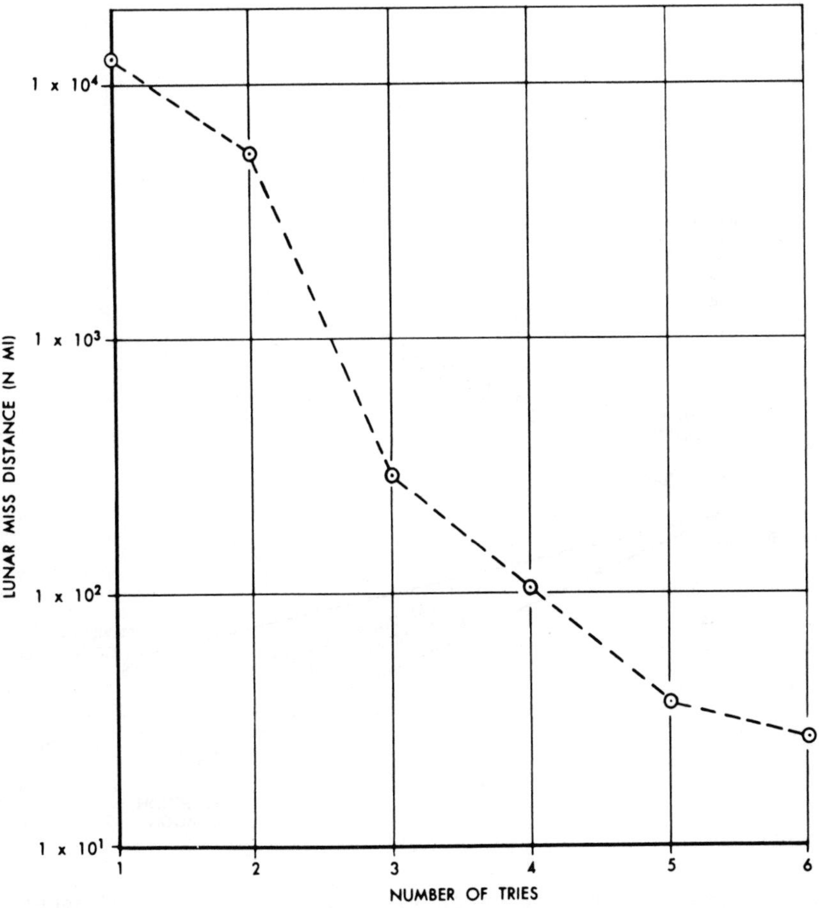


Figure 3. Convergence of the Lunar Hunting Procedure.

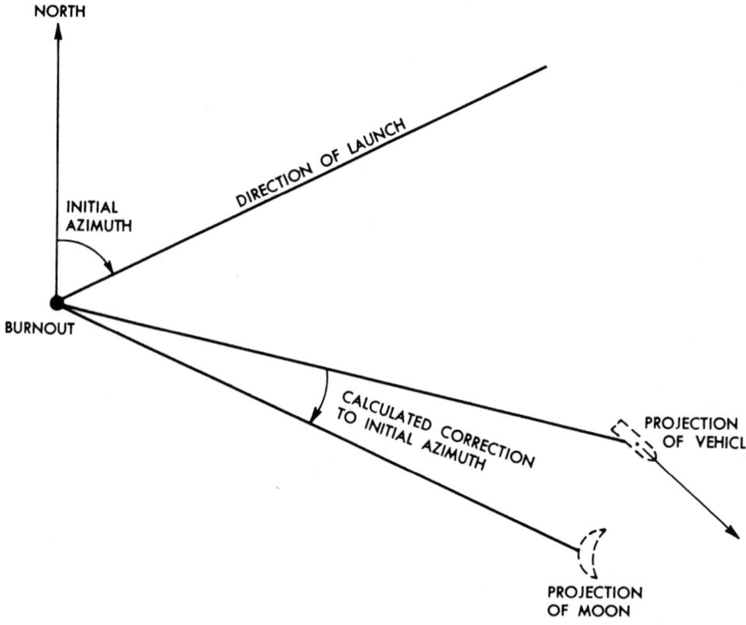


Figure 4. Projection of Miss Distance on Plan Tangent to the Earth at Point of Burnout.

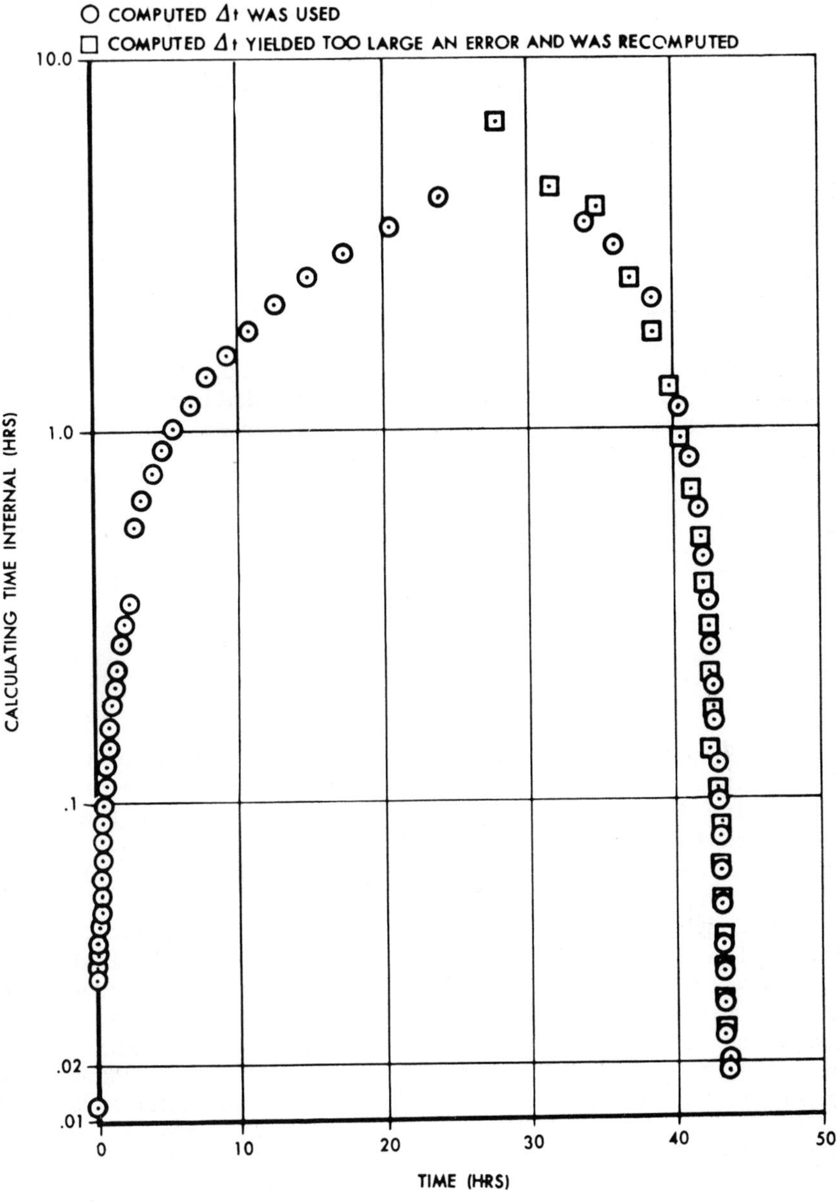


Figure 5. Computing Time Interval History for Typical Lunar Trajectory.

considered to be a function of initial velocity, $V_0$, flight path angle, $\gamma_0$, and azimuth of launch, $A_{Z_0}$. Fixed launch time and intercept time are assumed. Thus, Earth and Mars position and orientations are determined. From the initial trajectory, the partial derivative of each component with respect to one of the three input variables, e.g., velocity, $V_0$, is determined by running a trajectory varying only the initial velocity from the reference trajectory by a small increment $\Delta V$ and then making the approximation

$$\frac{\partial \Delta X_j}{\partial V} = \frac{\Delta X_j (\gamma_0, A_{Z_0}, V_0 + \Delta V) - \Delta X_j (\gamma_0, A_{Z_0}, V_0)}{\Delta V}, \quad j = 1,2,3$$

The partial derivatives with respect to flight path angle and azimuth angle are obtained from two more similar trajectories. If each component is expanded in Taylor Series about $(\gamma_0, A_{Z_0}, V_0)$

$$\Delta X_j (\gamma, A_Z, V) = \Delta X_j (\gamma_0, A_{Z_0}, V_0) + \frac{\partial \Delta X_j}{\partial \gamma} (\gamma - \gamma_0) + \frac{\partial \Delta X_j}{\partial A_Z} (A_Z - A_{Z_0}),$$

$$+ \frac{\partial \Delta X_j}{\partial V} (V - V_0) + \ldots , \quad j = 1,2,3$$

where all terms above the first order have been ignored, then for impact the righthand terms must equal zero. The only unknowns are $\gamma_0$, $A_{Z_0}$, and $V_0$ and hence the three equations may be solved to yield new estimates of these quantities. The resulting miss distance, from the center of the target planet, can be reduced to a desired value (but not less than the error due to computational inaccuracy) by repeated application of this correction procedure. The amount of improvement available for this application has been slightly less than one order of magnitude on most of the trajectories considered to date. This reduction is illustrated in figure 6 for a typical Earth-to Mars flight. The final trajectory is illustrated schematically in figure 7. Additional information about the final trajectory of this series is contained in Table 2 and figure 8. The IBM 704 computing time required to obtain these results was approximately twenty minutes, with each trajectory requiring about 2.4 minutes of machine time to simulate the trajectory from launch to point of closest approach to target planet. Five and one-half bodies were considered: Sun, Earth, Venus, Mars, Jupiter, and the vehicle. The choice of velocity magnitude, flight path angle, and azimuth as independent variables is quite arbitrary; it is only necessary that the three independent

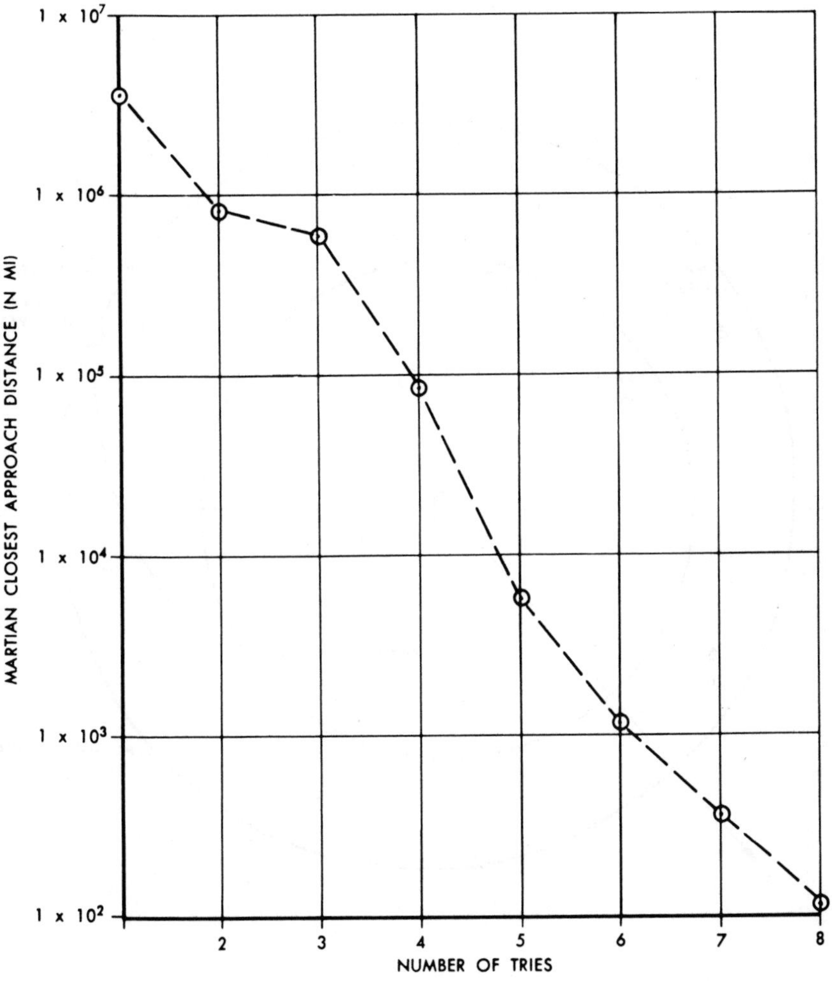


Figure 6. Convergence of the Interplanetary Hunting Procedure.

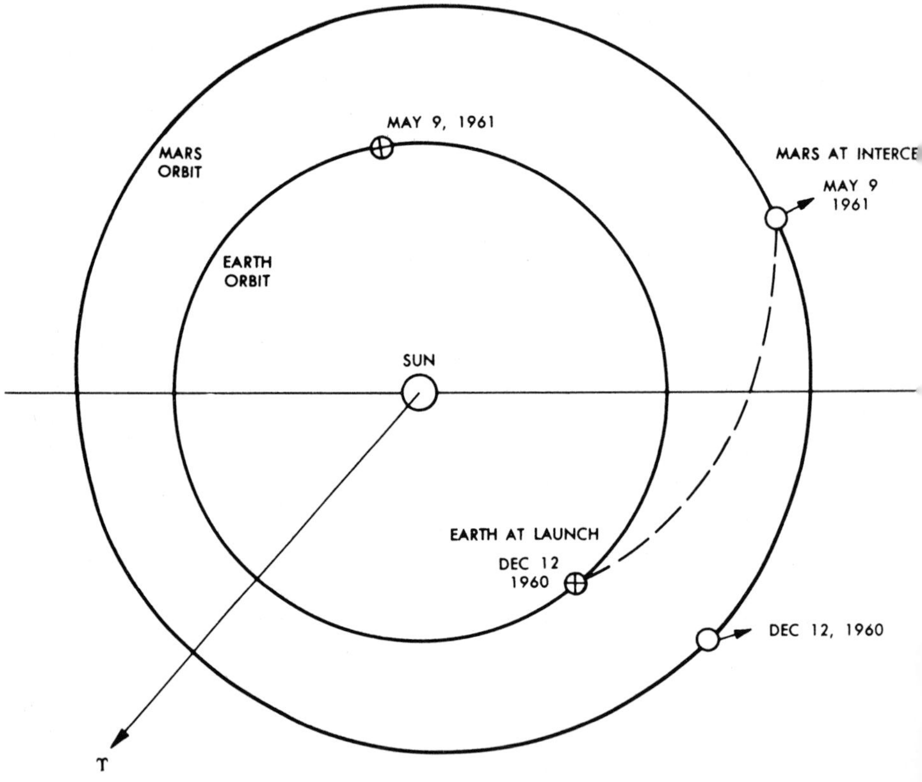


Figure 7. Typical Interplanetary Trajectory.

Table 2. Summary of Initial and Terminal Conditions and Permissible Deviations for Partian Impact

| | |
|---|---|
| LAUNCH DATE | 1960 DECEMBER 12 |
| LAUNCH TIME | $4^h\ 59^m\ 27.89814^s$ |
| TRANSFER ANGLE, $\bar{\beta}$, DEG. | 81.17 |
| **NOMINAL LAUNCH CONDITIONS** | |
| VELOCITY, $V_L$, FPS | 56,314.02 |
| FLIGHT PATH ANGLE, $\gamma_L$, DEG. | 89.8 |
| AZIMUTH ANGLE, $A_Z$, DEG. | 89.943506 |
| INCLINATION ANGLE, $\lambda$, DEG. | 1.10 |
| **TERMINAL CONDITIONS** | |
| VELOCITY AT IMPACT, $v_i$, FPS | 23,344.63 |
| IMPACT ANGLE, $\psi$, DEG. | 6.4002 |
| **PERMISSIBLE ERRORS** | |
| VELOCITY, $\Delta V_L$, FPS | 16.25 |
| FLIGHT PATH ANGLE, $\Delta\gamma_L$, DEG. | 0.00146 |
| AZIMUTH ANGLE, $\Delta A_Z$, DEG. | 0.33 |
| ASTRONOMICAL UNIT, $\frac{\Delta AU}{AU}$, % | 0.0245 |
| **TRANSFER TIME, t, DAYS** | 146.5 |

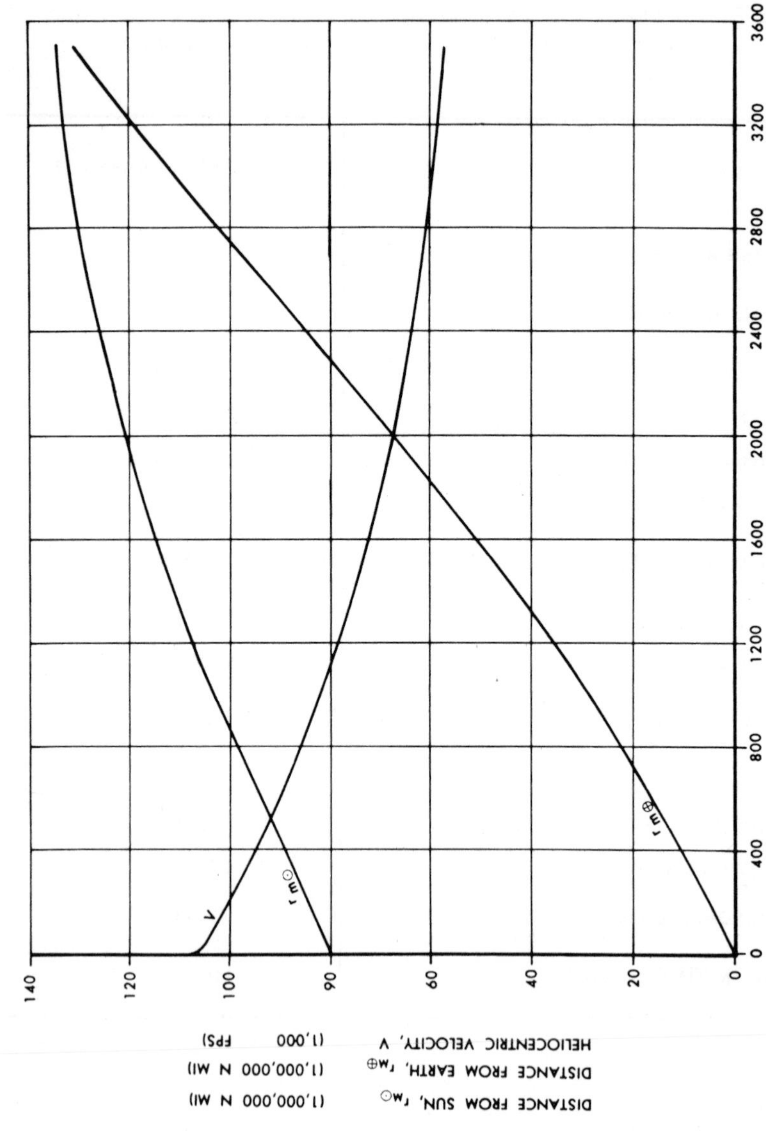


Figure 8. Velocity and Distance of Typical Martian Trajectory.

variables describe the initial velocity vector. Time interval versus time is indicated in figure 9. It is to be noted that the computing interval used is determined as an integral part of the program from an input accuracy requirement. This allows for the use of small increments in regions where gravitational forces are large (near planets) and large increments where gravitational forces are small (far from planets). Accordingly, much of the 2.4 minutes per trajectory is consumed in calculating the trajectory near the launch and target planet. The net result is that usage of the program for simulating trajectories of much greater duration does not require appreciably greater computation time. The total number of points required for the typical trajectory was 99.

As with the lunar case, trajectories were run with larger allowable errors. These indicated that the basic run's impact position on Mars had about 200 nautical miles of uncertainty due to integration error. The time of flight had an uncertainty of about six munutes due to the same cause. A similar check at a fixed time shortly before impact showed an uncertainty in missile position with respect to the Sun of 1070 miles, whereas the position of Mars checked within 13 miles. Since all programs must integrate the missile trajectory, it is felt that the much larger error in missile position supports the contention that no accuracy is lost by obtaining planetary positions by integration of the equations of motion.

## Extensions for Total Mission Simulation

This mechanization of the n-body problem has been designed to be combined with existing ballistic missile trajectory methods to provide a means of simulating a total space mission. A typical simulation of the flight of a multi-stage long range missile, with guidance, on a rotating spheroidal Earth, proceeds as follows (see figure 10):

The variations of atmosphere and gravity with altitude and latitude are specified for each case. From these and the statement of initial missile position, the environment in which the missile is operating may be evaluated. Adding the missile specifications and initial velocity, the orders that would be issued by the guidance may be calculated and the accelerations due to aerodynamics and propulsion may be evaluated in missile coordinates. Then typically these may be rotated through the inertial platform coordinates to a set of coordinates located at the center of Earth (which are considered inertial). At this point the gravitational accelerations are easily added and the result rotated to coordinates at the surface of the Earth (with due allowance for Coriolis and Centrifugal accelerations) where they are integrated for new velocities and positions as would be seen by an observer on the Earth.

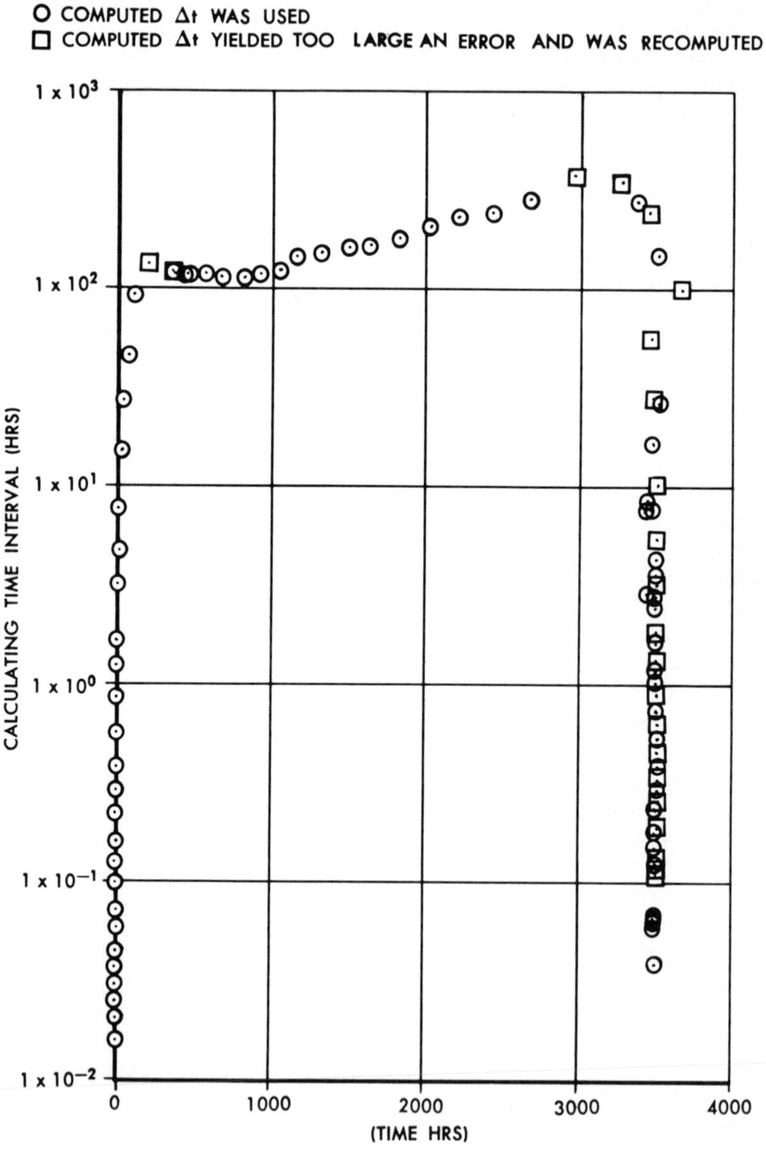


Figure 9. Computing Time Interval History for Typical Interplanetary Transfer.

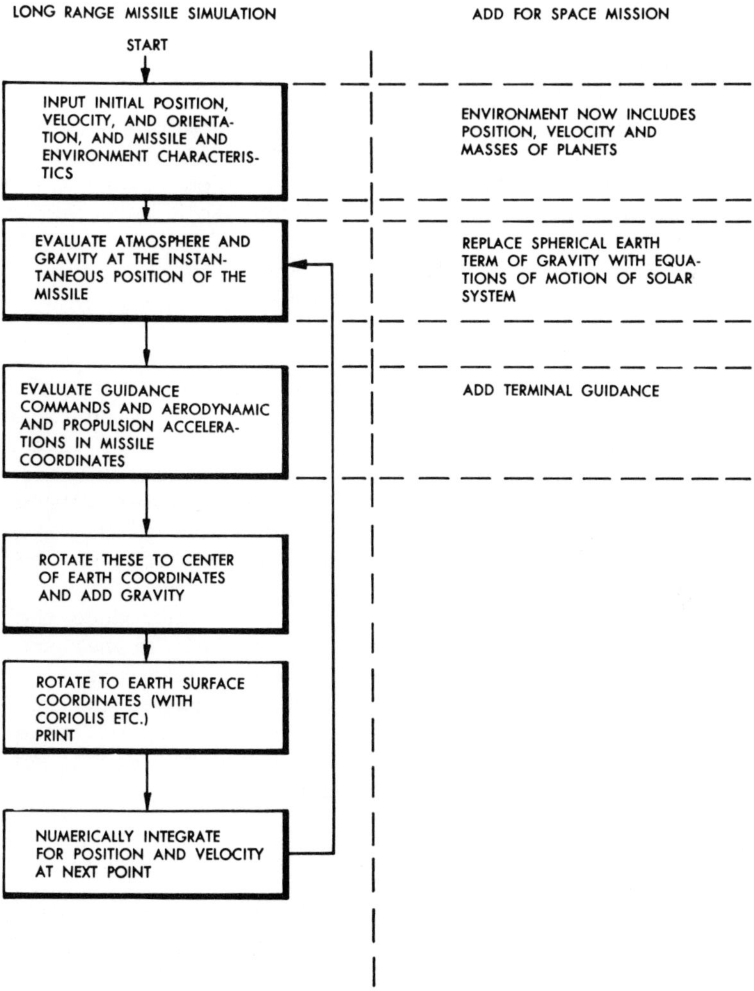
LONG RANGE MISSILE SIMULATION
ADD FOR SPACE MISSION
START
INPUT INITIAL POSITION, VELOCITY, AND ORIENTATION, AND MISSILE AND ENVIRONMENT CHARACTERISTICS
ENVIRONMENT NOW INCLUDES POSITION, VELOCITY AND MASSES OF PLANETS
EVALUATE ATMOSPHERE AND GRAVITY AT THE INSTANTANEOUS POSITION OF THE MISSILE
REPLACE SPHERICAL EARTH TERM OF GRAVITY WITH EQUATIONS OF MOTION OF SOLAR SYSTEM
EVALUATE GUIDANCE COMMANDS AND AERODYNAMIC AND PROPULSION ACCELERATIONS IN MISSILE COORDINATES
ADD TERMINAL GUIDANCE
ROTATE THESE TO CENTER OF EARTH COORDINATES AND ADD GRAVITY
ROTATE TO EARTH SURFACE COORDINATES (WITH CORIOLIS ETC.) PRINT
NUMERICALLY INTEGRATE FOR POSITION AND VELOCITY AT NEXT POINT

Figure 10. Relation Between Long Range Missile and Total Space Mission Simulation.

The changes to such a ballistic missile program to adapt it for a total simulation of a space mission would require:

(1) Specification of the atmosphere of each planet.
(2) Replacement of the spherical Earth term of the gravity calculation in the missile simulation by equations (4) in order to include the n-body effects and remove the assumption that the center of the Earth is inertially fixed.
(3) Additions to the guidance section for terminal and midcourse phases.

Obviously, forces that predominate in some portions of flight are insignificant in others. An efficient simulation will drop these out wherever possible, and will use four cycle integration where necessary and the simplified three cycle integration whenever possible.

## Conclusions

It is concluded:

1. That integration of the equations of motion of the solar system is a compact way of obtaining planetary positions and velocities as a function of time for use in the vehicle equations of motion.
2. That the errors in planetary coordinates introduced by this method run one to two orders of magnitude less than the error in vehicle position, and hence, are insignificant in all applications.
3. That the machine time required to introduce the n-body's effect on the vehicle in this manner are comparable to those of table-look-up programs.
4. That when the n-body problem is handled in this way, expansion to a more general simulation of the entire mission is quite simple and does not lead to as large a program as other approaches do.

## References


1. Gunkel, R. J., Lascody, D. N., Merrilees, D. S., Impulsive Midcourse Correction of an Interplanetary Transfer, Douglas Aircraft Company, Inc., Engineering Paper No. 804.

2. Scarborough, J. B., Numerical Mathematical Analysis, Oxford University Press, 1955.

3. Call, D. H., and Reeves, R. F., Error Estimation in Runge-Kutta Procedures, Communications of the Association for Computing Machinery, Volume 1, Number 9, September 1958.

4. The American Ephemeris and Nautical Almanac for the Year 1960, Nautical Almanac Office, United States Naval Observatory.

5. Walker, J. C., Interplanetary Trajectory Simulation, Douglas Aircraft Company, Inc., Report SM-27742, 10 September 1958.

6. Connaissance Des Tempes, Bureau de Longitude, Paris.

7. Allen, C. W., Astrophysical Quantities, University of London, Athlone Press, 1955.

8. Hunter, M. W., Klemperer, W. B., and Gunkel, R. J., Impulsive Midcourse Correction of a Lunar Shot, Douglas Aircraft Company, Inc., Engineering Paper No. 674.

9. Goldbaum, G. C., Gunkel, R. J., Comparison of Two Dimensional and Three Dimensional Analyses of Earth-Moon Flight, Douglas Aircraft Company, Inc., Engineering Paper No. 634.

# REGIONS ACCESSIBLE TO A BALLISTIC WEAPON*

Frederick L. Beckner
Military Physics Research Laboratory
The University of Texas
Austin, Texas

## Abstract

The problem of determining the curve bounding the region accessible to a weapon fired impulsively in a plane with either of two constraints on the velocity vector is considered. The bounding curve is found to be an ellipse if the weapon velocity vector is constant in magnitude but allowed to take on any direction in a plane. The bounding curve is found to be similar to a limaçon if the total weapon velocity vector is made up of the sum of a fixed velocity vector and one which is constant in magnitude but allowed to take on any direction in a plane, assuming the maximum possible velocity is less than escape velocity.

It is found that an elliptic-polar coordinate system simplifies the problem of determining the parameters of the minimum energy orbit between two points. The problem of coplanar orbital transfer using a minimum energy orbit is solved analytically, and a graphical method of obtaining an approximate solution is outlined.

## Introduction

The purpose of this paper is to report work done on the determination of optimum space weapon orbits.

The work reported includes the determination of the regions accessible to a ballistic weapon projected with a velocity vector of constant magnitude 1) from an arbitrary point in inertial space and 2) from an orbiting vehicle. Also

*This work was supported in whole or in part by the United States Air Force under Contract No. AF 08(635)-235 monitored by Air Proving Ground Center, Air Research and Development Command.

included is a treatment of the problem of determining the region of space from which a ballistic weapon with a velocity vector of constant magnitude has access to a given elliptical orbit. A ballistic weapon is said to have access to a particular point in space if there are no constraints on its motion that prevent it from reaching the particular point. The word "weapon" as used in this paper is defined to be any bullet, rocket, missile, or other device capable of acquiring a velocity vector of given magnitude in an arbitrarily short time. Where expedient, non-dimensional velocities and distances have been introduced. These velocities and distances are in units of circular velocity at a given point and the distance from the force center to the given point, respectively. All the trajectories or orbits discussed in this paper are assumed to be in an inverse-square-law central force field.

The second portion of this paper is a discussion of the region that is accessible to a ballistic weapon fired from an arbitrary point in inertial space with the constraint that the magnitude of its velocity vector is constant. It is found that the curve bounding the region of accessibility is an ellipse, called the bounding ellipse, with foci at the initial position of the projectile and the force center. This section points out that if a projectile is fired in any arbitrary direction and with a given velocity magnitude from the initial position, its trajectory would be an ellipse that is internally tangent to the bounding ellipse associated with the launch velocity. This trajectory from the initial point to the point of tangency with the bounding ellipse is a minimum energy trajectory between these two points.

The third part of the paper gives a derivation of two parametric equations defining the region from which a ballistic weapon with a constant magnitude velocity vector has accessibility to a given elliptical orbit. This derivation uses the concept of the bounding ellipse established in the second portion of the paper; the weapon is said to have ballistic accessibility to a point on the given elliptical orbit if the bounding ellipse associated with the weapon is tangent to the given orbit at the given point.

The last portion of the paper is a discussion of the problem of the determination of the region accessible to a ballistic weapon launched from an orbiting vehicle. The equations determining the bounding curve of the region of ballistic accessibility are derived, and plots of the bounding curve are presented. Appendix A gives the solution of a quartic equation presented in this section; Appendix B describes a graphical method for the determination of a quantity derived in the last section of the paper; and Appendix C presents a graphical method for solving orbital transfer problems. The transformation equations which allow computation of the bounding curve in planes other than that containing the satellite orbit are given in Appendix D. Appendix E explains the symbols used.

## Determination of the Region Accessible to a Weapon Having a Fixed $|\vec{V}|$

Suppose a weapon initially at rest in inertial space is launched in some direction with a fixed velocity $V_o$. Assume that the point of launch is a distance $R_o$ from the force center and that the velocity vector makes an angle $\psi_o$ with the line from the force center to the launch point.

The projectile will move in an elliptical orbit around the force center, the apogee of this orbit being at an angle $\alpha$ from the launch point. Furthermore, if a particular value of the polar angle $\gamma$, measured from the launch point, is chosen, this orbit will intersect the line $\gamma$ = constant at the point $(R, \gamma)$. It is desired to find the maximum possible value of R as a function of $\gamma$ with $V_o$ fixed and with $\psi_o$ allowed to vary over the complete range from 0 to 360 degrees. Figure 1 is a diagram of the geometry of this problem.

From Figure 1, the orbital equation is

$$R = \frac{A(1 - \epsilon^2)}{1 - \epsilon \cos(\gamma - \alpha)}$$

$$= \frac{A(1 - \epsilon^2)}{1 - \epsilon(\cos\gamma \cos\alpha + \sin\gamma \sin\alpha)} \qquad (1)$$

where

$$A = \mu R_o/(2\mu - R_o V_o^2) \qquad (1a)$$

$$1 - \epsilon^2 = R_o^2 V_o^2 \sin^2 \psi_o/\mu A \qquad (1b)$$

and $\mu$ = earth's gravitational constant. At $R = R_o$, this equation reduces to

$$R_o = \frac{A(1 - \epsilon^2)}{1 - \epsilon \cos\alpha}$$

Solving for $\cos\alpha$ gives

$$\cos\alpha = \frac{R_o - A(1 - \epsilon^2)}{R_o \epsilon}$$

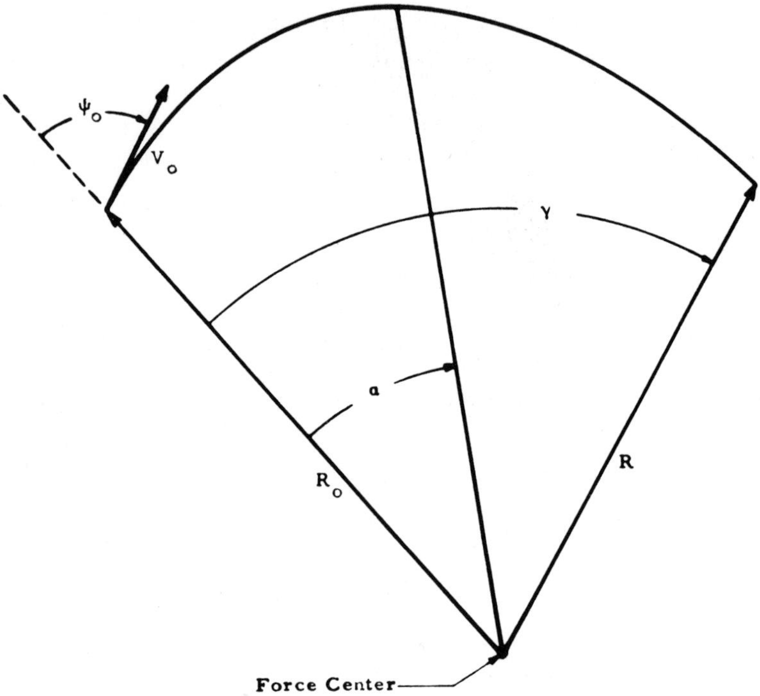


Figure 1

A Diagram of the Trajectory Through the Point (R, γ)

Substituting this value of cos $\alpha$ into Eq. (1) and simplifying gives

$$R = \frac{A(1-\epsilon^2)}{1-\cos\gamma+\frac{A}{R_o}\cos\gamma(1-\epsilon^2)-\sin\gamma\left\{\left(\frac{2A}{R_o}-1\right)(1-\epsilon^2)-\frac{A^2}{R_o^2}(1-\epsilon^2)^2\right\}^{\frac{1}{2}}} \qquad (2)$$

Since $V_o$ is a constant, A is also constant. Therefore, differentiating Eq. (2) with respect to $(1 - \epsilon^2)$ and equating to zero will give the value of $(1 - \epsilon^2)$ that extremalizes the radius vector at a given $\gamma$. Performing the differentiation and equating the numerator to zero gives

$$A\left[1-\cos\gamma+\frac{A}{R_o}\cos\gamma(1-\epsilon^2) - \sin\gamma\left\{\left(\frac{2A}{R_o}-1\right)(1-\epsilon^2)-\frac{A^2}{R_o^2}(1-\epsilon^2)^2\right\}^{\frac{1}{2}}\right]$$

$$-A(1-\epsilon^2)\left[\frac{A}{R_o}\cos\gamma - \sin\gamma\,\frac{\left(\frac{2A}{R_o}-1\right)-\frac{2A^2}{R_o^2}(1-\epsilon^2)}{2\left\{\left(\frac{2A}{R_o}-1\right)(1-\epsilon^2)-\frac{A^2}{R_o^2}(1-\epsilon^2)^2\right\}^{\frac{1}{2}}}\right] = 0$$

Solving this equation for $(1 - \epsilon^2)$ gives

$$1-\epsilon^2 = \frac{\frac{2A}{R_o}-1}{\left[\frac{\sin^2\gamma\left(\frac{2A}{R_o}-1\right)^2}{4(1-\cos\gamma)^2}+\frac{A^2}{R_o^2}\right]},\ 0 \qquad (3)$$

Substituting Eq. (3) into Eq. (2) gives, after algebraic manipulation,

$$R = \frac{4A(2A-R_o)}{4A-R_o-R_o\cos\gamma} \qquad (4)$$

which is the equation of an ellipse of eccentricity $\epsilon_b$ and semimajor axis $A_b$ where

$$\epsilon_b = \frac{R_o}{4A - R_o} \qquad (5)$$

and

$$A_b = \frac{4A - R_o}{2} \qquad (6)$$

For each angle $\gamma$, there is a corresponding angle $\psi_o$ which maximizes the R coordinate attainable at $\gamma$. To find $\psi_o(\gamma)$, or conversely $\gamma(\psi_o)$, the two expressions for $(1 - \epsilon^2)$ (the one found just below Eq. (1) and Eq. (3))are equated. Hence,

$$R_o^2 V_o^2 \sin^2 \psi_o = \frac{\mu A(\frac{2A}{R_o} - 1)}{\frac{(\frac{2A}{R_o} - 1)^2}{4 \tan^2 \gamma/2} + \frac{A^2}{R_o^2}} \qquad (7)$$

The equation

$$A = \frac{\mu R_o}{(2\mu - R_o V_o^2)}$$

implies that

$$(\frac{2A}{R_o} - 1) = \frac{R_o V_o^2}{2\mu - R_o V_o^2}$$

Substituting these results into Eq. (7) gives

$$\sin^2 \psi_o = \frac{4 \tan^2 \gamma/2}{\frac{R_o^2 V_o^4}{\mu^2} + 4 \tan^2 \gamma/2} \qquad (8)$$

Solving Eq. (8) for $\psi_o$ gives in non-dimensional units

$(v_o = \sqrt{\frac{R_o}{\mu}} V_o)$

$$\psi_o = \sin^{-1} \frac{2 \tan \gamma/2}{\sqrt{v_o^4 + 4 \tan^2 \gamma/2}} \tag{9}$$

Solving this equation for $\gamma$ gives

$$\tan \gamma/2 = \frac{v_o^2 \tan \psi_o}{2}$$

so

$$\gamma = 2 \tan^{-1} \left( \frac{v_o^2 \tan \psi_o}{2} \right) \tag{10}$$

Figure 2 is a plot of Eq. (10) showing $\gamma$ vs $\psi_o$ for $v_o = \sqrt{2}$, 1. All these curves are anti-symmetric about the lines $\gamma = 180^o$ and $\psi_o = 90^o$. The shaded regions contain the curves having $0 \leq v_o \leq 1$, or $1 \leq v_o \leq \sqrt{2}$ (in non-dimensional units, $\sqrt{2}$ = escape velocity).

Eq. (4) states that the curve bounding the region accessible to a projectile fired with a fixed velocity in a plane is an ellipse. It is interesting to note that the force center is at one focus of this ellipse and the other focus is at $R_o$. Equally interesting is the fact that all the trajectories obtained by launching a weapon from $R_o$ with a given velocity $V_o$ are minimum energy trajectories to points on the bounding ellipse corresponding to the velocity $V_o$. Further, all of these minimum energy trajectories are tangent to the bounding ellipse. Thus, since a satellite orbit can be thought of as a bounding ellipse, a weapon fired from the free focus of the orbit and with the velocity associated with that particular bounding ellipse, would move in a minimum energy trajectory to the bounding ellipse (or satellite orbit), and would also arrive tangential to the satellite orbit, regardless of the value of the angle $\psi_o$. By varying $\psi_o$ the point of tangency may be moved to any point on the orbit. Thus, a satellite is particularly vulnerable to projectiles fired from the free focus of its orbit since from this point a weapon may be fired at any time and still achieve tangential interception using a minimum energy weapon orbit.

If the velocity vector $\vec{V}_o$ is allowed to point in any direction, the bounding surface of the region accessible will be an ellipsoid of revolution. The axis of symmetry of this ellipsoid will be the line containing the force center and the initial point, $R_o$, since a rotation of the plane of the weapon

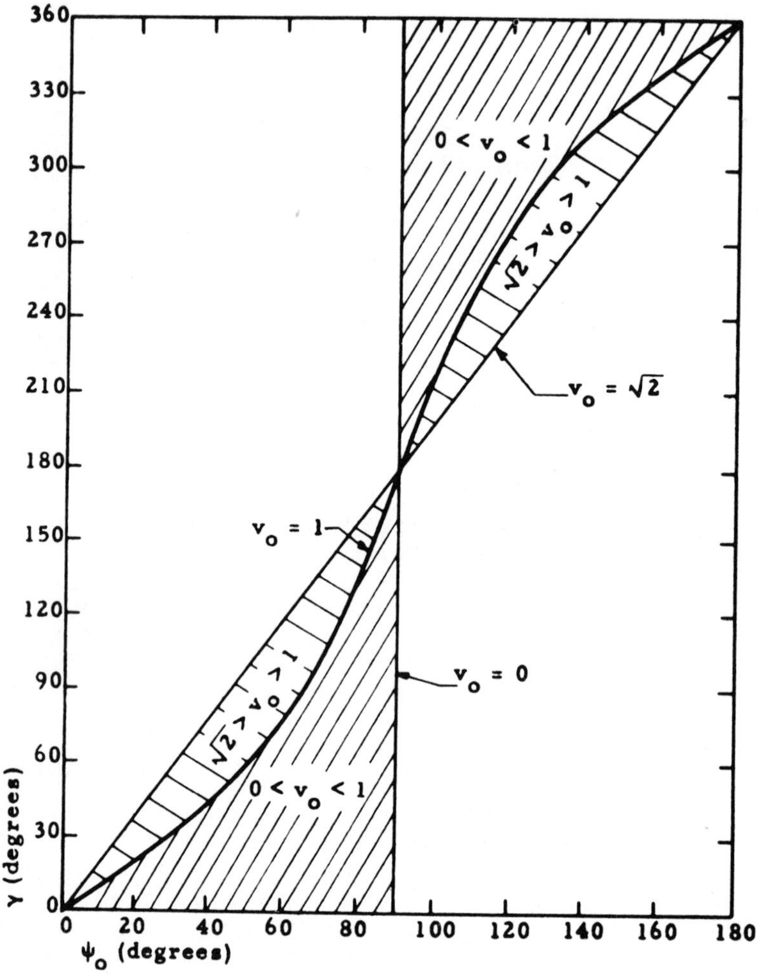


Figure 2

A Plot of $\gamma$ vs $\psi_o$

orbit about this line does not affect the semimajor axis or eccentricity of the bounding ellipse.

In non-dimensional units Eq. (4) may be written as

$$r = \frac{R}{R_o} = \frac{a_b(1 - \epsilon_b^2)}{(1 - \epsilon_b \cos \gamma)} \tag{11}$$

where

$$a_b = \frac{(2 + v_o^2)}{2(2 - v_o^2)} \tag{12}$$

$$\epsilon_b = \frac{2 - v_o^2}{2 + v_o^2} \tag{13}$$

$$v_o = \frac{V_o}{V_c}$$

where $V_c$ is the velocity required for a circular orbit at the radius in question.

Figure 3 shows plots of $a_b$ and $\epsilon_b$ versus $v_o$. The velocity for which $a_b = \epsilon_b$ may be found by equating Eqs. (12) and (13) and solving for $v_o$.

$$v_o = \sqrt{6 - \sqrt{32}} = 0.585788$$

Figure 4 is a plot of the bounding ellipses corresponding to $v_o = 0.3$, 0.4, 0.5, 0.6, 0.7, and Figure 5 is a plot of the bounding ellipses corresponding to $v_o = 0.8$, 0.9, 1.0, 1.1. This set of ellipses may be thought of as a set of constant energy lines or "equipotential" lines, since each ellipse is determined by a particular value of $v_o$ corresponding to a certain non-dimensional kinetic energy, $E = \frac{1}{2} v_o^2$. Substituting E for $\frac{1}{2} v_o^2$ in Eqs. (12) and (13) gives

$$a_b = \frac{1 + E}{2(1 - E)} \tag{14}$$

$$\epsilon_b = \frac{1 - E}{1 + E} \tag{15}$$

In any ellipse the distance between the two foci is equal to $2a\epsilon$. Eqs. (14) and (15) show that for the bounding ellipses

$$2a_b\epsilon_b = 1$$

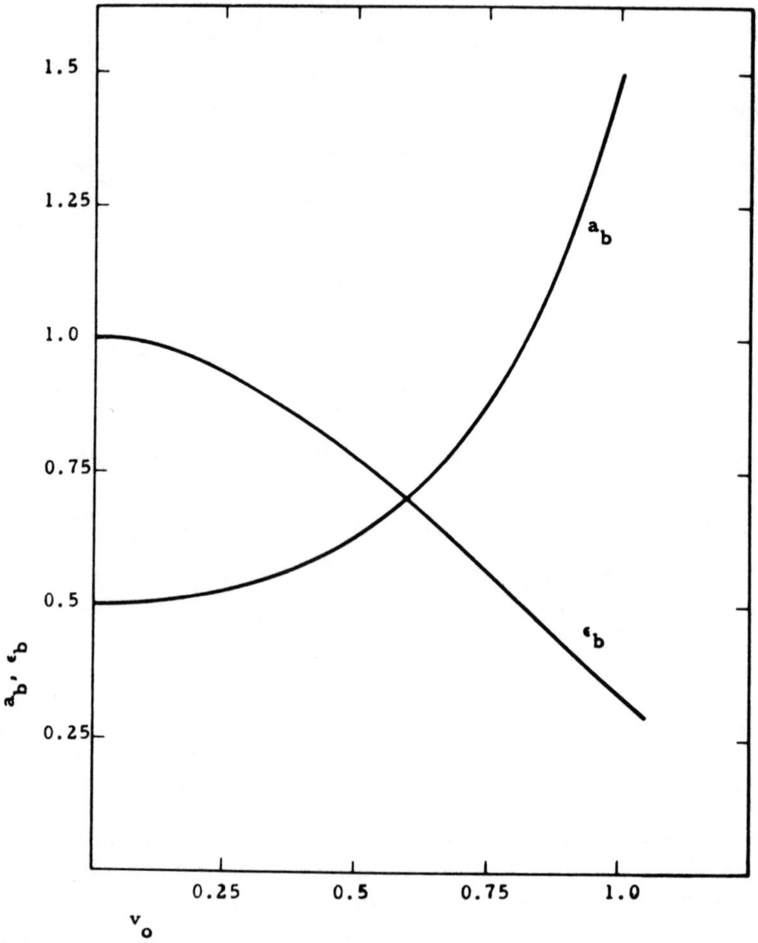


Figure 3

A Plot of $a_b$ and $\epsilon_b$ vs $v_o$

Therefore, the bounding ellipses are confocal, having the center of attraction as one focus and the initial point as the other. Substituting Eqs. (14) and (15) into Eq. (11) gives

$$r = \frac{2E}{(1 - E)(1 + E) - (1 - E)^2 \cos \gamma} \tag{16}$$

Eq. (16) is the equation of a one-parameter (E) family of confocal bounding ellipses.

In polar confocal elliptic coordinates, Eq. (16) may be written as

$$\xi = C_1, \text{ a constant}$$

where

$$\xi = \rho + r$$

$\rho$ being the distance in units of $r_o$ from the point $(r_o, 0)$ to the tip of the vector $\vec{r}$. Consequently, the equation of the family of hyperbolas orthogonal to the set of ellipses $\xi = C_1$ is

$$\eta = C_2, \text{ another constant} \tag{17}$$

where

$$\eta = \rho - r$$

From the law of cosines,

$$\rho = \sqrt{1 + r^2 - 2r \cos \gamma}$$

Substituting these values of $\rho$ and $\eta$ into Eq. (17) gives

$$\sqrt{(1 + r^2 - 2r \cos \gamma)} - r = \pm C_2 \tag{18}$$

where $C_2 > 0$ if $\rho > r$, and $C_2 < 0$ if $\rho < r$. Transposing and squaring leads to

$$1 - 2r \cos \gamma = C_2^2 \pm 2rC_2$$

Solving for r gives

$$r = \frac{1 - C_2^2}{2(\pm C_2 + \cos \gamma)} \tag{19}$$

Eq. (19) is the equation of a hyperbola having an eccentricity

$$\epsilon_h = \frac{1}{C_2}$$

and a semimajor axis

$$a_h = \frac{C_2}{2}$$

Since $2a_h \epsilon_h = 1$, these hyperbolas are confocal as expected, having the same foci as the bounding ellipses.

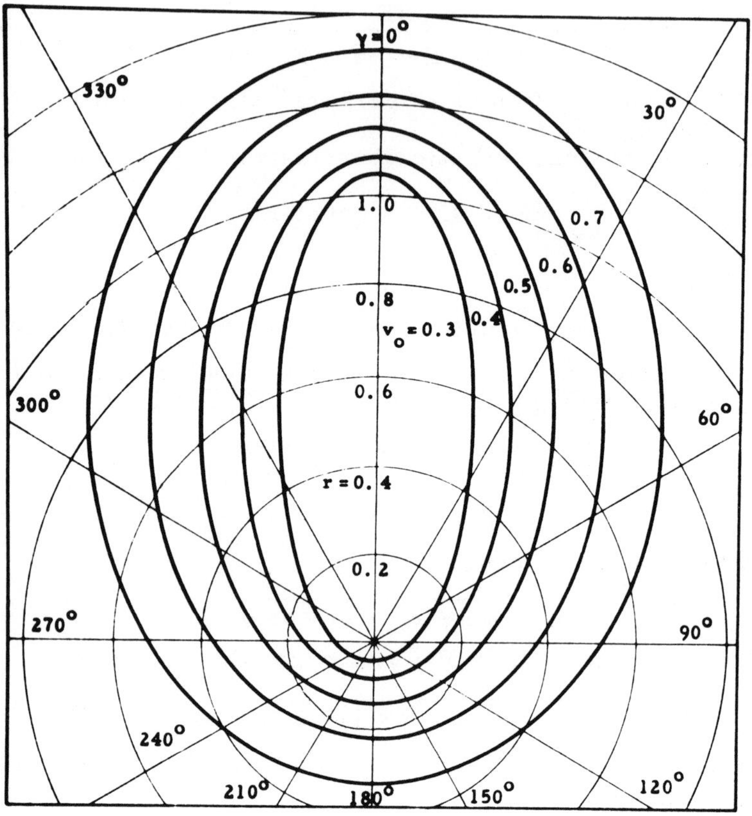


Figure 4

The Bounding Surfaces for $v_o = 0.3$, 0.4, 0.5, 0.6, 0.7

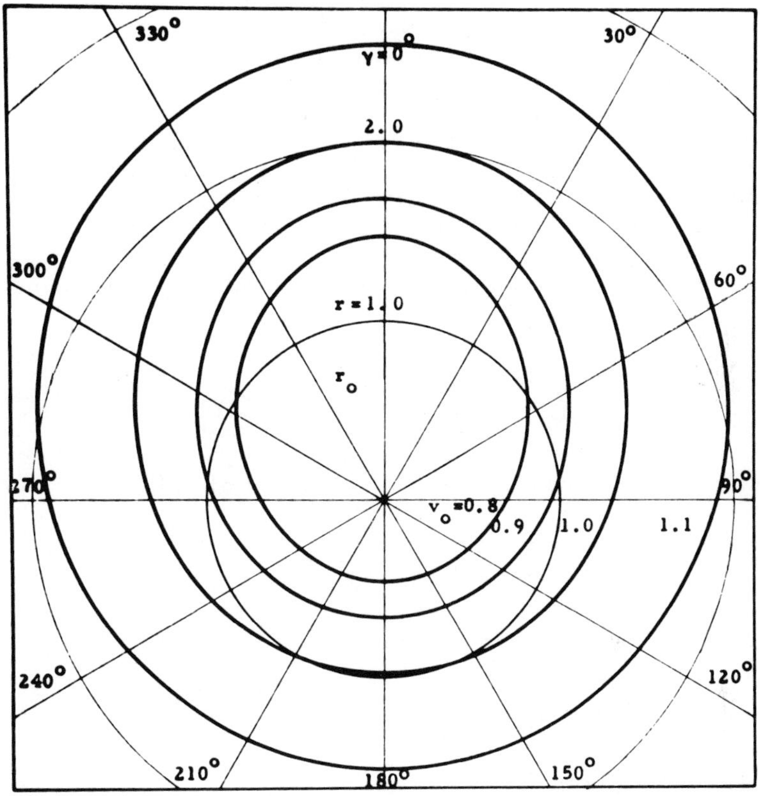


Figure 5

The Bounding Surfaces for $v_o = 0.8$, 0.9, 1.0, and 1.1

The significance of these hyperbolas is that they are the paths along which the rate of change of E with respect to the space variables is maximized. A possible application of this concept is in problems concerning evasive action taken by aircraft. Consider the problem of an aircraft trying to get out of range of an anti-aircraft gun as rapidly as possible (Figure 6). To do this the pilot must fly as fast as possible along a hyperbolic path given by Eq. (19), assuming the velocity he can attain is independent of the flight path. He is out of danger when he crosses the bounding ellipse corresponding to the muzzle velocity of the gun. There are space-to-space warfare counterparts of this example which have not been investigated because of lack of time.

The lines of constant $\psi_o$ may be found by eliminating E from Eq. (16). From Eq. (10)

$$E = \frac{\tan \frac{\gamma}{2}}{\tan \psi_o} = \frac{1 - \cos \gamma}{\sin \gamma \tan \psi_o}$$

Substituting this result into Eq. (16) and simplifying gives

$$r = \frac{2}{\sin \gamma \tan \psi_o - \frac{\sin \gamma}{\tan \psi_o} + 2 \cos \gamma} \qquad (20)$$

Substituting the following trigonometric identity

$$\tan \psi_o - \frac{1}{\tan \psi_o} = - \frac{2 \cos 2 \psi_o}{\sin 2 \psi_o}$$

into Eq. (20) gives

$$r = \frac{\sin 2 \psi_o}{\sin(2 \psi_o - \gamma)} \qquad (21)$$

Eq. (21) states that the lines of constant $\psi_o$ are straight lines emanating from the initial point. In a polar coordinate system $(\rho, \theta)$ centered at the initial point, the lines of constant $\psi_o$ are given by

$$\theta = 2 \psi_o \qquad (22)$$

where $\theta$ is measured from the local vertical.

Eq. (22) implies that given a point in an inverse-square-law force field and a weapon with a constant magnitude velocity vector, if it is desired to maximize the distance from the initial point to the intersection of the weapon trajectory with a ray (from the initial point) making an angle of $\theta$ with the

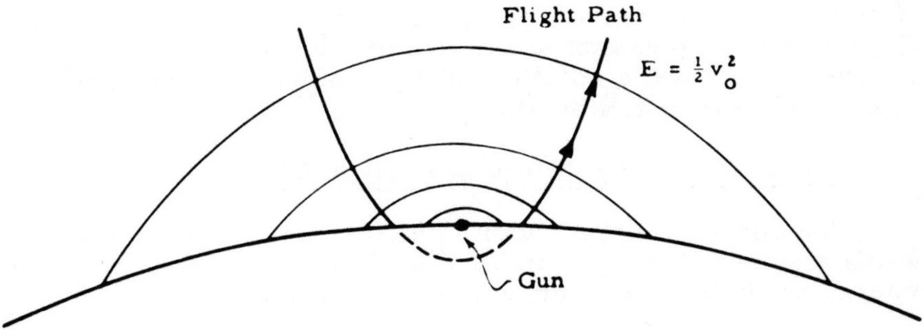


Figure 6

Optimum Aircraft Evasive Path

local vertical, then the projectile must be fired at an angle of $\theta/2$ from the local vertical.

From the preceding discussion it is clear that an elliptic polar coordinate system is best suited for working two-dimensional problems in ballistic accessibility with the constraint of a constant magnitude velocity vector. For three-dimensional problems having this constraint an ellipsoidal-spherical system is preferred. Figure 7 is a diagram of an elliptic polar coordinate system. In this system, a point in a plane is located by the intersection of an ellipse and a ray from one of its foci, the other focus being at the force center. In non-dimensional units, the distance between the two foci is unity. Any point in the plane may be described by two numbers, $(E, \theta)$, the value of E denoting a particular ellipse, and the value of $\theta$ (or $2\psi_o$), a particular ray from the free focus.

Note that this coordinate system is not orthogonal. Appendix C contains a discussion of the use of the elliptic polar coordinate system in the solution of the problem of finding minimum energy transfer orbits.

## Minimum Energy Orbits to a Given Elliptical Orbit

The concept of the bounding ellipse developed in the foregoing discussion gives a method of determining the minimum energy orbit from a point $(r_o, \beta)$ to a given ellipse

$$r_s = \frac{R_s}{R_o} = \frac{A_s(1 - \epsilon_s^2)}{R_o(1 - \epsilon_s \cos \gamma)} = \frac{a_s(1 - \epsilon_s^2)}{1 - \epsilon_s \cos \gamma} \tag{23}$$

Figure 8 shows the point $(r_o, \beta)$, the given elliptical orbit, and the bounding ellipse tangent to the orbit. A moment's study shows that the energy associated with the tangent bounding ellipse is the minimum energy required to go from the point $(r_o, \beta)$ to the given orbit.

The family of bounding ellipses associated with the point $(r_o, \beta)$ is given by

$$r_b = \frac{R_b}{R_o} = \frac{(1 - \epsilon_b^2)}{2\,\epsilon_b\{1 - \epsilon_b \cos(\gamma - \beta)\}} \tag{24}$$

The two ellipses given by Eq. (23) and (24) are tangent if

$$r_s = r_b \tag{25}$$

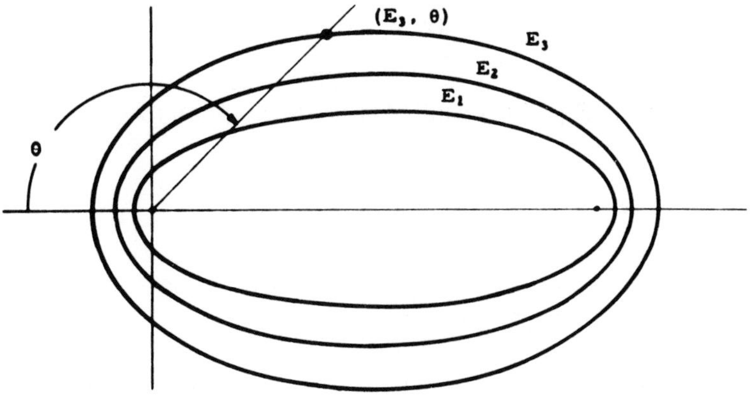


Figure 7

An Elliptic Polar Coordinate System

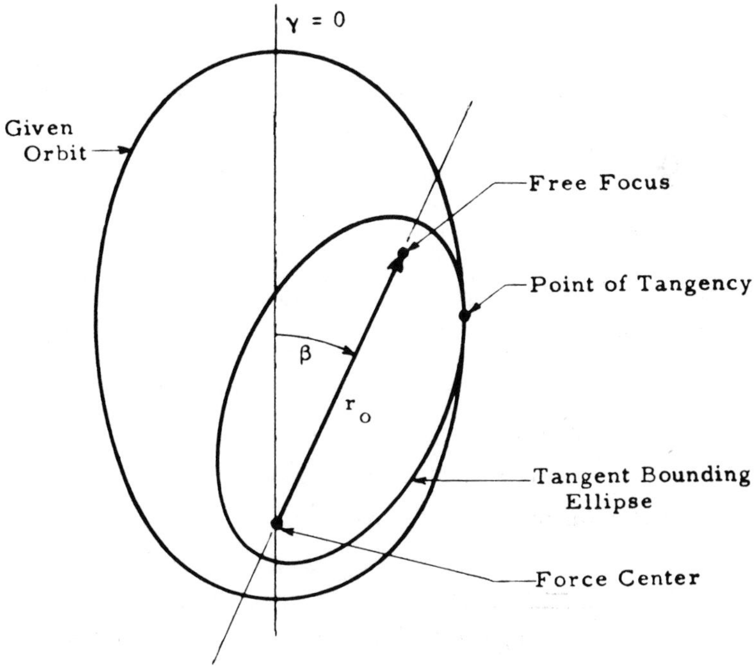


Figure 8

Geometry of the Orbital Transfer Problem

and

$$\frac{dr_s}{d\gamma} = \frac{dr_b}{d\gamma} \tag{26}$$

Differentiating Eq. (23) and (24) with respect to $\gamma$ gives

$$\frac{dr_s}{d\gamma} = -\frac{r_s \epsilon_s \sin\gamma}{1 - \epsilon_s \cos\gamma} \tag{27}$$

$$\frac{dr_b}{d\gamma} = -\frac{r_b \epsilon_b \sin(\gamma - \beta)}{1 - \epsilon_b \cos(\gamma - \beta)} \tag{28}$$

Substituting Eq. (27) and (28) into Eq. (26) and dividing by Eq. (25) gives

$$\frac{\epsilon_s \sin\gamma}{1 - \epsilon_s \cos\gamma} = \frac{\epsilon_b \sin(\gamma - \beta)}{1 - \epsilon_b \cos(\gamma - \beta)}$$

Solving this equation for $\epsilon_b$ yields

$$\epsilon_b = \frac{\epsilon_s \sin\gamma}{\epsilon_s \sin\beta + \sin(\gamma - \beta)} \tag{29}$$

Substituting Eq. (29) into Eq. (24) and equating the result to Eq. (23) gives after considerable simplification

$$2a_s\epsilon_s(1 - \epsilon_s^2)\sin\gamma = \sin(\gamma - \beta) + 2\epsilon_s \sin\beta - \epsilon_s^2 \sin(\gamma + \beta)$$

Collecting terms gives

$$\sin\gamma(2a_s\epsilon_s - \cos\beta)(1 - \epsilon_s^2) + \cos\gamma(1 + \epsilon_s^2)\sin\beta = 2\epsilon_s \sin\beta \tag{30}$$

Eq. (30) is of the form

$$\sin\gamma \sin\phi + \cos\gamma \cos\phi = \text{constant}$$

which may be written as

$$\cos(\gamma - \phi) = \text{constant}$$

Thus the solution of Eq. (30) for $\gamma$ is

$$\gamma = \cos^{-1} \frac{2\epsilon_s \sin\beta}{\sqrt{(2a_s\epsilon_s - \cos\beta)^2(1 - \epsilon_s^2)^2 + (1 + \epsilon_s^2)^2 \sin^2\beta}}$$

$$+ \cos^{-1} \frac{(1 + \epsilon_s^2)\sin\beta}{\sqrt{(2a_s\epsilon_s - \cos\beta)^2(1 - \epsilon_s^2)^2 + (1 + \epsilon_s^2)^2 \sin^2\beta}} \tag{31}$$

The velocity required for transfer may be found by substituting the value of $\epsilon$ given in Eq. (13) for $\epsilon$ in Eq. (29). This results in

$$\frac{2 - v_o^2}{2 + v_o^2} = \frac{\epsilon_s \sin\gamma}{\epsilon_s \sin\beta + \sin(\gamma - \beta)}$$

Solving this equation for $v_o$ gives

$$v_o = \sqrt{2}\left\{\frac{\epsilon_s \sin\beta + \sin(\gamma - \beta) - \epsilon_s \sin\gamma}{\epsilon_s \sin\beta + \sin(\gamma - \beta) + \epsilon_s \sin\gamma}\right\}^{\frac{1}{2}} \qquad (32)$$

Substituting for $\gamma$ from Eq. (31) will give the value of the minimum velocity required to reach the ellipse from the point $(R_o, \beta)$.

Given $\gamma$ and $v_o$, the angle $\psi_o$ between the projectile velocity vector and the local vertical at launch may be found from Eq. (10) by replacing $\gamma$ with $(\gamma - \beta)$. This substitution gives

$$\gamma - \beta = 2\tan^{-1}\left(\frac{v_o^2 \tan\psi_o}{2}\right)$$

Solving for $\psi_o$ gives

$$\psi_o = \tan^{-1}\frac{2\tan\left(\frac{\gamma - \beta}{2}\right)}{v_o^2} \qquad (33)$$

The radial distance to the point of tangency of the projectile orbit with the given orbit may be found from either Eq. (23) or (24)

Reintroducing dimensional units, Eqs. (30) and (32) may be written as

$$\sin\gamma\left(\frac{2A_s\epsilon_s}{R_o} - \cos\beta\right)(1 - \epsilon_s^2) + \cos\gamma(1 + \epsilon_s^2)\sin\beta = 2\epsilon_s \sin\beta \qquad (34)$$

$$\sqrt{\frac{R_o}{\mu}}\, V_o = \sqrt{2}\left\{\frac{\epsilon_s \sin\beta + \sin(\gamma - \beta) - \epsilon_s \sin\gamma}{\epsilon_s \sin\beta + \sin(\gamma - \beta) + \epsilon_s \sin\gamma}\right\}^{\frac{1}{2}} \qquad (35)$$

Elimination of $\gamma$ from these two equations will give $R_o$ as a function of $V_o$, $\beta$, $A_s$, and $\epsilon_s$. Thus for a given ellipse, these equations determine a curve in r, $\gamma$ space. This curve bounds the region from which an elliptical orbit is accessible to a weapon launched with a given velocity. Figure 9 is a plot of such curves for the orbit $a_s = 2$, $\epsilon_s = 0.5$. The velocities

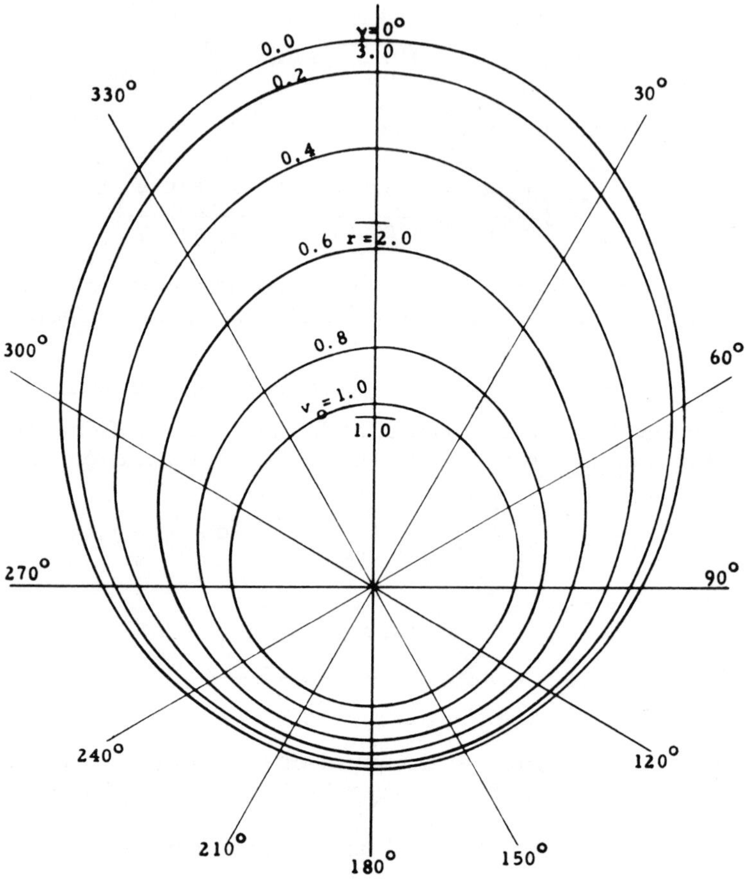


Figure 9

The Lines of Constant Minimum Velocity Required for Accessibility To the Orbit $a_s = 2.0$, $\epsilon_s = 0.5$

shown on this plot are in units of circular velocity at r = 1.0.

## Determination of the Region Accessible to a Weapon Launched from a Satellite

Given a satellite in an elliptical orbit with constants $A_s$, $\epsilon_s$, and $\phi_s$. Suppose at some time a weapon is impulsively ejected from the satellite with a velocity $V_w$ relative to the satellite. It is desired to determine the boundary of the region accessible to the weapon. To simplify the problem somewhat the motion of the weapon is restricted to the plane of the original orbit.

Assume the distance from the force center to the satellite at the point of ejection is $R_o$ and the velocity of the satellite is $V_s$, making an angle $\psi_s$ with the local vertical. The weapon velocity vector makes an angle of $\psi_w$ with the local vertical. Figure 10 is a diagram which shows the orientation of the satellite and weapon velocity vectors.

From the law of cosines, the magnitude of the resultant velocity vector is found to be

$$V_o = \{V_s^2 + V_w^2 + 2V_sV_w\cos(\psi_s - \psi_w)\}^{\frac{1}{2}} \tag{36}$$

The angle the resultant velocity vector makes with the local vertical, $\psi_o$, is given by

$$\psi_o = \psi_w + \Delta \tag{37}$$

Again, from the law of cosines

$$V_s^2 = V_w^2 + V_s^2 + V_w^2 + 2V_sV_w\cos(\psi_s - \psi_w)$$
$$- 2V_w\{V_s^2 + V_w^2 + 2V_sV_w\cos(\psi_s - \psi_w)\}^{\frac{1}{2}}\cos\Delta \tag{38}$$

Solving Eq. (38) for $\Delta$ gives

$$\Delta = \cos^{-1}\frac{V_w + V_s\cos(\psi_s - \psi_w)}{\{V_s^2 + V_w^2 + 2V_sV_w\cos(\psi_s - \psi_w)\}^{\frac{1}{2}}} \tag{39}$$

Substituting Eqs. (36), (37), and (39) into the equations for A and $\epsilon$ (Eqs. (1a) and (1b)), and substituting these values of A and $\epsilon$ into Eq. (2) gives R as a function of $\gamma$, $V_w$, $V_s$, $\psi_s$, and $\psi_w$.

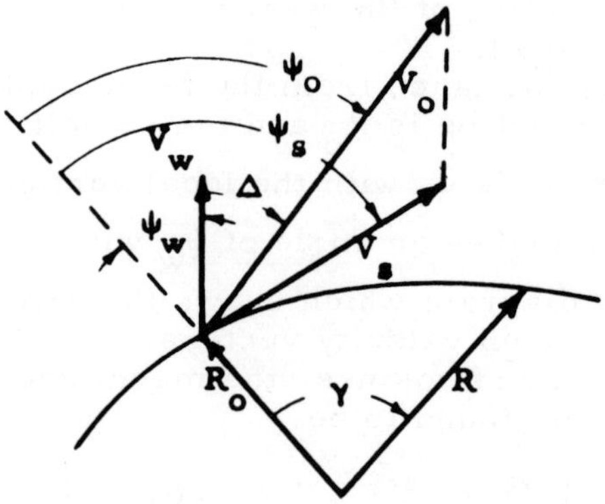


Figure 10

Orientation of Weapon and Satellite Velocity Vectors

$$R = R_o^2\{V_w^2 \sin^2\psi_w + V_s^2 \sin^2\psi_s + 2V_sV_w \sin\psi_s \sin\psi_w\}/\mu \Big[ 1 - \cos\gamma + \frac{\cos\gamma}{\mu} R_o\{V_w^2 \sin^2\psi_w + V_s^2 \sin^2\psi_s + 2V_sV_w \sin\psi_s \sin\psi_w\} - \frac{\sin\gamma}{\mu} R_o\{V_w \sin\psi_w + V_s \sin\psi_s\}\{V_w \cos\psi_w + V_s \cos\psi_s\} \Big] \tag{40}$$

Differentiating this equation with respect to $\psi_w$ and equating to zero gives

$$\Big[ 1 - \cos\gamma - \frac{\sin\gamma}{\mu} R_o\{V_w^2 \sin\psi_w \cos\psi_w + V_wV_s \sin\psi_w \cos\psi_s + V_wV_s \sin\psi_s \cos\psi_w + V_s^2 \cos\psi_s \sin\psi_s\} \Big] \{2V_w^2 \sin\psi_w \cos\psi_w + 2V_sV_w \cos\psi_w \sin\psi_s\} - \{V_w^2 \sin^2\psi_w + V_s^2 \sin^2\psi_s + 2V_sV_w \sin\psi_w \sin\psi_s\} \Big[ -\frac{\sin\gamma}{\mu} R_o\{V_w^2 \cos^2\psi_w - V_w^2 \sin^2\psi_w + V_wV_s \cos\psi_w \cos\psi_s - V_wV_s \sin\psi_s \sin\psi_w\} \Big] = 0$$

Simplification of this equation yields

$$2\cos\psi_w(1 - \cos\gamma) = \frac{\sin\gamma}{\mu} R_o \Big[ V_w \sin\psi_w + V_s \sin\psi_s \Big] \cdot \Big[ V_w + V_s \cos(\psi_s - \psi_w) \Big] \tag{41}$$

At this point the straight-forward procedure for obtaining the bounding curve would be to solve Eq. (41) for $\psi_w$ and to substitute this result into Eq. (40). Unfortunately the roots of a quartic equation are required for solving Eq. (41) (the solution of Eq. (41) for $\psi_s = \pi/2$ is given in Appendix A). Fortunately, however, Eq. (41) may be solved for $\gamma$ in terms of $V_w$, $\psi_w$, $V_s$, and $\psi_s$.

Before proceeding with the solution of Eq. (41), it is worthwhile to introduce the non-dimensional velocities

$$v_w = \left[\frac{R_o}{\mu}\right]^{\frac{1}{2}} V_w$$

and

$$v_s = \left[\frac{R_o}{\mu}\right]^{\frac{1}{2}} V_s$$

Substituting these relations into Eq. (41) and rearranging gives

$$\frac{(1 - \cos\gamma)}{\sin\gamma} = \frac{\{v_w \sin\psi_w + v_s \sin\psi_s\}\{v_w + v_s \cos(\psi_s - \psi_w)\}}{2\cos\psi_w} \tag{42}$$

Let the right-hand member of this equation be represented by the symbol U, then

$$\frac{1 - \cos\gamma}{\sin\gamma} = U \tag{43}$$

Utilizing a trigonometric substitution and squaring gives

$$1 - 2\cos\gamma + \cos^2\gamma = U^2(1 - \cos^2\gamma)$$

Collecting terms gives the following quadratic equation in $\gamma$

$$(1 + U^2)\cos^2\gamma - 2\cos\gamma + (1 - U^2) = 0$$

Application of the quadratic formula yields

$$\cos\gamma = \frac{2 \pm \sqrt{4 - 4(1 - U^4)}}{2(1 + U^2)}$$

$$= \frac{1 \pm U^2}{1 + U^2}$$

The solution obtained from using the plus sign of $U^2$ is uninteresting ($\gamma = 0$); therefore

$$\cos\gamma = \frac{1 - U^2}{1 + U^2} \tag{44}$$

In practice U may either be computed from the right-hand member of Eq. (42) or a less accurate estimate of U may be found graphically. Appendix B outlines the graphical determination of U. Utilizing the trigonometric identity

$\sin U = \sqrt{1 - \cos^2 U}$ and Eq. (44) gives

$$\sin\gamma = \frac{2U}{1 + U^2} \tag{45}$$

Substituting Eqs. (44) and (45) into Eq. (40) gives, in non-dimensional units

$$r = (1+U^2)(v_w \sin\psi_w + v_s \sin\psi_s)^2 \Big/ [2U^2 + (1-U^2)(v_w \sin\psi_w + v_s \sin\psi_s)^2 - 2U(v_w \sin\psi_w + v_s \sin\psi_s)(v_w \cos\psi_w + v_s \cos\psi_s)]$$

Substituting for U gives

$$r = [4\cos^2\psi_w + (v_w \sin\psi_w + v_s \sin\psi_s)^2 \{v_w + v_s \cos(\psi_s - \psi_w)\}^2] \Big/ [4\cos^2\psi_w - (v_w \sin\psi_w + v_s \sin\psi_s)^2 \{v_w + v_s \cos(\psi_s - \psi_w)\}^2 + 2\cos\psi_w \{v_w + v_s \cos(\psi_s - \psi_w)\}\{\sin\psi_w (v_w \sin\psi_w + v_s \sin\psi_s) - \cos\psi_w (v_w \cos\psi_w + v_s \cos\psi_s)\}] \quad (46)$$

Eqs. (44) and (46) are the equations of the bounding curve in parametric form. Appendix D gives the transformation equations which allow computation of the bounding curve in planes other than that containing the satellite orbit, thus allowing computation of the three dimensional bounding surface.

If the weapon and satellite velocity vectors are equal in magnitude, and if $\psi_s = \pi/2$, Eq. (42) may be solved for $\sin\psi_w$ in the following manner.

If $v_w = v_s$ and $\psi_s = \pi/2$, Eq. (42) reduces to

$$\frac{1-\cos\gamma}{\sin\gamma} \equiv F(\gamma) = \tan\frac{\gamma}{2} = v_s^2 \, \frac{(1+\sin\psi_w)^2}{2\sqrt{1-\sin^2\psi_w}} \quad (47)$$

Squaring both sides of this equation and expanding gives

$$\frac{4F^2(\gamma)}{v_s^4}(1-\sin\psi_w) = 1 + 3\sin\psi_w + 3\sin^2\psi_w + \sin^3\psi_w$$

Grouping terms containing like powers of $\sin\psi_w$ gives

$$\sin^3 \psi_w + 3 \sin^2 \psi_w + \sin \psi_w \left(3 + \frac{4F^2(\gamma)}{v_s^4}\right) + 1 - \frac{4F^2(\gamma)}{v_s^4} = 0 \tag{48}$$

Let

$$\sin \psi_w = X - 1 \tag{49}$$

Then Eq. (48) reduces to

$$X^3 + C_3 X + C_4 = 0$$

where

$$C_3 = \frac{4F^2(\gamma)}{v_s^4}$$

$$C_4 = - \frac{8F^2(\gamma)}{v_s^4}$$

Notice that $C_4 = -2C_3$.

So

$$\frac{4C_3^2}{4} + \frac{C_3^3}{27} = C_3^2 \left(1 + \frac{C_3}{27}\right) = \frac{16F^4(\gamma)}{v_s^8} \left(1 + \frac{4F^2(\gamma)}{v_s^4}\right) \geq 0$$

Hence, if $F(\gamma) \neq 0$ there is one real root

$$X_1 = \left[ + C_3 + \sqrt{C_3^2 \left(1 + \frac{C_3}{27}\right)} \right]^{1/3} + \left[ + C_3 - \sqrt{C_3^2 \left(1 + \frac{C_3}{27}\right)} \right]^{1/3}$$

$$= C_3^{1/3} \left[ \left\{1 + \sqrt{1 + \frac{C_3}{27}}\right\}^{1/3} + \left\{1 - \sqrt{1 + \frac{C_3}{27}}\right\}^{1/3} \right]$$

Therefore

$$\sin \psi_w = C_3^{1/3} \left[ \left\{1 + \sqrt{1 + \frac{C_3}{27}}\right\}^{1/3} + \left\{1 - \sqrt{1 + \frac{C_3}{27}}\right\}^{1/3} \right] - 1 \tag{50}$$

As an example, let

$$\gamma = 90^{\circ}, \; F(\gamma) = 1, \; C_3 = 4, \; v_s = 1$$

Substituting these values into Eq. (50) gives

$$\sin\psi_w = (4)^{1/3}\left[\left(1+\sqrt{1+\frac{4}{27}}\right)^{1/3} + \left(1-\sqrt{1+\frac{4}{27}}\right)^{1/3}\right] - 1$$

$$= 1.587401\left[(1+\sqrt{1.148148})^{1/3} + (1-\sqrt{1.148148})^{1/3}\right] - 1$$

$$= 1.587401\left[-(.0715167)^{1/3} + (2.0715167)^{1/3}\right] - 1$$

$$= .36466$$

$$\psi_w = 21^\circ 23'$$

Figures 11 and 12 show the bounding curves for two sets of conditions, the varying parameter being $v_w$ with $v_s = 1$ and $\psi_s = \pi/2$. If $v_w = 0$, all points accessible to the weapon lie on a circle of unit radius (not shown in either figure). As $v_w$ increases ($0 < v_w < \sqrt{2} - 1$), the circle (for $v_w = 0$) becomes two loops, one longer and one shorter than the original circle in the direction containing the launch point and the force center. Figure 11 shows the bounding curve for $v_w = .25$ which has the general appearance of a limaçon. If $\sqrt{2} - 1 < v_w < \infty$, the outer loop is joined at infinity. The inner loop continues to shrink for $\sqrt{2} - 1 < v_w < 1$. At $v_w = 1$, the inner loop collapses to a line along the radius vector from the force center to the launch point as shown in Figure 12. The dashed portion of the bounding curve in Figure 12 is not accessible to the weapon. This is due to the assumption that the satellite velocity vector is pointed in the direction $\psi_s = +\pi/2$ instead of $-\pi/2$. All of the points on this bounding curve for which $|\gamma| < 53^\circ 08'$ may be reached by weapon orbits which are elliptical and tangent to the bounding curve. The points $\gamma = \pm 53^\circ 08'$ correspond to a weapon orbit that is parabolic ($\psi_w = 0$), and the points for which $|\gamma| > 53^\circ 08'$ correspond to hyperbolic orbits.

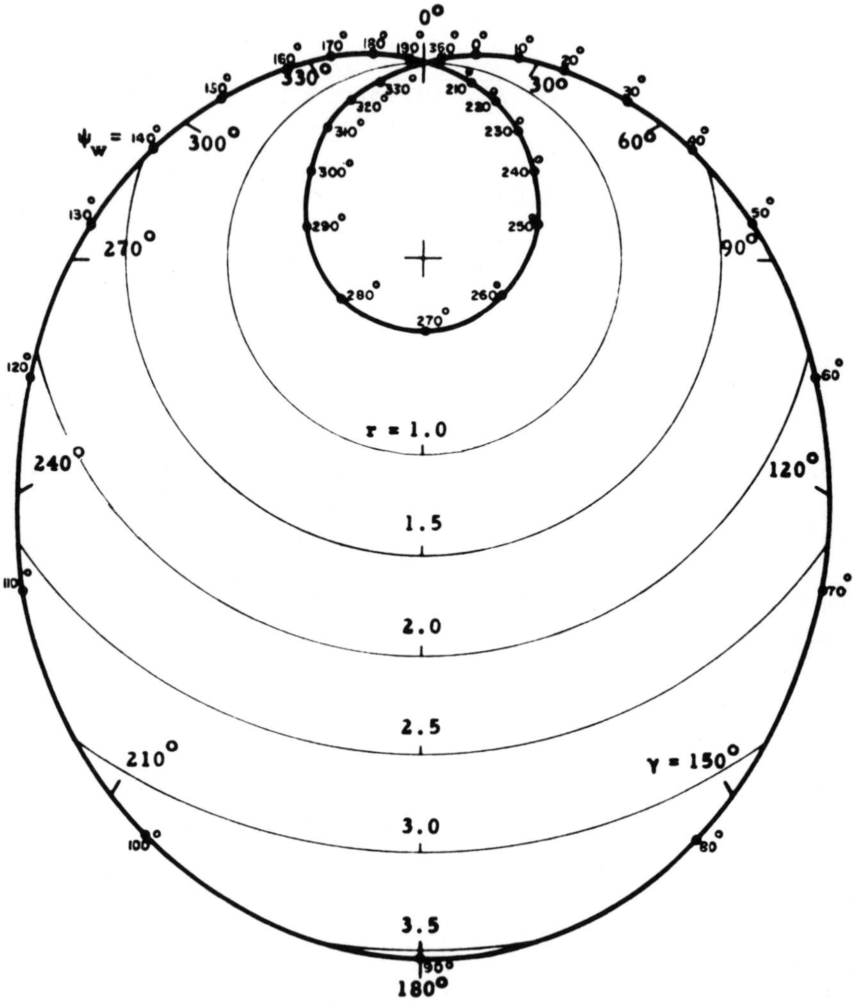


Figure 11

The Bounding Curve for $v_s$ = 1.0, $\psi_s = \pi/2$, and $v_w$ = 0.25

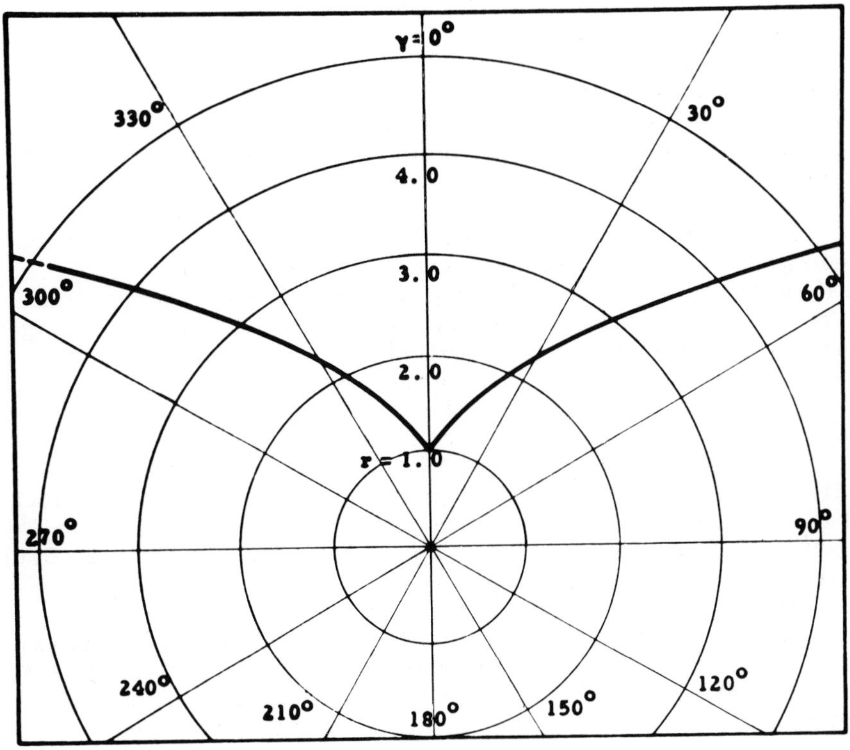


Figure 12

The Bounding Curve for $v_s = 1.0$, $\psi_s = \pi/2$, and $v_w = 1.0$

Figure 13 is a plot of a bounding curve for the satellite velocity vector not perpendicular to the local vertical at launch. In this figure $v_s = 1$, $\psi_s = \pi/4$, and $v_w = 0.1$.

## Conclusions

The main results of the work reported in this note may be summarized as follows:

1) An analytical expression has been derived for the curve bounding the region accessible to a ballistic weapon fired from a fixed point with a constant magnitude velocity vector. These curves were found to be ellipses with foci at the initial point and the force center. In three dimensions the bounding curve is an ellipsoid of revolution.

2) Given an initial point in an inverse-square-law force field and a weapon with a fixed magnitude velocity vector, if it is desired to maximize the distance of the intersection of the weapon orbit along a ray from the initial point making an angle $\theta$ with the local vertical at the launch point, then the weapon's initial velocity vector should be coplanar with the initial radius vector and the target ray and make an angle of $\theta/2$ with the local vertical at launch.

3) The lines of constant $\theta$ (rays emanating from the initial point) and constant kinetic energy E (ellipses with foci at the initial point and the force center) form a coordinate system in which each point in space has the coordinates $(E, \theta)$. E is the kinetic energy and $\theta$ is twice the angle of fire required at the origin to pass a minimum energy orbit between the particular point and the origin. Thus, given two points described in any coordinate system, the velocity vector required at either of the points to pass a minimum energy orbit between them may be found by a transformation of coordinates.

4) The transformation equations between $(r, \gamma)$ space and $(E, \theta)$ space are given in Appendix C. This appendix also gives a method of solving orbital transfer problems using a template which transforms $(r, \gamma)$ coordinates into $(E, \theta)$ coordinates.

5) The point or points of minimum ballistic accessibility on any arbitrary curve in space relative to any given point in space are the points where the curve and members of the set of bounding ellipses associated with the given point have points of tangency.

6) The parametric equations of the curve bounding the region of ballistic accessibility to an arbitrary elliptical orbit are derived using the concept given in the previous paragraph.

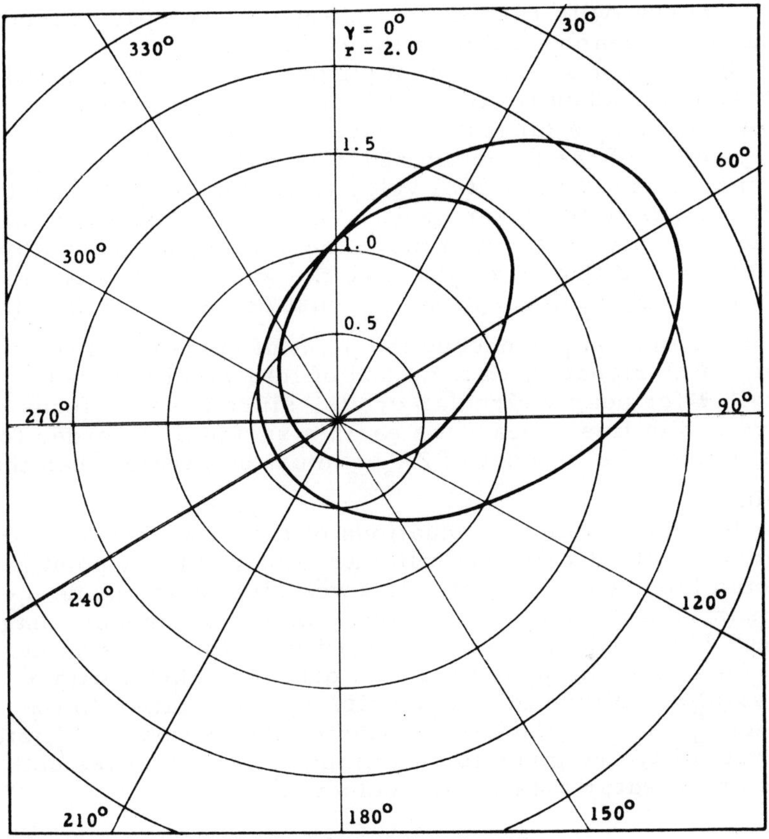


Figure 13

The Bounding Curve for $v_s = 1.0$, $\psi_s = \pi/4$, and $v_w = 0.1$

7) The family of hyperbolas orthogonal to the family of bounding ellipses associated with a given point are found to be the paths which maximize the rate of change of the minimum energy (with respect to a change in the space variables) required to reach a point on the path.

8) Given a satellite in an elliptical orbit, it is found that a weapon launched from the free focus and in the plane of the orbit will make a tangential rendezvous with this orbit, independent of the direction of the initial velocity vector, if the magnitude of the initial velocity vector is such that it corresponds to the given orbit. Varying the direction of the initial velocity vector will move the point of tangency along the orbit, and thus alter the time the weapon takes to reach the orbit. For interception, $\psi_o$ must be so chosen that the satellite and weapon occupy the point of tangency at the same time. Unfortunately this method of interception is not possible for nearly circular orbits, since the free focus of these orbits lies beneath the earth's surface. In order to use this method the product of $2A_s \epsilon_s$ must be greater than the radius of the earth.

9) The parametric equations of the curve bounding the region of ballistic accessibility are derived for a point mass ejected from a fixed point with a velocity vector made up of the sum of a constant vector and a vector of constant magnitude. This constraint on the velocity vector is the same as that on a weapon ejected from an orbiting vehicle with a constant magnitude initial velocity vector relative to the vehicle. Plots of the curve bounding the region of ballistic accessibility are given for maximum total velocities both less and greater than escape velocity.

## Appendix A: The Solution of Eq. (41) for $\psi_w$ as a Function of $\gamma$, $v_s$, and $v_w$ ($\psi_s = \pi/2$)

Eq. (41) reduces to

$$F(\gamma) = \frac{1 - \cos\gamma}{\sin\gamma} = \frac{(v_w \sin\psi_w + v_s)(v_w + v_s \sin\psi_w)}{2\cos\psi_w} \tag{51}$$

Expanding this equation and squaring gives

$$4F^2(\gamma)(1-\sin^2\psi_w) = \sin^4\psi_w v_s^2 v_w^2 + \sin^3\psi_w\, 2v_w v_s(v_w^2+v_s^2)$$
$$+ \sin^2\psi_w (v_w^4 + v_s^4 + 4v_w^2 v_s^2)$$
$$+ \sin\psi_w\, 2v_w v_s (v_w^2+v_s^2) + v_w^2 v_s^2$$

Rearranging gives the following quartic equation in $\sin\psi_w$

$$\sin^4\psi_w + \sin^3\psi_w \frac{2(v_w^2+v_s^2)}{v_w v_s} + \sin^2\psi_w \frac{v_w^4 + 4v_w^2 v_s^2 + 4F^2(\gamma) + v_s^4}{v_w^2 v_s^2}$$
$$+ \sin\psi_w \frac{2(v_w^2+v_s^2)}{v_w v_s} + 1 - \frac{4F^2(\gamma)}{v_w^2 v_s^2} = 0 \tag{52}$$

Now let

$$\sin\psi_w = y - \frac{(v_w^2+v_s^2)}{2v_w v_s} \tag{53}$$

Eq. (52) then reduces to

$$y^4 + a'y^2 + b'y + c' = 0 \tag{54}$$

where

$$a' = \frac{-(v_w^2 - v_s^2)^2 + 8F^2(\gamma)}{2v_w^2 v_s^2}$$

$$b' = \frac{-4F^2(\gamma)(v_s^2+v_w^2)}{v_w^3 v_s^3}$$

$$c' = \frac{(v_w^2 - v_s^2)^2}{16 v_w^4 v_s^4}\left[(v_w^2 - v_s^2)^2 + 16F^2(\gamma)\right]$$

The resolvent cubic equation is

$$t^3 + \frac{a'}{2}t^2 + \frac{(a'^2 - 4c')}{16}t - \frac{b'^2}{64} = 0 \tag{55}$$

Substituting for a', b', and c' in this equation gives

$$t^3 + \frac{-(v_w^2 - v_s^2)^2 + 8F^2(\gamma)}{4 v_w^2 v_s^2} t^2 + \frac{\{2F^2(\gamma) - (v_w - v_s)^2\} F^2(\gamma)}{2 v_w^4 v_s^4} t$$

$$- \frac{(v_w^2 + v_s^2)^2 F^4(\gamma)}{4 v_w^6 v_s^6} = 0 \tag{56}$$

Now let $t = x + \dfrac{(v_w^2 - v_s^2)^2 - 8F^2(\gamma)}{12 v_w^2 v_s^2}$ (57)

Eq. (56) reduces to

$$x^3 + \alpha' x + \beta' = 0$$

where

$$\alpha' = - \frac{(v_w^2 - v_s^2)^4 + 8F^2(\gamma)(v_w^2 - v_s^2)^2 + 16F^4(\gamma)}{48 v_w^4 v_s^4}$$

or

$$\alpha' = - \frac{[(v_w^2 - v_s^2)^2 + 4F^2(\gamma)]^2}{48 v_w^4 v_s^4}$$

$$\beta' = - \frac{\{[(v_w^2 - v_s^2)^2 + 4F^2(\gamma)]^3 + (2)^5(27) v_w^2 v_s^2 F^4(\gamma)\}}{(27)(4)^2(2) v_w^6 v_s^6}$$

Now

$$\frac{\beta'^2}{4} + \frac{\alpha'^3}{27} = \frac{F^4(\gamma)[(v_w^2 - v_s^2)^2 + 4F^2(\gamma)]^3 + (2)^4(27) v_w^2 v_s^2 F^8(\gamma)}{(27)(2)^6 v_w^{10} v_s^{10}}$$

So

$$-\frac{\beta'}{2} \pm \sqrt{\frac{\beta'^2}{4} + \frac{\alpha'^3}{27}} = \frac{[(v_w^2 - v_s^2)^2 + 4F^2(\gamma)]^3 + (2)^5(27)v_w^2 v_s^2 F^4(\gamma)}{(27)(2)^6 v_w^6 v_s^6}$$

$$\pm \sqrt{\frac{F^4(\gamma)[(v_w^2 - v_s^2)^2 + 4F^2(\gamma)]^3 + (2)^4(27)v_w^2 v_s^2 F^8(\gamma)}{(27)(2)^6 v_w^{10} v_s^{10}}}$$

$$= \frac{[(v_w^2 - v_s^2)^2 + 4F^2(\gamma)]^3 + (2)^5(27)v_w^2 v_s^2 F^4(\gamma)}{(27)(2)^6 v_w^6 v_s^6}$$

$$\pm \frac{F^2(\gamma)}{(2)^3 v_w^5 v_s^5} \sqrt{\frac{[(v_w^2 - v_s^2)^2 + 4F^2(\gamma)]^3 + (2)^4(27)v_w^2 v_s^2 F^4(\gamma)}{27}}$$

Therefore from the theory of the general cubic equation

$$x_1 = \frac{1}{12 v_w^2 v_s^2} \Bigg[ \Big( [(v_w^2 - v_s^2)^2 + 4F^2(\gamma)]^3 + (2)^5(27)v_w^2 v_s^2 F^4(\gamma)$$

$$+ (2)^3 v_w v_s F^2(\gamma) \sqrt{27[(v_w^2 - v_s^2)^2 + 4F^2(\gamma)]^3 + (2)^4(27)^2 v_w^2 v_s^2 F^4(\gamma)} \Big)^{1/3}$$

$$+ \Big( [(v_w^2 - v_s^2)^2 + 4F^2(\gamma)]^3 + (2)^5(27)v_w^2 v_s^2 F^4(\gamma)$$

$$- (2)^3 v_w v_s F^2(\gamma) \sqrt{27[(v_w^2 - v_s^2)^2 + 4F^2(\gamma)]^3 + (2)^4(27)^2 v_w^2 v_s^2 F^4(\gamma)} \Big)^{1/3} \Bigg]$$

$$x_2, x_3 = -\frac{1}{(2)(12)v_w^2 v_s^2}\left[\left(\left[(v_w^2 - v_s^2)^2 + 4F^2(\gamma)\right]^3 + (2)^5(27)v_w^2 v_s^2 F^4(\gamma)\right.\right.$$

$$+ (2)^3 v_w v_s F^2(\gamma)\sqrt{27[(v_w^2 - v_s^2)^2 + 4F^2(\gamma)]^3 + (2)^4(27)^2 v_w^2 v_s^2 F^4(\gamma}$$

$$+ \left(\left[(v_w^2 - v_s^2)^2 + 4F^2(\gamma)\right]^3 + (2)^5(27)v_w^2 v_s^2 F^4(\gamma)\right.$$

$$- (2)^3 v_w v_s F^2(\gamma)\sqrt{27[(v_w^2 - v_s^2)^2 + 4F^2(\gamma)]^3 + (2)^4(27)^2 v_w^2 v_s^2 F^4(\gamma)}\Big)^1$$

$$\pm \frac{i\sqrt{3}}{(2)(12)v_w^2 v_s^2}\left[\left(\left[(v_w^2 - v_s^2)^2 + 4F^2(\gamma)\right]^3 + (27)(2)^2 v_w^2 v_s^2 F^4(\gamma)\right)^1\right.$$

$$- \left(\left[(v_w^2 - v_s^2)^2 + 4F^2(\gamma)\right]^3 + (2)^5(27)v_w^2 v_s^2 F^4(\gamma)\right.$$

$$- (2)^3 v_w v_s F^2(\gamma)\sqrt{27[(v_w^2 - v_s^2)^2 + 4F^4(\gamma)]^3 + (2)^4(27)^2 v_w^2 v_s^2 F^4(\gamma)}\Big)^1$$

Transforming gives the solutions of Eq. (55)

$$t_1 = \frac{1}{12v_w^2 v_s^2}\left[\left(\left[(v_w^2 - v_s^2)^2 + 4F^2(\gamma)\right]^3 + (2)^5(27)v_w^2 v_s^2 F^4(\gamma)\right.\right.$$

$$+ 2v_w v_s F^2(\gamma)\sqrt{27[(v_w^2 - v_s^2)^2 + 4F^2(\gamma)]^3 + (2)^4(27)^2 v_w^2 v_s^2 F^4(\gamma)}\Big)^{1/3}$$

$$+ \left(\left[(v_w^2 - v_s^2)^2 + 4F^2(\gamma)\right]^3 + (2)^5(27)v_w^2 v_s^2 F^4(\gamma) - (2)^3 v_w v_s F^2(\gamma)\cdot\right.$$

$$\sqrt{27[v_w^2 - v_s^2)^2 + 4F^2(\gamma)]^3 + (2)^4(27)^2 v_w^2 v_s^2 F^8(\gamma)}\Big)^{1/3} + (v_w^2 - v_s^2)^2 - 8F^2(\gamma$$

$$t_2, t_3 = -\frac{1}{(2)(12)v_w^2 v_s^2}\Bigg[\bigg(\left[(v_w^2 - v_s^2)^2 + F^2(\gamma)\right]^3 + (2)^5(27)v_w^2 v_s^2 F^4(\gamma)$$

$$+ (2)^3 v_w v_s F^2(\gamma)\sqrt{27\left[(v_w^2 - v_s^2)^2 + 4F^2(\gamma)\right]^3 + (2)^4(27)^2 v_w^2 v_s^2 F^4(\gamma)}\bigg)^{1/3}$$

$$+\bigg(\left[(v_w^2 - v_s^2)^2 + 4F^2(\gamma)\right]^3 + (2)^5(27)v_w^2 v_s^2 F^4(\gamma) - (2)^3 v_w v_s F^2(\gamma)\cdot$$

$$\sqrt{27\left[(v_w^2 - v_s^2)^2 + 4F^2(\gamma)\right]^3 + (2)^4(27)^2 v_w^2 v_s^2 F^4(\gamma)}\bigg)^{1/3} - 2(v_w^2 - v_s^2)^2$$

$$+ 16F^2(\gamma)\Bigg] \pm \frac{i\sqrt{3}}{(2)(12)v_w^2 v_s^2}\Bigg[\bigg(\left[(v_w^2 - v_s^2)^2 + 4F^2(\gamma)\right]^3 + (2)^5(27)v_w^2 v_s^2 F^4(\gamma)$$

$$+ (2)^3 v_w v_s F^2(\gamma)\sqrt{27\left[(v_w^2 - v_s^2)^2 + 4F^2(\gamma)\right]^3 + (2)^4(27)^2 v_w^2 v_s^2 F^4(\gamma)}\bigg)^{1/3}$$

$$- \bigg(\left[(v_w^2 - v_s^2)^2 + 4F^2(\gamma)\right]^3 + (2)^5(27)v_w^2 v_s^2 F^4(\gamma)$$

$$- (2)^3 v_w v_s F^2(\gamma)\sqrt{27\left[(v_w^2 - v_s^2)^2 + 4F^2(\gamma)\right]^3 + (2)^4(27)^2 v_w^2 v_s^2 F^4(\gamma)}\bigg)^{1/3}\Bigg]$$

Now from the theory of equations the solutions of Eq. (54) are

$$y_1 = \pm\left(-\sqrt{t_1} - \sqrt{t_2} - \sqrt{t_3}\right)$$

$$y_2 = \pm\left(-\sqrt{t_1} + \sqrt{t_2} + \sqrt{t_3}\right)$$

$$y_3 = \pm\left(\sqrt{t_1} - \sqrt{t_2} + \sqrt{t_3}\right)$$

and

$$y_4 = \pm\left(\sqrt{t_1} + \sqrt{t_2} - \sqrt{t_3}\right)$$

To save space the symbols [+] and [-] are defined such that

$$t_1 = \frac{1}{12 v_w^2 v_s^2} \left\{ [+] + (v_w^2 - v_s^2)^2 - 8F^2(\gamma) \right\}$$

$$t_2, t_3 = - \frac{1}{(2)(12) v_w^2 v_s^2} \left\{ [+] - 2(v_w^2 - v_s^2)^2 + 16F^2(\gamma) \right\} \cdot \qquad (58)$$

$$\pm \frac{i\sqrt{3}}{(2)(12) v_w^2 v_s^2} [-]$$

The theory of complex numbers states that

$$(A + iB) = (A^2 + B^2)^{\frac{1}{2}} e^{i\theta}$$

where

$$\theta = \sin^{-1} B/(A^2 + B^2)^{\frac{1}{2}}$$

Similarly

$$(A - iB) = (A^2 + B^2)^{\frac{1}{2}} e^{i\phi}$$

where

$$\phi = \sin^{-1} - B/(A^2 + B^2)^{\frac{1}{2}}$$

Now

$$\sin(-\theta) = -\sin\theta$$

So

$$A + iB = (A^2 + B^2)^{\frac{1}{2}} e^{i\theta}$$

$$A - iB = (A^2 + B^2)^{\frac{1}{2}} e^{-i\theta}$$

Taking the square root gives

$$\sqrt{A+iB} = (A^2+B^2)^{\frac{1}{4}} e^{i\theta/2} = (A^2+B^2)^{\frac{1}{4}} (\cos\frac{\theta}{2} + i\sin\frac{\theta}{2})$$

$$\sqrt{A-iB} = (A^2+B^2)^{\frac{1}{4}} e^{-i\theta/2} = (A^2+B^2)^{\frac{1}{4}} (\cos\frac{\theta}{2} - i\sin\frac{\theta}{2})$$

Inspection reveals that the only real roots of Eq. (54) are $y_1$ and $y_2$ which are

$$y = \pm(-\sqrt{t_1} \pm \frac{1}{\sqrt{6}v_w v_s} \{[+]^2 + 4(v_w^2 - v_s^2)^4 + 256\,F^4(\gamma)$$

$$-4(v_w^2 - v_s^2)^2[+] + 32F^2(\gamma)[+] - (4)(16)(v_w^2 - v_s^2)^2 F^2(\gamma)$$

$$+ 3[-]^2\}^{\frac{1}{4}} \cos\frac{\theta}{2})$$

where

$$\theta = \sin^{-1} \frac{\sqrt{3}[-]}{\left[\{[+] - 2(v_w^2 - v_s^2)^2 + 16\,F^2(\gamma)\}^2 + 3[-]^2\right]^{\frac{1}{2}}}$$

Transforming according to Eq. (53) gives

$$\sin\psi_w = \frac{1}{2v_w v_s}\left[\pm\left\{\frac{[+] + (v_w^2 - v_s^2)^2 - 8F^2(\gamma)}{3}\right\}^{\frac{1}{2}} \pm \frac{2\cos\frac{\theta}{2}}{\sqrt{6}}\right.\,.$$

$$\{[+]^2 + 4(v_w^2 - v_s^2)^4 + 256F^4(\gamma) - 4(v_w^2 - v_s^2)^2[+] \tag{59}$$

$$\left. + 32F^2(\gamma)[+] - 64(v_w^2 - v_s^2)^2 F^2(\gamma) + 3[-]^2\}^{\frac{1}{4}} - (v_w^2 + v_s^2)\right]$$

where

$$[\pm] = \Bigg[\Bigg(\big[(v_w^2 - v_s^2)^2 + 4F^2(\gamma)\big]^3 + (2)^5(27)\,v_w^2 v_s^2 F^4(\gamma)$$

$$+ (2)^3 v_w v_s F^2(\gamma)\sqrt{27\big[(v_w^2 - v_s^2)^2 + 4F^2(\gamma)\big]^3 + (2)^4(27)^2 v_w^2 v_s^2 F^4(\gamma)}\Bigg)$$

$$\pm \Bigg(\big[(v_w^2 - v_s^2)^2 + 4F^2(\gamma)\big]^3 + (2)^5(27)\,v_w^2 v_s^2 F^4(\gamma)$$

$$- (2)^3 v_w v_s F^2(\gamma)\sqrt{27\big[(v_w^2 - v_s^2)^2 + 4F^2(\gamma)\big]^3 + (2)^4(27)^2 v_w^2 v_s^2 F^4(\gamma)}\Bigg)^{1}$$

## Appendix B: The Graphical Determination of the Quantity U

In Eq. (43) there appears the quantity

$$U = \frac{(v_w \sin\psi_w + v_s \sin\psi_s)\{v_w + v_s \cos(\psi_s - \psi_w)\}}{2\cos\psi_w}$$

This quantity may be evaluated graphically in the following manner.

Step 1. On rectangular coordinate paper draw the non-dimensional satellite velocity vector $v_s$ from the origin (Figure B1).

Step 2. Draw a circle of radius $v_w$ about the end of $v_s$ (Figure B2).

Step 3. Draw a line through the center of the circle making an angle $\psi_w$ with the y-axis. Drop a perpendicular from the point of intersection of the circle and this line to the x-axis. Note the value of the abcissa (x). It is numericall equal to $(v_w \sin\psi_w + v_s \sin\psi_s)$ (Figure B3).

Step 4. Draw the tangent to the line representing the weapon velocity vector. Note the y intercept of the tangent line (y) (Figure B4).

Step 5. Calculate U from the equation

$$U = \frac{xy}{2}$$

In the example shown in Figures B1 - B4, the value of U obtained graphically is 0.27805, whereas that obtained from direct computation is 0.27855. The error in this method increases as $\psi_w$ approaches $\pm 90^\circ$. Also the application of this method is limited to angles $\psi_w$ remote from $\pm 90^\circ$, since angles on the order of $\pm 90^\circ$ have very large values of y and may fall outside the range of the graph.

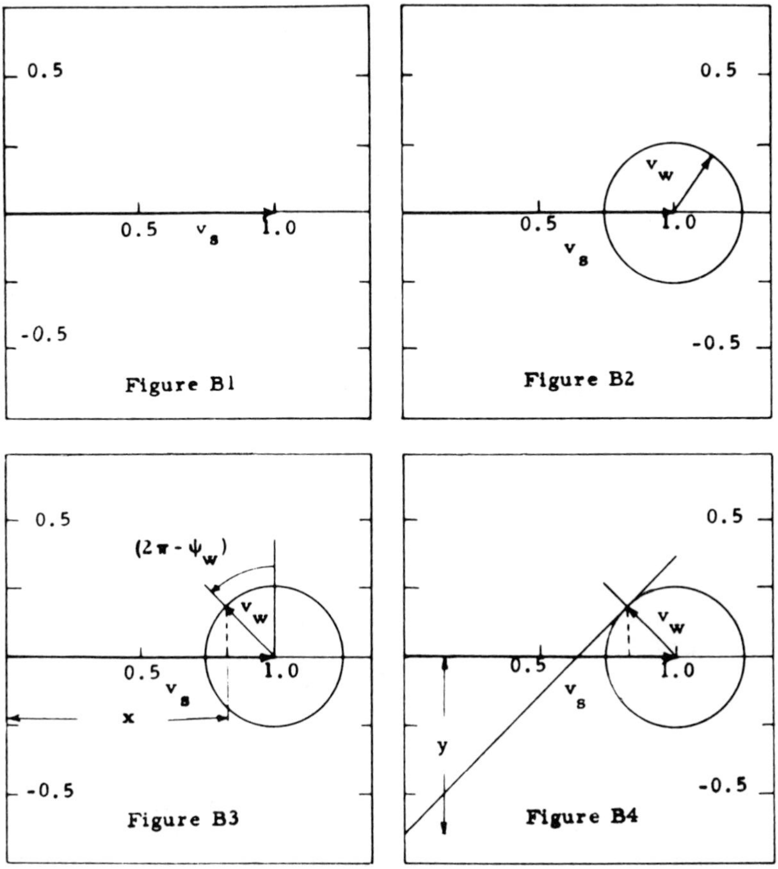


Figures B1-B4

Steps in the Graphical Determination of U

## Appendix C: A Method of Determining Minimum Energy Orbits

The elliptical-polar coordinate system described in the second part of this paper can be used to solve several interesting problems. One of these is the determination of points of minimum ballistic accessibility from a given point with an arbitrary constraint on the velocity vector at the given point.

The velocity constraining equation is (in non-dimensional units)

$$|\vec{v}| = v(\psi)$$

By transforming this equation into elliptic-polar coordinates having foci at the given point P and the force center, there results the equation of the locus of points having minimum ballistic accessibility from P. The transformation equations are

$$E = \tfrac{1}{2}v^2$$

$$\theta = 2\psi_o$$

Thus the equation of the locus of points of minimum ballistic accessibility from P is

$$E = \frac{1}{2}\left[v\left(\frac{\theta}{2}\right)\right]^2$$

A point Q is said to be a point of minimum ballistic accessibility relative to another point P if there exists no constraint on the velocity vector at P preventing the weapon from taking a minimum energy orbit from Q to P.

Another problem that can be solved by using elliptic-polar coordinates is that of finding the parameters of the minimum energy orbit between any two given points. To solve this problem set up an elliptic-polar coordinate system with one focus at the point from which the weapon is to be launched, and with the other focus at the force center. Transform the non-dimensional $(r, \gamma)$ coordinates of the other point into the elliptic-polar system. The transformation equations are

$$E = \frac{-(1 - r\cos\gamma) + \sqrt{1 - 2r\cos\gamma + r^2}}{r(1 + \cos\gamma)}$$

$$\theta = \sin^{-1} \frac{r \sin \gamma}{\sqrt{1 + r^2 - 2 r \cos \gamma}}$$

Once E and $\theta$ are found, the parameters v and $\psi_o$ of the minimum energy orbit may be found from

$$v = \sqrt{2E}$$

$$\psi_o = \frac{\theta}{2}$$

The points of minimum ballistic accessibility on an arbitrary curve in space relative to any given point may be found analytically by determining the points of tangency between the given curve and the coordinate lines E = constant. If the arbitrary curve is written as

$$E = E(\theta)$$

the points of minimum ballistic accessibility may be found from the equation

$$\frac{dE}{d\theta} = 0$$

An approximate solution to this problem, using the template shown in Figure C1, may be found as follows:

1) Plot the given curve on polar-coordinate paper to the same non-dimensional scale as the template (R in units of $R_o$).

2) Place the point marked O on the template over the origin of the polar plot and rotate the template until the $\gamma = 0$ line is superimposed on the $\psi = 0$ line.

3) From the template read the values of $\psi_o$ and v at the points of tangency of the curve and the elliptical field on the template.

4) Read the r, $\gamma$ coordinates of the points of tangency from the polar plot.

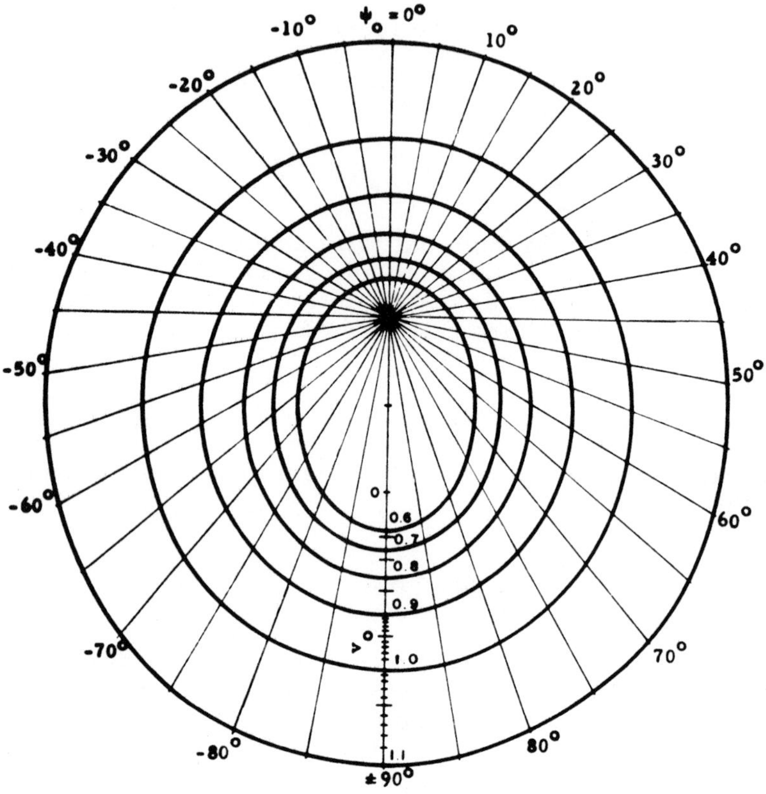


Figure C1

A Template for Solving Minimum Energy Orbital Transfer Problems

## Appendix D: The Surface Bounding the Region Accessible to a Weapon Launched from a Satellite

The surface bounding the region accessible to a weapon launched from a satellite may be found by an extension of the results presented in the fourth section of this paper, in which the parametric equations of the curve bounding the region accessible to a weapon launched from a satellite were derived under the assumptions that the weapon was launched in the satellite's orbital plane. Figure D1 shows how these equations may be used to define the three-dimensional bounding surface. The figure shows that if the total weapon velocity vector is constrained to lie in a plane containing the geocentric position vector of the satellite at launch time and if this plane is rotated through an angle β with respect to the plane of the satellite orbit, the parametric equations of the bounding curve in this new plane are simply the ones derived in the fourth section of this paper with the satellite and weapon velocity vectors transformed according to the following equations:

$$V_S(\beta) = V_S \cos\beta \tag{60}$$

$$V_W(\beta) = (V_W^2 - V_S^2 \sin^2\beta)^{\frac{1}{2}} \tag{61}$$

It may also be shown that the maximum angle through which the plane of the weapon orbit may be rotated is given by the expression

$$\beta_{max} = \sin^{-1}\frac{V_W}{V_S} \tag{62}$$

## Appendix E: List of Symbols

| | |
|---|---|
| A | The semimajor axis of an elliptical orbit (dimensional units) |
| a | The semimajor axis of an elliptical orbit (non-dimensional units) |
| C | A constant |
| E | The initial kinetic energy of the weapon (non-dimensional units) |
| $F(\gamma)$ | $\tan\gamma/2$ |
| i | $\sqrt{-1}$ |

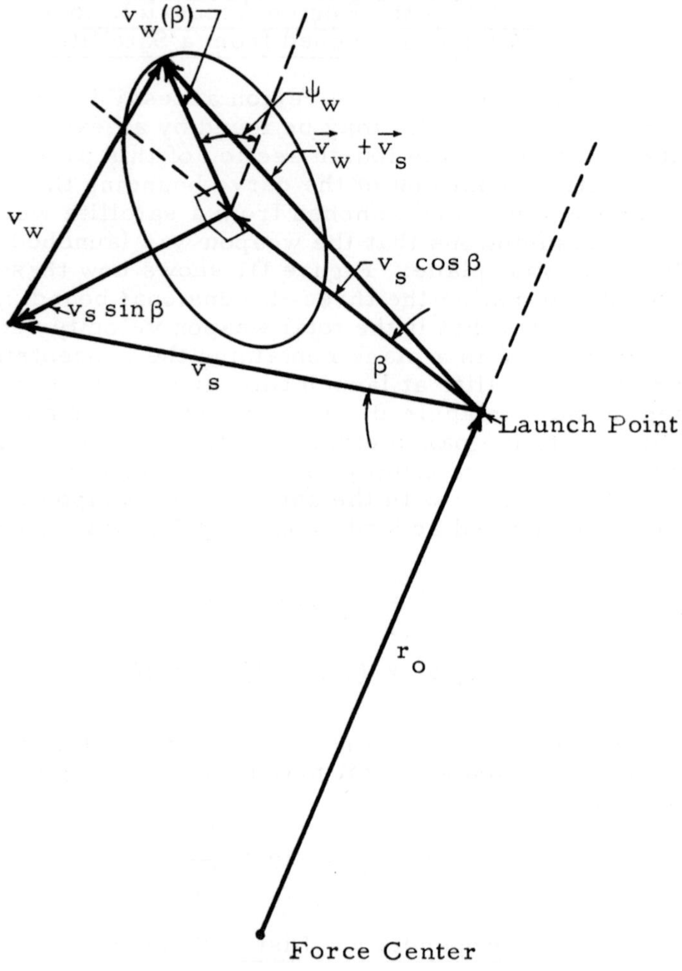


Figure D1

Geometry of the Satellite and Weapon Velocity Vectors

| | |
|---|---|
| $R$ | The radial distance to a point measured from the force center (dimensional units) |
| $r$ | The radial distance to a point measured from the force center (non-dimensional units) |
| $t$ | A variable in Eq. (55) |
| $U$ | A function in Eq. (43) |
| $V$ | The magnitude of a velocity vector (dimensional units) |
| $v$ | The magnitude of a velocity vector (non-dimensional units) |
| $X$ | A variable defined by Eq. (49) |
| $x$ | A variable defined by Eq. (57) |
| $y$ | A variable defined by Eq. (53) |
| $\alpha$ | The $\gamma$ coordinate of the weapon orbit apogee |
| $\beta$ | The $\gamma$ coordinate of the initial point |
| $\gamma$ | A polar angle measured about the force center from the line containing the initial point and the force center |
| $\Delta$ | The angle between the weapon's relative velocity vector and its total velocity vector |
| $\epsilon$ | The eccentricity of an ellipse or elliptical orbit |
| $\eta$ | A polar confocal elliptic coordinate |
| $\theta$ | An elliptic polar coordinate (the angle measured about the initial point from the line containing the initial point and the force center) |
| $\mu$ | The earth's gravitational constant |
| $\xi$ | A polar confocal elliptic coordinate |
| $\rho$ | The radial distance to a point measured from the initial point |
| $\phi$ | A phase angle |
| $\psi$ | The $\theta$ coordinate of a velocity vector |

Subscripts

| | |
|---|---|
| o | Refers to conditions at the initial point |
| 1, 2, 3. . . | Label different constants |
| s | Refers to quantities associated with the satellite |
| w | Refers to quantities associated with the weapon |

# SPACE PHYSICS

# PLASMA PROBES FOR SPACE EXPLORATION

Bernard Raab
Republic Aviation Corporation
Missile Systems Division
Mineola, New York

## Abstract

A probe which may be useful for determining the existence and measuring the properties of a relatively low temperature low density plasma constituent of space is described. The theory of such a probe is discussed, and in a series of laboratory experiments the probe is seen to be useful for the determination of plasma velocity and linear dimension (if limited), electron temperature and, possibly, ion density. The circuitry requirements are demonstrated to be simple and the data are easily analyzed. For use in space the probe elements would have to be separated by approximately 25 to 100 meters and be several square meters or more in area. An asymmetric probe which proves the existence of positive ions for a plasma of known propagating direction is described and its operation is experimentally demonstrated.

## A. Introduction

The measurement of a relatively low energy particle constituent of space would provide an important addition to current knowledge of the space environment. In particular, measurements of the density, temperature and velocity of the solar wind at various points in the solar system, as well as the detection of relatively low energy particles associated with solar flares or other cosmic events would be of great interest. Recent experience has demonstrated the futility of trying to predict in advance the determinations of most space probes. Scientific curiosity is usually sufficient motivation for such measurements.

The usefulness of single-particle detectors for measuring the material constitution of space is severely limited when information is desired in the energy range of from several to perhaps 100 electron volts. It may be possible, however, to measure this constituent as a plasma and bring to bear the various techniques which have been developed for the measurement of plasmas in the laboratory.

The particle densities of interest probably range from $10^2$ to $10^5$ particles per cubic centimeter. While certain optical and radiofrequency measurements are still possible at such densities, physical probes may be a primary measurement mechanism.

Perhaps the plasma probe most commonly used in the laboratory, as well as in ionospheric sounding experiments, is the single-wire probe, basically as developed by Langmuir and Mott-Smith in 1924 (1). This has been successfully used to determine electron temperature and plasma density in numerous experiments. The use of the Langmuir probe involves a variation of probe-to-plasma potential and simultaneous measurement of the consequent variation in electron probe current. In the laboratory, a convenient plasma-probe reference potential is generally available since access to the terminals of the discharge circuit and to a convenient ground is generally possible. In space, however, no such convenient reference potential presents itself, and the interaction of the plasma itself with the space vehicle is relied upon to establish the necessary potentials. For the tenous plasmas of interest here, however, this reliance will not, in general, be justified.

A plasma probe in space is basically a "floating" probe system (i.e., floating in potential), so that it would seem reasonable to seek the development of a symmetric double floating probe, such as described by Johnson and Malter, (2), for the measurements of interest here. Such a probe draws significantly less electron current from the plasma than the Langmuir probe, and has been seen to be both useful and accurate in measuring the properties of a gaseous discharge plasma (2, 3). The experiments described in this report were performed in an effort to determine its usefulness in measuring a freely propagating plasma -- unconnected to a potential source. The Bostick plasma "button-gun" was employed as a convenient source of plasma. Since this imparts a significant translational kinetic energy to the plasma, which arrives at the probe position with a rather sharply defined leading edge, this may correspond to the plasma emission of a solar flare.

In section B, the theory of the symmetric dual probe is reviewed and the effects of an external magnetic field are indicated. The experiments are described in section C, followed by experiments with asymmetric probe symmetry, and the results are analyzed. Section D contains the conclusions of the study.

## B. Probe Theory

### (1) Symmetric dual probe

The symmetric-probe technique involves the use of a pair of probes, each floating in potential with respect to the plasma and kept at some potential difference with respect to each other by an external source. This probe configuration may be employed to determine electron temperature and plasma density by the method to be outlined. The action of these probes is described qualitatively in the following paragraph.

A plasma in thermal equilibrium will, in general, tend to assume a potential that is slightly positive with respect to the most positive conductor it contacts. The electrons, with their greater random velocities, tend to produce a greater electron than ion current to each probe. Since the probes are floating, this tends to drive their potentials negative until a sufficient number of electrons is repelled to establish an equivalence of electron and ion currents. This is the equilibrium condition and results in each probe being surrounded by a small region of rising potential known as the "sheath." The ions move through the plasma under the influence of zero electric field. Upon entering a sheath region, however, they will be accelerated toward the probes and collected. Since the plasma will always be at a higher potential than the highest potential probe, the ion current to each probe will remain approximately constant over a large range of potential differences between probes. When a potential is applied between the probes, therefore, the net current flow in the circuit is strictly due to changes in electron flow to the respective probes. The general potential diagram for such a plasma probe configuration is shown in Fig. 1. $V_1$ and $V_2$ are the probe-to-plasma potentials for each probe. $V_D$ is the externally imposed potential; $j_1$ and $j_2$ are the random electron current densities in the regions near probes 1 and 2, respectively. $V_c$ represents any small potential difference in the plasma (which would tend to approach zero for highly conducting plasmas in field-free space) as well as any contact potentials acting on the system. As $V_D$ varies, the net current flowing between the probes will follow a function similar to that represented in Fig. 2 which is a somewhat idealized voltage-current characteristic for a floating dual-probe system. In Fig. 2, $i_{p_1}$ and $i_{p_2}$ are the saturated positive ion currents to probes 1 and 2, respectively. As discussed previously, these currents change insignificantly for applied potentials between points a and b. The electron currents in this region, however, will vary sensitively, thereby producing the net current flow, $i_D$, shown in Fig. 2. Electron currents $i_{e_1}$ and $i_{e_2}$ are flowing to probes 1 and 2, respectively. The absolute values of the total ion and electron currents to the probe system must be equal.

$$\left| i_{p_1} \right| + \left| i_{p_2} \right| = \left| i_{e_1} \right| + \left| i_{e_2} \right| \qquad (1)$$

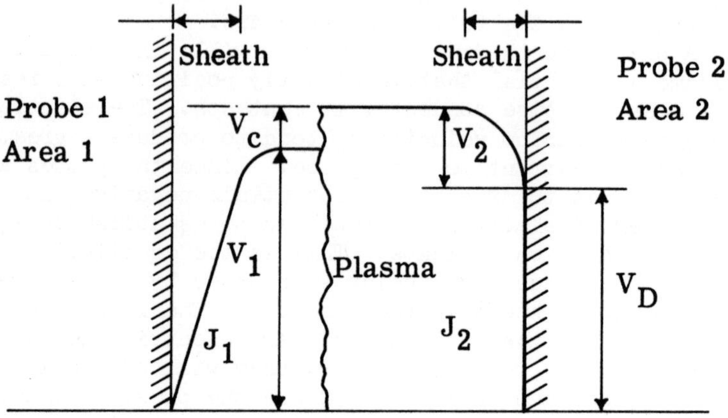


Figure 1. Potential Diagram--Dual Probe System.

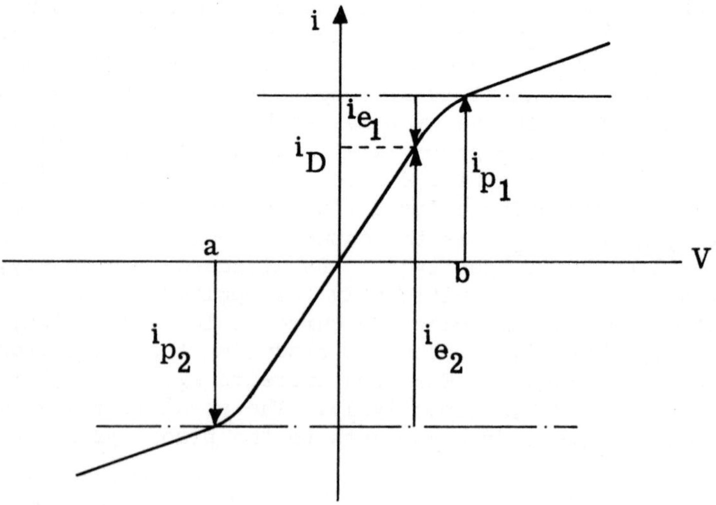


Figure 2. Probe Potential vs Current.

For voltages less than a or greater than b in Fig. 2, the current should ideally remain constant. In practice, however, there is some increase in positive ion currents in these regions due to a gradually increasing sheath area.

From the Boltzmann relation, the electron currents to each probe may be expressed as a function of the random electron currents in the vicinity of each probe multiplied by an exponential function of plasma-probe potential and electron temperature:

$$i_{e_1} = A_1 j_1 e^{-\phi V_1} \tag{2}$$

$$i_{e_2} = A_2 j_2 e^{-\phi V_2}$$

where $A_1$ and $A_2$ are the areas of probe plates 1 and 2 respectively, and $\phi = e/kT$, the inverse of temperature in electron volts. Substituting into Eq. (1), where all terms represent absolute magnitudes,

$$I_p = A_1 j_1 e^{-\phi V_1} + A_2 j_2 e^{-\phi V_2} \tag{3}$$

where $I_p = i_{p_1} + i_{p_2}$

From Fig. 1, however,

$$V_1 + V_c = V_2 + V_D \tag{4}$$

Substituting this expression into Eq. (2) yields

$$\Gamma_1 = \frac{A_2 j_2}{A_1 j_1} e^{-\phi (V_c - V_D)} \tag{5}$$

where $\Gamma_1 = \frac{I_p}{i_{e_1}} - 1$

Similarly,

$$\Gamma_2 = \frac{A_1 j_1}{A_2 j_2} e^{\phi (V_c - V_D)} \tag{6}$$

where $\Gamma_2 = \frac{I_p}{i_{e_2}} - 1$

so that $\Gamma_1 = \Gamma_2^{-1}$. Rewriting Eqs. (5) and (6),

$$\ln \Gamma_1 = -\phi(V_c - V_D) + \ln \frac{A_2 j_2}{A_1 j_1}$$

$$\ln \Gamma_2 = \phi(V\ -V\ ) - \ln \frac{A_2 j_2}{A_1 j_1} \tag{7}$$

Therefore,

$$\frac{d}{dV_D} \ln \Gamma_1 = \phi \ ; \ \frac{d}{dV_D} \ln \Gamma_2 = -\phi \tag{8}$$

so that a plot of ln $\Gamma$ vs $V_D$ should yield a straight line with a slope which is the inverse of electron temperature in electron volts. The line will pass through the origin if $A_1 j_1 = A_2 j_2$ and if $V_c = 0$, i.e., if there are no contact potentials or potential gradients within the plasma. Evaluating the left side of Eq. (8),

$$\frac{d}{dV_D} \ln \Gamma_1 = \frac{1}{\Gamma_1} \frac{d\Gamma_1}{dV_D} = \frac{I_p}{i_{e_1} i_{e_2}} \quad \frac{di_{e_1}}{dV_D} \tag{9}$$

Since the quantity $\frac{di_{e_1}}{dV_D}$, or its practical equivalent $\frac{di_D}{dV_D}$, is constant in the region between a and b (Fig. 2), the quantity $I_p/i_{e_1} i_{e_2}$ must also be constant in this region. That this is not true in general can be seen from the fact that

$$\frac{I_p}{i_{e_1} i_{e_2}} = \frac{1}{i_{e_1}} + \frac{1}{i_{e_2}} \tag{10}$$

It would appear, therefore, that $\phi$, and hence the temperature, is not constant with a variation of potential applied between the probes. This may be explained, however, by remembering that Eq. (2) is based upon a Maxwellian distribution of electron velocities which an applied potential tends to upset. Since we are actually interested in the temperature of the unperturbed plasma, Eq. (9) should be evaluated at $V_D = V_c$, that is, where the applied field just cancels out the field due to contact potentials or ambipolar charge diffusion in the plasma. It is not necessary to determine $V_c$ explicitly, however, since at $V_D = V_c$, $V_1 = V_2$ (Eq. (4)), and $i_{e_1} = i_{e_2} = i_e$ (Eq. (2)). Eq. (9), therefore, becomes

$$\phi = \frac{I_p}{i_e^2} \left(\frac{di_D}{dV_D}\right)_{V_D = V_c} \tag{11}$$

or since $I_p = 2i_e$

$$T = \frac{I_p}{4\left(\frac{di_D}{dV_D}\right)_{V_c = V_D}} \quad \text{electron volts} \tag{12}$$

which is the form derived by Biberman & Panin (4). Since $di_D/dV_D$ is constant over the range of $V_D$ from a to b (Fig. 2), it is only necessary to determine the saturated positive ion currents to each probe and the slope of the current vs voltage curve in the linear region of the curve. Tverdokhlebov has shown (5) that the Langmuir probe characteristic may be derived as a special case of the dual-probe characteristic, that is, where $V_2$ = constant.

From a knowledge of the saturated positive ion current $i_{p_1}$ and ion temperature, it is possible to calculate ion density and, hence, electron density, if plasma neutrality is assumed.

If the mean-time for electron-ion energy equilibration is short compared to the time since generation of the plasma, it may be assumed that ion temperature is essentially equal to electron temperature. Otherwise, it would be necessary to make an independent measurement of ion temperature by some means such as spectral-line broadening, if such a measurement is possible. In any event, the measurement is not critical for an order-of-magnitude determination of plasma density since temperature appears to the one-half power. In general, the ion density $n_i$ is given by:

$$n_i = \frac{j_p}{eW_{av}} \tag{13}$$

where $j_p$ = ion current density
$e$ = electronic charge
$W_{av}$ = average drift velocity of ions

In general:

$$W_{av} = \frac{1}{4} W_p \tag{14}$$

where $W_p = 1.87 \times 10^{-8} (T_p/m_i)^{\frac{1}{2}}$ average ion velocity averaged over a Maxwellian distribution
$T_p$ = plasma temperature, degrees Kelvin
$m_i$ = ion mass

and

$$j_p = \frac{i_p}{A_s} \tag{15}$$

where $i_p = i_{p_1} = i_{p_2}$, saturated positive ion current to probe
$A_s$ = sheath area

Therefore, Eq. (13) becomes

$$n_i = \frac{1.34 \times 10^{27} i_p}{A_s} \sqrt{\frac{m_i}{T_p}} \ (\text{cm})^{-3} \tag{16}$$

where $i_p$ is in amperes, $A_s$ in square centimeters, $m_i$ in grams, and $T_p$ in degrees Kelvin.

(2) Symmetric dual probe in a magnetic field

The previous discussion considers the behavior of a plasma subjected to an external electric field and the information which may be derived from the variation of current to the probes with a variation of electric field strength, where no magnetic field is assumed to be present. In general, however, it will be necessary to operate in a region of external magnetic field, which may significantly alter the voltage-current characteristic of the probes. While no attempt has been made to rederive the general theory presented in subsection 1 for the case of an externally imposed magnetic field, the general trend of effects may be noted.

The primary effect of the magnetic field will be produced when the magnetic field is perpendicular to the electric field, i.e., parallel to the probes (see Fig. 3).

In this case, ignoring sheath formation and assuming penetration of the electric field into the plasma as a whole, the net effect will be to give rise to a Lorentz drift, $\vec{W}_E$ , in the positive y direction, given by

$$\vec{W}_E = \frac{\vec{E} \times \vec{B}}{B^2} \tag{17}$$

In the case where a plasma sheath is formed, there is no loss of generality in this discussion since the equations will apply to the plasma regions into which electric field does penetrate, i.e., the sheath regions.

The effect of accelerating the plasma in the y direction is to produce an "inertial" drift, $W_i$ in the x direction, given by

$$\vec{W}_i = \frac{m}{qB^2}\left[\vec{B} \times \frac{d\vec{w}_E}{dt}\right] \tag{18}$$

Substituting Eq. (18) into Eq. (17),

$$\vec{W}_i = - \frac{m}{qB^2}\left[\frac{d}{dt}\left(\frac{\vec{E} \times \vec{B}}{B^2}\right) \times \vec{B}\right] \tag{19}$$

Assuming that $\vec{B}$ is constant in time,

$$\begin{aligned} W_{i_x} &= \frac{m}{qB^4} \dot{E}B^2 \\ &= \frac{m}{qB^2} \dot{E} \end{aligned} \tag{20}$$

Therefore, this drift, which is dependent on charge and mass, will provide a net flow of current in the direction of the electric field. Assuming that no collisions occur, this current density may be expressed by

$$j_x = \sum_k n_k q_k W_{i_k} \tag{21}$$

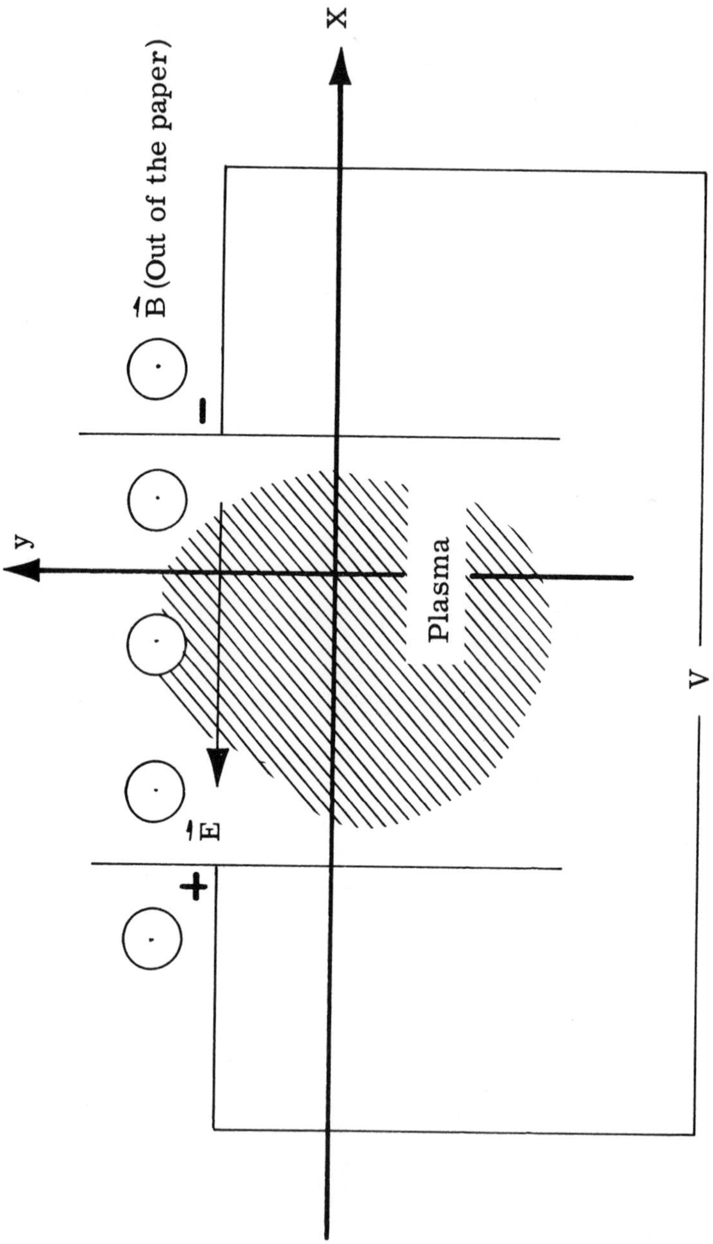


Figure 3. Magentic Field Orientation.

where the summation is performed over groups of various charges and masses. Assuming singly charged ions of equal mass and electrons only, from Eq. (20),

$$j_x = nq\left(\frac{m_i}{qB^2} + \frac{m_e}{qB^2}\right)\dot{E} = \frac{n(m_i + m_e)}{B^2}\dot{E} \qquad (22)$$

where $m_i$ = ion mass

$m_e$ = electron mass

Eq. (22) indicates that a simultaneous measurement of the rate of change of the electric field with the current to the probes will yield information on plasma density.

Although it has not been explicitly stated, it is assumed in this analysis that the separation distance between probe plates (or the thickness of the sheath) is greater than either the ion or electron gyroradius in the magnetic field. This condition will be much more readily met for the electrons than for the ions, so that the ion current will very likely remain a function of ion temperature, as in the case of no magnetic field, while the electron current will depend on electron temperature only insofar as this will determine the electron gyroradius. If this radius is smaller than the separation distance between probe plates, the electron current will be given by Eq. (22), with $m_i = 0$.

## C. Experimental Results

### (1) Solid-foil symmetric probe

The dual-probe technique has been successfully employed in measuring the properties of a gaseous discharge (2). In order to determine the feasibility of performing such measurements on freely propagating plasmas, a series of experiments was conducted in the absence of external magnetic field. A conveniently repeatable source of high-speed plasma, the Bostick plasma button-gun, was employed. This type of plasma source is described in detail in (6). A probe was constructed which consisted of two square parallel plates of tinned copper foil, each 1 square centimeter in area and separated by approximately 2.5 millimeters. These were oriented parallel to the direction of plasma propagation and biased by a static electric field. The complete experimental configuration is shown in Fig. 4. The pulse transformer serves to isolate the probes from ground. The low-pass filter, which cuts off at approximately 20 megacycles, serves to minimize high frequency background noise

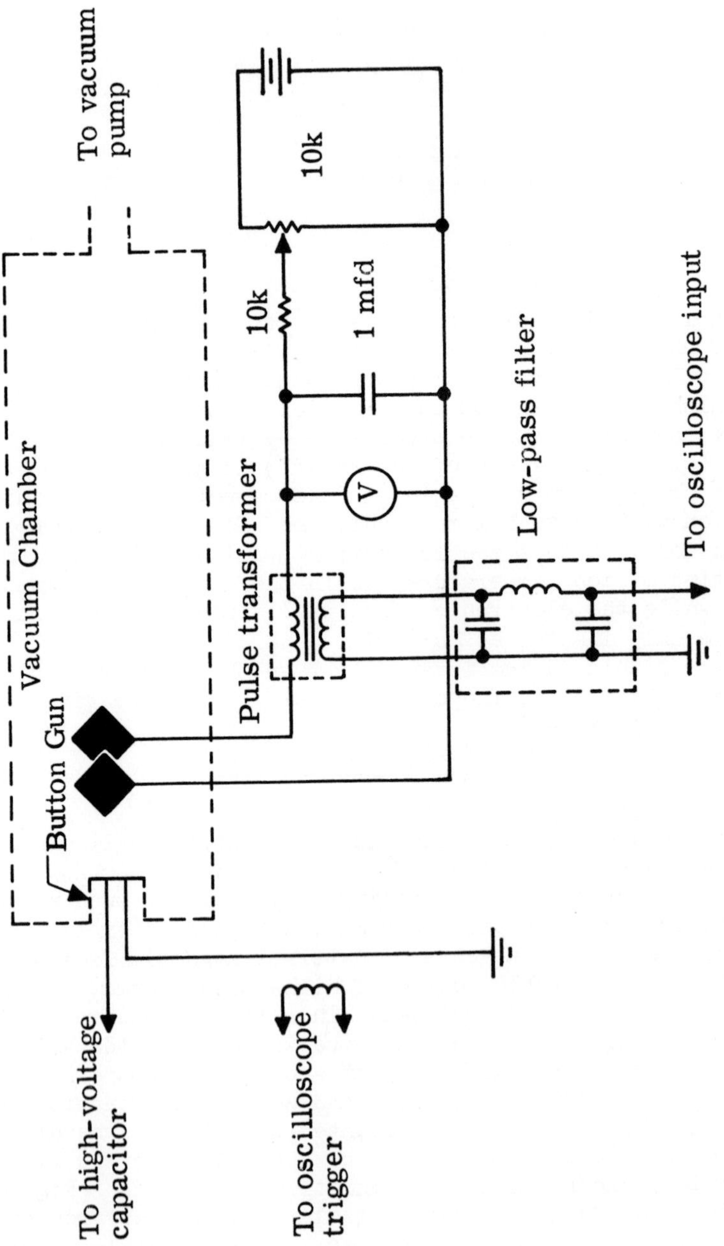


Figure 4. Experimental Configuration.

caused by the gun discharge. The 1-microfarad capacitor, which is charged from the variable battery supply, provides the potential on the probes which is measured by the voltmeter, V. The passage of plasma between the probe plates discharges the capacitor through the pulse transformer. This current produces a potential drop across the oscilloscope input resistance which is reflected into the primary circuit of the pulse transformer without attenuation (1:1 windings ratio). The oscilloscope, therefore, serves as an ammeter and should be shunted to a relatively low input resistance. The oscilloscope input resistance in these experiments was 170 ohms.

A series of experiments was performed with the probes placed at a distance of 20 centimeters from the plasma gun. The plasma gun was activated from a 0.3-microfarad capacitor bank charged to 2 kilovolts. Chamber pressure was $8 \times 10^{-6}$ millimeter of mercury. The results of varying probe bias from -40 to +40 volts are shown in Fig. 5. The trace is triggered by the discharge of the button-gun via a pick-up loop and proceeds from right to left in the photographs. The abscissa is marked in 2-microsecond intervals; the ordinate is marked in 5-volt, hence 29 milliampere, intervals. The data thus obtained may be plotted on a linear scale to give the current-voltage characteristic (Fig. 6). In view of the fact that each measurement was made only once, and each with a separately generated plasma, the experimental points fit the curve remarkably well. A calculation of electron temperature from Fig. 6 by the methods outlined earlier yields a value of approximately 9 electron volts. Calculating plasma density on the basis of a similar ion temperature results in a density of the order of $10^{12}$ particles per cubic centimeter. These values are considered reasonable on the basis of previous button-gun experiments and tend to lend confidence to the probe measurements. Plasma density may seem somewhat high, but it is unlikely that thermal equilibrium between ions and electrons exists at the point of measurement, so that the ion temperature may be considerably less than 9 ev. In addition, the plasma has long since expanded to the walls of the chamber and has been cooled by interaction with the walls.

In addition to measurement of electron temperature and plasma density, the symmetric dual probes may be seen to be useful for determining plasma propagation velocity and linear dimension. Since the trace in Fig. 5 is triggered at the time of initiation of the discharge, the distance of the probes from the source divided by the time-of-arrival of the leading edge of the signal gives a value of average plasma velocity over the time-of-flight to the probes. This measurement was made at various gun-to-probe distances to determine the effect of possible jitter in the triggering mechanism as well as possible existence of accelerations or decelerations operating over the time of flight of the plasma (7). The pertinent oscilloscope

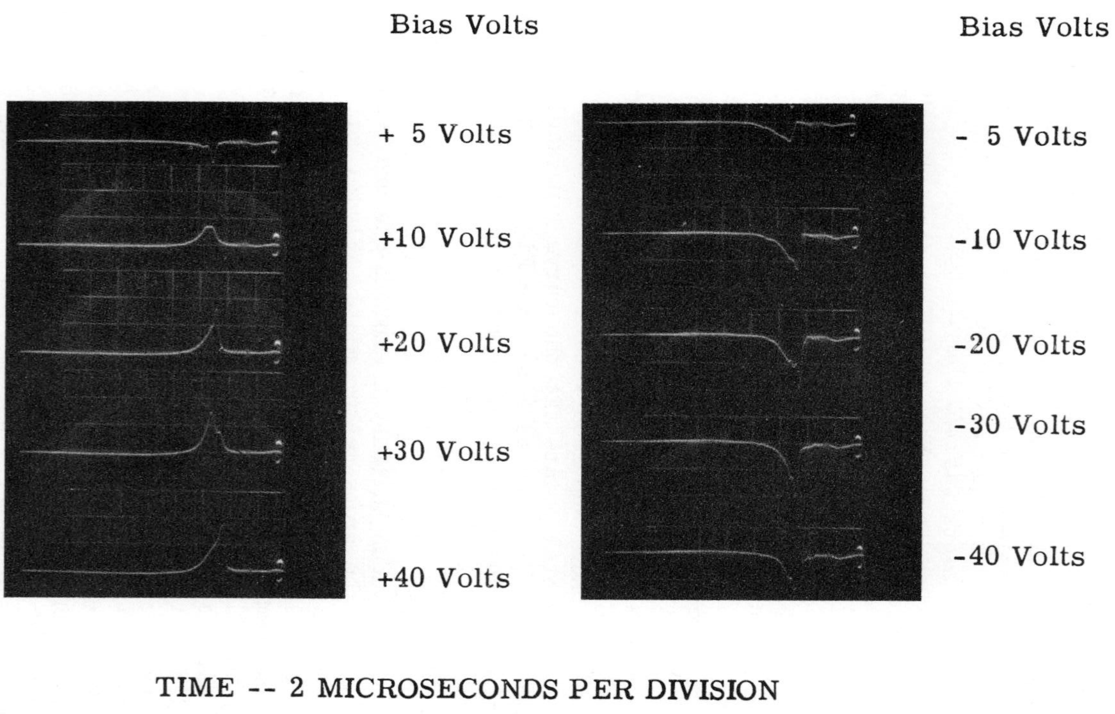


Figure 5. Probe Signals at Various Bias Voltages.

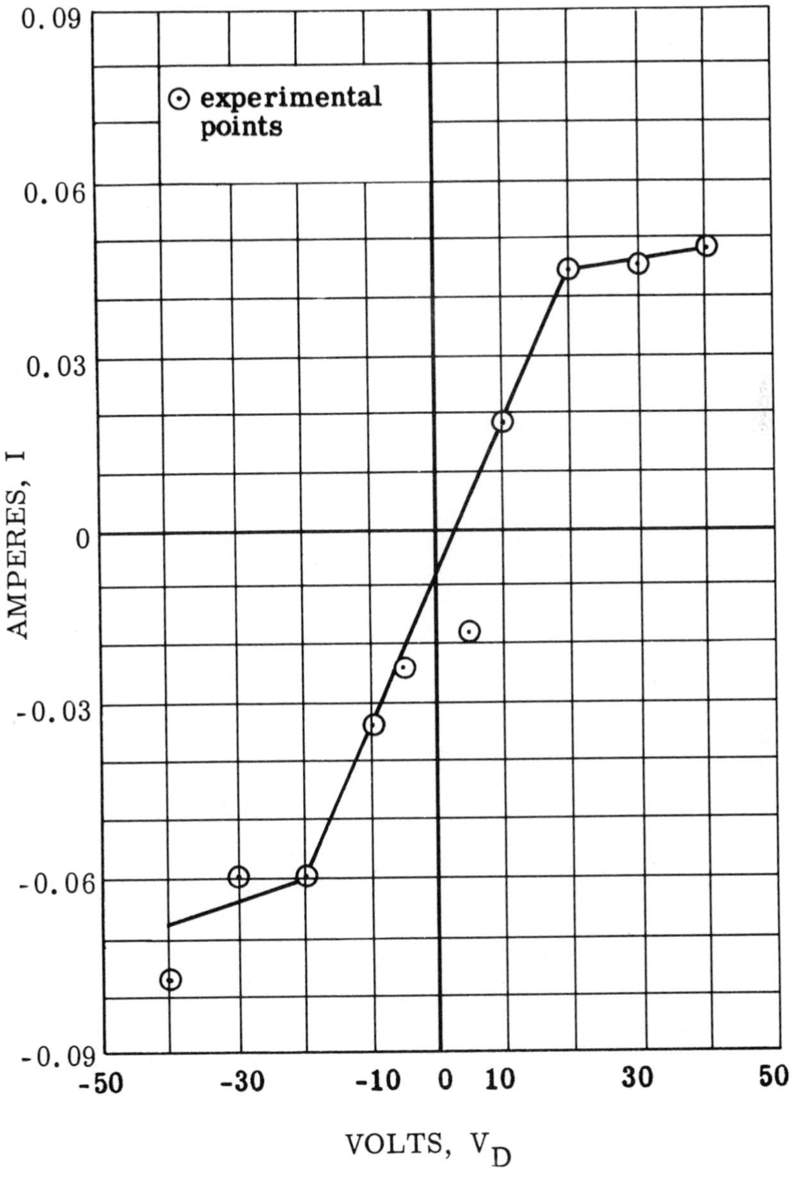


Figure 6. Current-Voltage Characteristic--Experimental.

data are reproduced in Fig. 7. The conditions are basically the same as those of Fig. 5, except that ambient chamber pressure was $5 \times 10^{-5}$ millimeter of mercury, and the battery was connected directly across the probe-pulse transformer combination at a potential of 22.5 volts. The gun-to-probe distance was varied from 9 to 21 centimeters, and the plasma velocity ($4.5 \times 10^{6}$ centimeters per second) was quite uniform over this interval. This value has been corroborated by microwave doppler shift measurements (8).

A knowledge of plasma velocity permits a calculation of the effective dimensions of the plasma in the direction of plasma propagation on the basis of observed pulse width. The pulse width is approximately 2.5 microseconds from 9 to 21 centimeters from the source; therefore, this dimension is approximately 10 centimeters.

(2) Wire-mesh symmetric probe

A disadvantage to the solid foil probes is that if the probes are oriented perpendicular to the direction of plasma propagation, one probe effectively shields the other and prevents plasma from propagating into the probe region. This is a particularly serious deficiency where measurements are desired in the presence of a magnetic field with the probes oriented both parallel and perpendicular to the magnetic field.

It was thought desirable, therefore, to construct a set of similar probes of copper wire mesh. These would present a smaller physical area to the plasma, thereby causing less disruption to plasma flow, and could possibly be oriented perpendicular to the principal direction of plasma propagation. Moreover, the configuration of the electric field between the probes would be unchanged, so that the dynamic behavior of the probe system should be similarly unchanged. The sheath area is formed, as previously, only on the sides of the probes facing each other, so that plasma can propagate through the wire mesh into the probe region freely before being influenced by the applied electric field of the probe system.

Consequently, two probes of copper wire mesh were fabricated to the same dimensions as the foils described previously (1 square centimeter each, over-all, mounted parallel to each other, 2.5 millimeters apart, on an insulated brass support arm and feed-through in the experimental chamber). The parallel foil probes, in duplicate relative geometry, were still in the chamber, mounted on a separate support arm, for comparative purposes.

The basic operation of the wire-mesh probes was first checked in comparison with the solid-foil probes in successive trials. The experimental circuit is shown in Fig. 7. Both the solid-foil probes and the wire-mesh probes were inter-

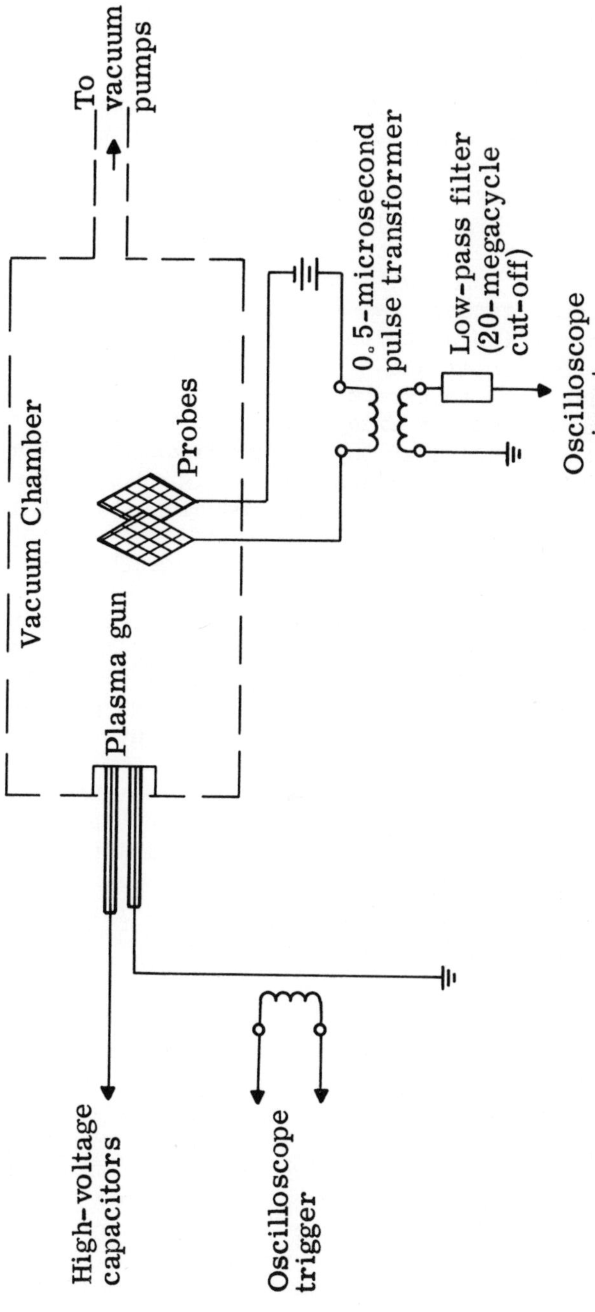


Figure 7. Experimental Circuit.

changeably connected to the same circuit for the comparison test. The test consisted of firing the plasma gun through the foil probes, which were oriented parallel to the principal direction of plasma propagation, while alternating the polarity of probe potential. The resultant oscilloscope traces (right-to-left) are shown in Fig. 8. The plasma gun was fired by the discharge of a 0.3-microfarad capacitor bank charged to 2 kilovolts. Chamber pressure varied between $5 \times 10^{-6}$ and $2 \times 10^{-5}$ millimeter of mercury. The abscissas are marked in 2-microsecond intervals. Fig. 9(a) shows the result of the solid-foil probe potential at 22.5 volts and with alternating polarity. The last trace was taken with zero probe potential as a control. The gun-to-probe distance was kept constant at 12 centimeters throughout the series of tests. The ordinate in Fig. 9(a) is marked in 28-volt intervals.

The series was then repeated with the wire-mesh probes under the same conditions except that the wire-mesh probes were oriented perpendicular to the principal direction of plasma propagation. The results are shown in Fig. 9(b). The ordinate is marked in 40-volt intervals. Reproducibility between the two sets of measurements appears quite satisfactory except for an apparent increase in signal strength obtained by the use of the wire-mesh probes.

This may be due to increased plasma density between the probes due to the removal of much of the self-shielding action of the solid-foil probes, or it may possibly be due to some effect associated with the direction of plasma propagation. This may be checked by a series of measurements at various probe potentials and orientations.

An additional check of the usefulness of the wire-mesh probes was obtained by a series of experiments at increasing gun-to-probe distances (Fig. 10). The conditions were the same as for Fig. 9(b) except that the runs were made at distances of 9, 12, 15, 18, and 21 centimeters, respectively. Plasma propagation speed is seen to be $4.5 \times 10^6$ centimeters per second, precisely as measured previously with the solid-foil probes.

(3) Asymmetric Probe

Plasma probe measurements are frequently suspected of yielding signals due to factors other than the existence of plasma in the vicinity of the probe. In particular, probe measurements are open to suspicion of conduction by an electron cloud composed either of electrons emitted from the source or of photoelectrons produced at the probe by ultraviolet emission at the source. While the latter possibility is effectively excluded by a signal variation in time as a function of distance from the source, an asymmetric probe configuration was devised which would permit definite identification of the existence of

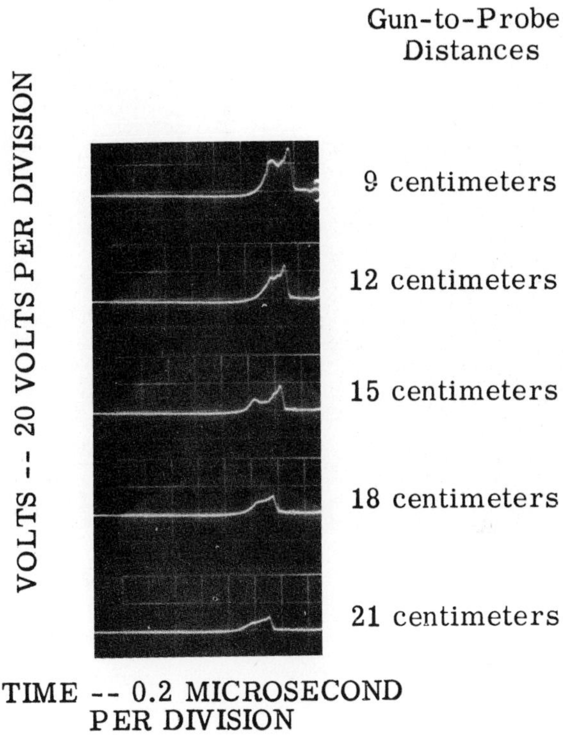


Figure 8. Probe Signals at Various Gun-to-Probe Distances.

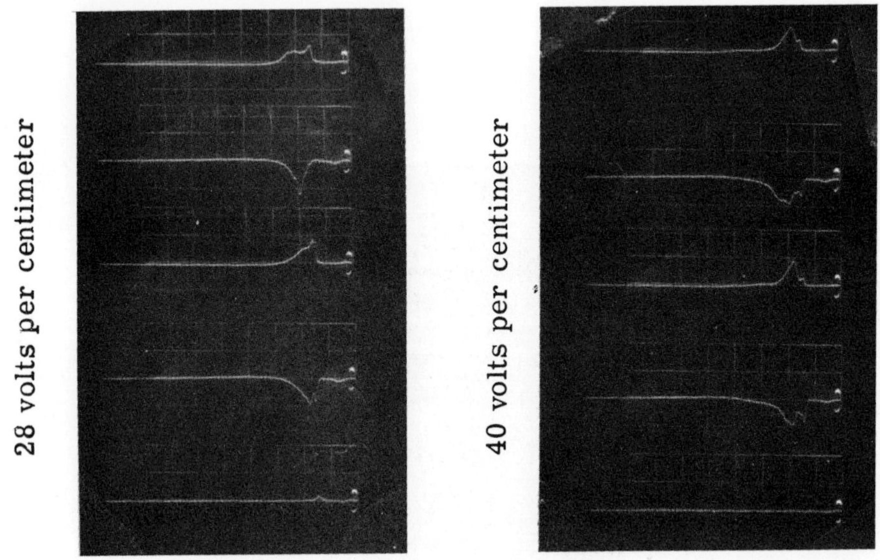


2 microseconds per centimeter
(a) Solid-foil probes

2 microseconds per centimeter
(b) Wire-mesh probes

Figure 9. Results of Probe Measurements.

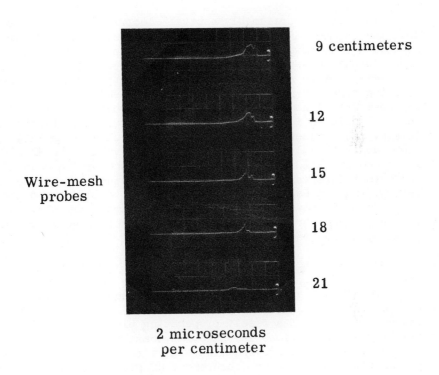

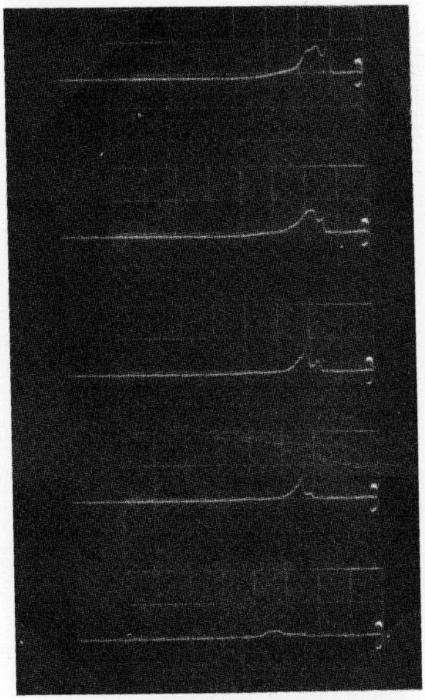


Figure 10. Results of Measurements Made at Varying Distances.

propagating positive ions. This configuration consisted of a disc of copper screen, 2 inches in diameter, set parallel to and separated by 1 centimeter from a solid copper disc 1 inch in diameter. These were oriented in a plane perpendicular to the direction of plasma propagation; the screen was placed nearer to the plasma gun. The circuit is the same as that used in the previous experiments except that the copper screen is grounded (Fig. 11).

The plasma, presumably neutral electrically, propagates down the chamber and through the screen relatively undisturbed. At this point, however, it enters a region of electric field which induces a separation of charge and a consequent reduction of electric field strength which results in a signal. An increasing negative bias on the plate will result in an increasing positive signal (until the saturation voltage is reached) only if positive ions are present. This is seen to be the case in Fig. 12. Traces a, b, c, d, and e were taken with -25, -50, -100, and -125 volts on the plate, respectively. The abscissa is marked in 2-microsecond intervals, and the ordinate is marked in 80-volt intervals. The gun-to-probe distance was 19 centimeters, and chamber pressure was about $10^{-5}$ millimeter of mercury

Positive bias on the plate yielded strong signals, but they were much more widely spread. At biases of 40 volts and greater, plasma oscillations were induced.

## E. Conclusions

The floating dual-probe system has been demonstrated to be a useful device for the determination of the velocity and linear dimension of a freely propagating plasma "blob." For velocity determinations in space, at least two such probes, suitably separated, are required. A voltage excursion of the probes with simultaneous measurement of probe current is sufficient for a determination of electron temperature. An independent measurement of ion temperature or an inference of electron-ion thermal equilibrium permits the calculation of ion density.

Although experience with the wire-mesh probes to date is incomplete, it appears at present perfectly feasible and desirable to use them for measuring the plasma properties that have previously been measured by the solid-foil probes with some success. It has been demonstrated that measurements may be taken with the wire-mesh probes oriented perpendicular to the principal direction of plasma propagation.

An asymmetric probe system is described and demonstrated to be useful for a determination of the existence of propagating plasma in the region of the probes, rather than a group of high-velocity electrons propagating through a background plasma cloud, or electrons produced at the probes by electromagnetic radiation from distant points.

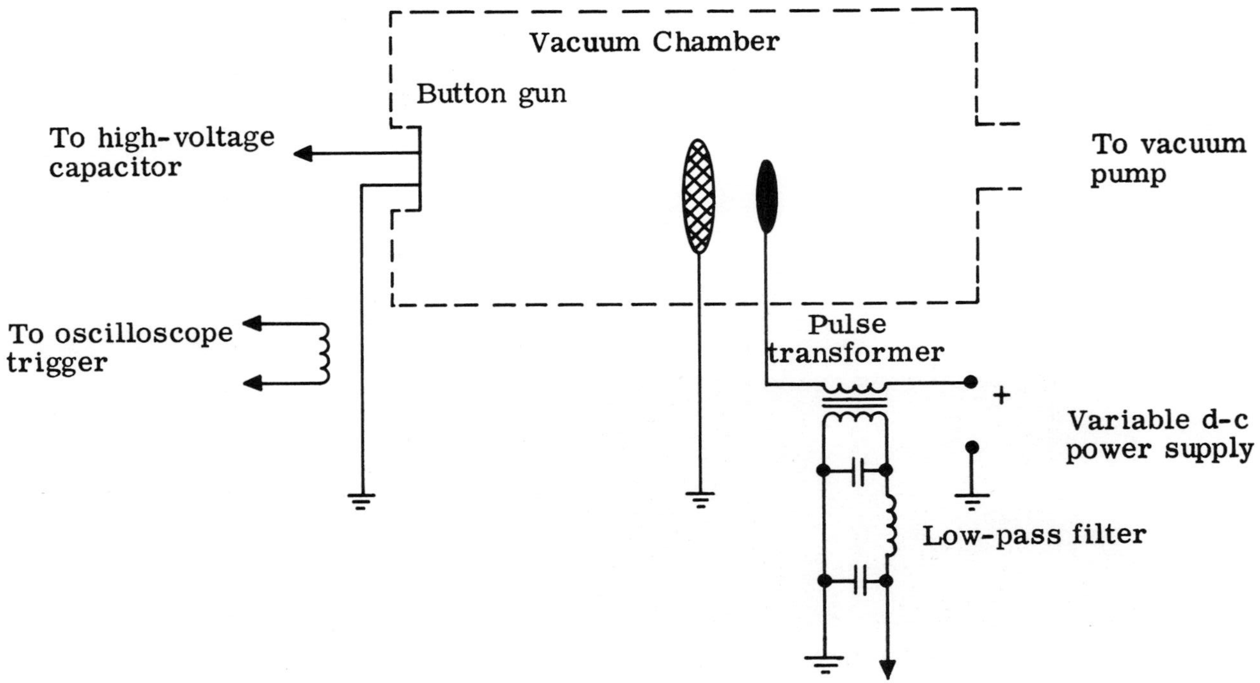


Figure 11. Asymmetric Probe Circuit.

VOLTS -- 80 VOLTS PER DIVISION

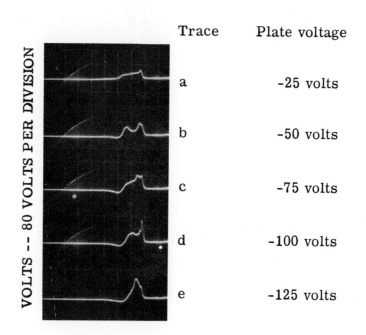

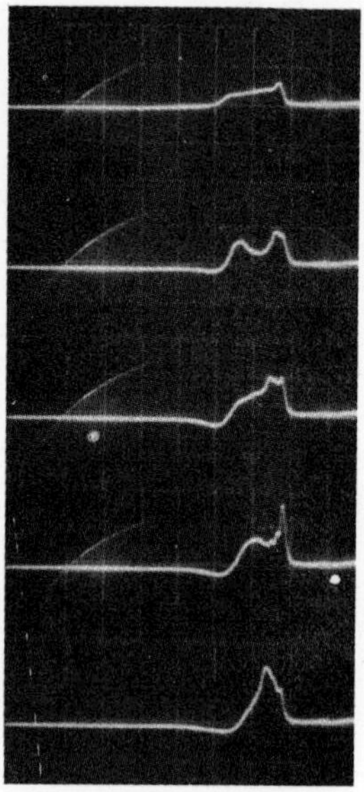

| Trace | Plate voltage |
|---|---|
| a | -25 volts |
| b | -50 volts |
| c | -75 volts |
| d | -100 volts |
| e | -125 volts |

TIME -- 2 MICROSECONDS PER DIVISION

Gun-to-probe distance -- 19 centimeters

Chamber pressure -- $10^{-5}$ millimeter of mercury

Figure 12. Probe Signals for Various Negative Plate Voltages

The theory of the symmetric dual-probes as reviewed in section B assumes the formation of a plasma-sheath on the effective probe face. In order for this to occur, the probes must be separated by a distance equal to several Debye lengths in the plasma. The maximum Debye length for the plasmas of interest will occur at the maximum temperatures and minimum densities of interest. If these are arbitrarily defined as 100 electron-volts and 100 per cubic centimeter respectively, the maximum Debye length will be approximately 7 meters. Therefore, under these conditions, the probe separation distance should be of the order of 20 to 100 meters. Probe currents of the order of microamperes would result from probe areas of the order of several square meters.

## F. Acknowledgements

The experiments reported herein were performed in the Plasma Laboratory of the Department of Physics of the Stevens Institute of Technology. The author wishes to acknowledge the hospitality and valued suggestions offered by the members of this department, in particular by Drs. Winston H. Bostick, Samuel J. Koslov, and George Schmidt. The assistance of the Publications Section of Republic Aviation Corporation, Missile Systems Division in the preparation of this report is acknowledged. This research was supported by the Physics Division, Research Directorate Air Force Special Weapons Center, Air Research and Development Command, Kirtland Air Force Base, Albuquerque, New Mexico.

## References

1. Langmuir, I., and Mott-Smith, H.M., General Electric Review, vol. 27, 1924. pp. 449, 538, 616, 762, 810.

2. Johnson, E.O., and Malter, L., Physical Review, vol. 80, 1950. p.1.

3. Dzherpetov, Kh.A., and Pateiuh, G.M., Soviet Physics (JETP), vol. 28, 1955. p.3.

4. Biberman, G.L., and Panin, B., Journal of Technical Physics (USSR), vol. 21, 1951. p.1.

5. Tverdokhlebov, V.I., Soviet Physics (JETP), vol. 2, 1957. p.4.

6. Bostick, W.H., Physical Review, vol. 104, 1956. p.2.

7. Raab, B., "Experimental Research on Expanding Plasmas and Plasmoids," Republic Aviation Corporation Report No. MSD 206-956, AFSWC-TR-59-65, 9 November 1959.

8. DiMarco, J., unpublished data, Department of Physics, Stevens Institute of Technology.

# RADIO PROPAGATION EXPERIMENTS FOR INVESTIGATING THE SOLAR WIND*

S. Rubin and S. D. Softky
Stanford Research Institute
Menlo Park, California

## Abstract

Velocity and density data on the solar wind plasma can be obtained by analysis of frequency differences in radio signals propagated between separated vehicles outside of the earth's atmosphere. Two different types of experiments are proposed: (1) to measure the effect of solar flares on the solar wind by means of the anomalous Doppler shift generated by the changing refractivity of the medium, and (2) to study the "steady state" solar wind by means of the difference in Doppler shifts between two oppositely moving vehicles in a moving medium. The magnitudes of the frequency changes are estimated and shown to be within present measurement capabilities.

## Introduction

Several of the basic properties of the solar wind and of solar flare effects, such as density, homogeneity, velocity, and dimensions, can be investigated by means of the interaction between the ionized hydrogen of the solar atmosphere and radio-frequency radiation transmitted through it. In particular, frequency perturbations offer a fruitful opportunity for making measurements, because of the very great precision with which frequencies can be measured.

In this paper some experiments are proposed by which some of the properties of the solar wind may be directly and continuously observed, and by which solar flare clouds may be studied by utilizing their intermittent perturbation of the solar wind parameters.

These experiments are based on the fact that the refractive indices of a plasma are known functions of frequency and of electron density. Consequently, electron densities can be

* This research was sponsored by Lawrence Radiation Laboratory, under Project Agreement No. 22, Subcontract 122.

determined by "radio-optical" experiments designed to yield refractive indices at appropriate frequencies.

By considering a somewhat generalized theory of Doppler shift, which takes into account the properties of the medium along the ray path between a radiation source and a receiver, as well as their relative motions, it is found that measurable effects arising from the time variation of the density of the medium can be obtained.

Furthermore, in a homogeneous medium, a relativistic Doppler theory yields a means of direct measurement of the velocity of the medium, as well as its density.

If the electron density in the solar wind is about $10^3$ $cm^{-3}$ at one A.U. from the sun, the critical plasma oscillation frequency, $\nu_c$, is about 300 kilocycles $sec^{-1}$. Any frequency higher than this will be propagated, and the medium will have relatively large refractive effects at frequencies slightly greater than $\nu_c$. The choice of frequencies to be used will depend on the range of densities to be investigated in any particular experiment. For some experiments, more than one frequency is required to give an explicit solution of the equations.

## Detection of Solar Flares and Other Inhomogeneities in the Solar Wind

Consider a source of frequency $\nu$ at point b and a detector at point a, such that both a and b may be functions of time (i.e., source and detector both moving), and consider that the intervening medium along the ray path has a refractive index varying in both space and time. The source frequency $\nu$ is assumed to be constant.

If W is the number of wavelengths between the source at b and the detector at a,

$$W = \int_a^b \frac{dx}{\lambda} = \frac{\nu}{c} \int_a^b n_p dx \qquad (1)$$

where $n_p$ is the phase index of refraction and c is the velocity of light.

The total frequency shift, $\Delta\nu$, between the source frequency and that measured by the detector is the rate of change of W:

$$\Delta\nu = \nu_{det.} - \nu_{source} = - \frac{dW}{dt} = - \frac{\nu}{c} \cdot \frac{d}{dt} \int_a^b n_p dx \qquad (2)$$

From Peirce's Table of Integrals - No. 857:

$$\frac{d}{dt}\int_a^b n dx = \int_a^b \frac{\partial n}{\partial t} dx + n(b)\frac{db}{dt} - n(a)\frac{da}{dt}$$

We define the refractivity, $\eta$, by $\eta = 1-n$. Therefore one may replace $\partial n/\partial t$ in the integral by $-\partial\eta/\partial t$. This may be more convenient because $\eta$ is proportional to the density of the medium.

Let $\eta = \alpha\rho$, where $\rho$ is the density of the medium. Then

$$\frac{c}{\nu}\Delta\nu = \alpha\int_a^b \frac{\partial\rho}{\partial t} dx - n(b)\frac{db}{dt} + n(a)\frac{da}{dt} \qquad (3)$$

We note that the second and third terms on the right side are proportional to the velocity components of the source, (db/dt), and the detector, (da/dt), parallel to the ray path at their corresponding positions (that is, along the x-coordinate). Therefore, these will be termed the source and detector Doppler shifts, respectively, corresponding to common usage.

The integral term gives an additional frequency shift which is not explicitly a function of the source or detector velocities, but is dependent only on the homogeneity and time dependence of the medium itself. We shall call this the "refractivity shift".

The time variation of the density along the ray path may be due to motion of an inhomogeneous medium across the ray path; to lateral displacement of the ray path due to components of the velocities of either the source or the detector perpendicular to the ray direction at each; to changes in the direction of the ray path resulting from the varying refraction of the medium; to purely time-dependent variations in the medium; or to combinations of any of these.

The determination of the velocity of a vehicle from frequency shift measurements requires that the effects of refractivity be taken into consideration. In some cases of interest, the local point is stationary with respect to the surrounding medium so that $da/dt = 0$; $db/dt = V$. If $\eta \ll 1$, we can write the refractivity in the form:

$$\eta = f(\nu)\rho$$

then

$$\frac{c}{\nu}\Delta\nu = f(\nu)\int_a^b \frac{\partial\rho}{\partial t} dx - (1 - f(\nu)\rho_b)V$$

$$= -V + f(\nu)\left[\int_a^b \frac{\partial\rho}{\partial t} dx + \rho_b V\right] \qquad (4)$$

We note that the bracketed factor is the rate of change of the integrated density along the ray path,

$$\frac{c}{\nu} \Delta\nu = - V + f(\nu) \frac{d}{dt} \int_a^b \rho \, dx \tag{5}$$

To solve for V by measuring frequency shifts, one must know the explicit form of the dispersion law, $f(\nu)$.

The phase refractive index, $n_p$, for a plasma is given by

$$n_p^2 = 1 - \frac{\nu_c}{\nu}^2 \quad . \tag{6}$$

so that

$$f(\nu) = \frac{k}{\nu^2} \tag{7}$$

Let

$$\frac{d}{dt} \int_a^b \rho dx = M(t)$$

Then

$$\frac{c}{\nu} \Delta\nu = - V + \frac{kM(t)}{\nu^2}$$

$$kM = V\nu_1^2 + c\nu_1\Delta\nu_1 = V\nu_2^2 + c\nu_1\Delta\nu_2$$

$$\frac{V}{c} = \frac{\nu_2\Delta\nu_2 - \nu_1\Delta\nu_1}{\nu_1^2 - \nu_2^2} \quad . \tag{8}$$

Although one can determine velocities by measuring the frequency shifts at two frequencies, in any medium for which the dispersion law is known, it is not possible to separate explicitly the refractive index at the vehicle from the time dependence of refractivity along the path. In situations in which there is independent evidence that the time dependence of the refractivity is negligible, then one obtains the following expression for the phase index of a plasma at the vehicle:

$$n_1 = \frac{\left(\frac{\nu_2}{\nu_1}\right)^2 - 1}{\frac{\nu_2}{\nu_1}\left(\frac{\Delta\nu_2}{\Delta\nu_1}\right) - 1} \tag{9}$$

It appears feasible to use the refractive shift to investigate the hydrogen emissions resulting from solar flares. It is believed that an average flare emits $\sim 10^{15}$ g of hydrogen (1).

If the density of the flare cloud is $\sim 10^5$ atoms $cm^{-3}$ at the earth's orbit (2), corresponding to the onset of a geomagnetic storm, then the diameter of the cloud can be estimated to be $\sim 10^6$ km. Its velocity is apparently $\sim 10^3$ km $sec^{-1}$, based on the delay time between the occurrence of a flare on the sun, and on the onset of the resulting geomagnetic storm. This velocity is also consistent with the measurements of Biermann (3) on the deflection of comet tails.

The critical frequency of the plasma is given by

$$\nu_c^2 = 8 \times 10^7 N \qquad (10)$$

where N is the electron density in $cm^{-3}$. For a density of $10^5$ ionized hydrogen atoms $cm^{-3}$, the critical frequency is 2.8 Mc.

To make observations with the receiver on the surface of the earth, the transmitted frequency should be at least 20 Mc to penetrate the ionosphere. If we choose 100 Mc for convenience, the refractivity of the cloud will be $4 \times 10^{-4}$, which will give relatively large effects. Since the density of the solar wind outside the cloud is $\sim 10^3$ atoms $cm^{-3}$, its refractivity may be neglected compared with that of the cloud.

When such a cloud intercepts the ray path between the transmitter and receiver, there will be a frequency shift corresponding to the rate of change of path length measured in wavelengths.

For a plane front moving at velocity S across the ray path at angle $\theta$, the frequency shift, $\Delta\nu$, is given by

$$\frac{\Delta\nu}{\nu} = \frac{S\,\eta}{c\cos\theta} \,. \qquad (11)$$

By neglecting the angular dependence, we can obtain a lower limit to the refractivity shift. Thus for

$\nu = 100$ Mc $= 10^8$ cps
$S = 10^3$ km $sec^{-1}$
$\eta = 4 \times 10^{-4}$
$c = 3 \times 10^5$ km $sec^{-1}$

$$\Delta\nu \geq \frac{10^8 \times 4 \times 10^{-4} \times 10^3}{3 \times 10^5} \approx 100 \text{ cps.}$$

It appears, therefore, that the predicted effect is large enough to be easily measured. The observed shift at any frequency will be the sum of the Doppler and the refractive shifts; however, as shown above, the velocity of the vehicle can be determined by use of two different frequencies.

For a vehicle velocity of $\sim 3$ km $sec^{-1}$, and $\nu = 100$ Mc, the Doppler shift is $10^3$ cps. With two frequencies one can measure both total frequency shift and Doppler shift. From Eq. (4) the difference between them is equal to

$$\frac{\nu}{c} f(\nu)\left[\int_a^b \frac{\partial\rho}{\partial t}\, dx + \rho_b\, V\right]$$

Since the first term has the magnitude of the density variation times the velocity of the inhomogeneities, and the velocities of flare clouds and of other inhomogeneities in the solar wind will generally be very large compared with the vehicle velocity, the first term in the bracket will dominate, unless the medium is extremely homogeneous.

The magnitude of the refractive shift and its time dependence can be used to give some information on the size and shape of the flare cloud. If the vehicle is sufficiently far away, and the full diameter of the cloud crosses the ray path, the phase shift will be $\sim 10^5$ cycles for a cloud diameter of $10^6$ km.

There remains the problem of planning an experimental configuration which would have a reasonable probability of observing the unpredictable occurrence of one or more solar flares. A vehicle orbiting the earth at the maximum stable radius would be advantageous from the standpoint of readiness. To obtain distances as large as $10^6$ km may require a solar orbit. A solar orbit sufficiently near that of the earth may permit the vehicle to remain within transmission range for many months. One could also launch a probe vehicle at the time a large solar flare is observed on the sun. Since the flare cloud or magnetic storm takes at least two days to arrive at the earth's distance, this would allow the probe to reach about $10^5$ km from the earth, if its average speed is 1 km $sec^{-1}$, before the cloud would intercept the transmission path.

Because of the large magnitude of the refractive shift at solar wind velocities, particularly for motions perpendicular to the ray path, it may also be possible to detect more or less continuous inhomogeneities or turbulence effects in the "normal" solar wind, rather than only the relatively rare solar flares. This, of course, would require detecting frequency shifts of the order of 1 cps or smaller.

Observations of such small frequency shifts place more stringent requirements both on the stability of the oscillators and on the possible effects of perturbations introduced by the earth's ionosphere. There is some evidence that the magnitude of the short-term refractivity shifts in the ionosphere at 20-40 Mc are of the order of 10 cps (4). Other observations of ionospheric scintillations on Sputnik III, Vanguard, and Explorer I are reported by Hutchinson and Arendt (5). The largest such effect was observed from Vanguard on 29 March 1958, when a frequency anomaly up to about 50 cps out of 108 Mc lasted about 3 minutes. The total phase shift was nearly 5000 cycles.

It is obvious that these ionospheric effects would mask any weak effects due to the solar wind. Therefore, to apply refractivity shift measurements to the study of the solar wind, it is necessary to place the receiver on a satellite outside of the ionosphere and to telemeter the observed frequency shifts to an earth station. If the source and receiver are both outside the ionosphere, then it is possible to use much lower frequencies, for which the refractivity of the solar wind is much larger.

The problem of oscillator stability can be solved by using a reference oscillator on the earth and by transmitting a suitable reference frequency to both satellites. However, a better solution would be the development of an extremely stable lightweight frequency standard which could be carried in the satellites. A possible device for this purpose is the rubidium vapor optical pump, using the field-independent levels of rubidium. This device is said to have a frequency stability as good as one part in $10^{12}$ (6).

Although this discussion deals only with phase velocities and CW transmission, similar results should be obtainable with equivalent techniques based on group velocity measurements and pulsed transmission.

## Velocity of the Solar Wind

It is very desirable to find a method for obtaining a direct measurement of solar wind velocity, especially if it can be done on a continuous basis for correlation with other solar and cosmic ray phenomena.

One method which was investigated was the possibility of using the Fresnel drag coefficient of a moving medium. However, it was found that the Fresnel drag of a plasma can be shown to be exactly zero; i.e., the refractive indices measured by an observer moving with respect to the medium are the same function of observed frequency as those measured by a stationary observer.

There is another effect in special relativity involving a moving medium, and that is the effect of the motion of the medium on the Doppler shift between a source and receiver which are in relative motion. This is shown to be a measurable effect for solar wind velocities of the order of $10^3$ km sec$^{-1}$, and for frequencies near the critical frequency.

If the detector is in motion relative to the source, and both are moving with respect to a homogeneous plasma, we can calculate the frequency seen by the detector by first transforming from source coordinates to medium coordinates, then again from medium to detector.

Let us number two vehicles 1 and 2, moving with parallel relative velocities $c\beta_1$ amd $c\beta_2$ with respect to the plasma, and located on a line parallel to the direction of motion.

$\nu$ = source frequency

$\nu'$ = frequency observed in medium

$\nu_1''$ = frequency observed at 1, when source is at 2

$\nu_2''$ = frequency observed at 2, when source is at 1

$n'$ = phase index of medium (for observer stationary in mediur

$V = c(\beta_2-\beta_1)$ = relative velocity of separation of vehicles

$U = \frac{c}{2}(\beta_1+\beta_2)$ = velocity of plasma with respect to the average velocity of vehicles.

The Doppler shift equations for radiation transmitted from 1 to 2 are:

$$\frac{\nu}{\nu'} = \frac{1 - \beta_1 n'}{\sqrt{1 - \beta_1^2}} \qquad (12a)$$

$$\frac{\nu_2''}{\nu'} = \frac{1 - \beta_2 n'}{\sqrt{1 - \beta_2^2}} \quad , \qquad (12b)$$

so that

$$\frac{\nu_2''}{\nu} = \frac{(1 - \beta_2 n')}{(1 - \beta_1 n')} \cdot \frac{\sqrt{1 - \beta_1^2}}{\sqrt{1 - \beta_2^2}} \qquad (13a)$$

The reverse of this procedure, with radiation transmitted from 2 to 1, is described by the same equation with $\beta_1$ and $\beta_2$ interchanged and reversed in sign.

$$\frac{\nu_1''}{\nu} = \frac{(1 + \beta_1 n')}{(1 + \beta_2 n')} \cdot \frac{\sqrt{1 - \beta_2^2}}{\sqrt{1 - \beta_1^2}} \qquad (13b)$$

Therefore, if the two transmitters send identical frequencies, the ratio of the frequencies of the two received signals will be:

$$\frac{\nu_2''}{\nu_1''} = \frac{(1 - \beta_1^2)}{1 - (\beta_1 n')^2} \cdot \frac{1 - (\beta_2 n')^2}{(1 - \beta_2^2)} \qquad (14)$$

For $\beta_1$, $\beta_2 \ll 1$:

$$\frac{\nu_2''}{\nu_1''} = \left[1 - \beta_2^2(n'^2-1)\right]\left[1 + \beta_1^2(n'^2-1)\right]$$

$$= 1 + (\beta_2-\beta_1)\ (\beta_1+\beta_2)\ (1-n'^2)$$

$$\frac{\nu_2''}{\nu_1''} = 1 + \frac{2VU\ (1-n'^2)}{c^2} \quad . \qquad (15)$$

Let

$$\nu_2'' - \nu_1'' = \delta\nu$$

Then

$$\frac{\delta\nu}{\nu} = \frac{2VU\,(1-n'^2)}{c^2} \tag{16}$$

We call $\delta\nu/\nu$ the "differential Doppler shift" for reciprocal transmission between two vehicles in a moving medium. We see that, as one would expect, the differential Doppler shift goes to zero if there is no relative velocity between the vehicles, if the medium is stationary, or if the medium is a vacuum.

The "one-way" Doppler shift can be used to determine the refractive index of the medium. Approximating Eqs. (13a) and (13b), since $\beta_1$, $\beta_2 \ll 1$.

$$\frac{\nu_2''}{\nu} = 1 - (\beta_2-\beta_1)n' = \frac{\nu_1''}{\nu} \tag{17}$$

Let

$$\nu'' - \nu = \Delta\nu \quad .$$

Then

$$\frac{\Delta\nu}{\nu} = -\frac{Vn'}{c} \quad . \tag{18}$$

This experiment requires that two earth satellites be in roughly circular orbits, traveling in opposite directions in the same plane. This plane should contain the sun-earth line, and the satellites should preferably pass each other when moving parallel to it. However, since slightly different orbital velocities would cause the passing point to precess around the earth, the above condition would be met periodically. The orbit radii should be around $10^5$ km so that the satellites will be well beyond the range of geomagnetic effects. At this radius, their orbital velocities will be about 2 km/sec.

The equations give the velocity of the medium in terms of the relative velocity between the two satellites and the refractive index of the medium. In the case of satellites around the earth, we can determine their relative velocity with good accuracy from independent observations of the orbit parameters, such as the period. Therefore the two measurements of ordinary and differential Doppler shift suffice to measure the density and the velocity of the solar wind.

Both satellites will radiate continuously at a frequency slightly above the critical frequency to obtain the largest possible value of $(1-n'^2)$. However, because of the great uncertainty in the electron density in this region, and the probability that it may vary, several different frequencies should be used. For these calculations, an electron density of

$10^3$ electrons/$cm^3$ will be assumed, giving a critical frequency of 280 kc, or a wavelength of about 1 km.

A tuned receiver on each satellite will pick up the signal and compare it with the frequency of the local oscillator. At the relative velocity of 4 km/sec, and a wavelength of 1 km, there will be a 4-cps beat frequency. This beat frequency can be telemetered to the earth by a sharp pulse signal each time the received and local frequencies are exactly in phase. Since the test frequencies are about $10^5$ times the beat, the in-phase condition can be detected precisely by the simultaneity of a null of both the received and the local signal. This eliminates the necessity of precise amplitude matching.

The relative magnitude of the solar wind effect can be estimated if it is assumed that $(1-n'^2)$ is a small number of the order of unity. Then

$$\delta\nu \sim \frac{2x10^3 \ x \ 3x10^5 \ x \ 4}{10^{11}} = 2x10^{-2} \text{ cps.}$$

This is about $10^{-7}$ of the oscillator frequency so that oscillator stability of the order of $10^{-8}$ is necessary to obtain a useful measurement. However, since each measurement of the differential Doppler shift can probably be made over an approach distance of $10^4$ km (0.1 radian), the duration of each measurement will be about 1 hour. Consequently, the precision of measurement of the Doppler shift frequencies can be of the order of $10^{-4}$, provided that the oscillators are as stable as $10^{-9}$. This order of stability should permit measuring solar wind velocities to an accuracy of about 1%.

The simple equations above assumed that the two local oscillators are at exactly the same frequency. If there is a small difference between them, then the error in the difference between the beat frequencies will be twice the frequency discrepancy between oscillators.

As the satellites pass each other, both U and V in our notation change sign, so that the sign of $\delta\nu$ is independent of whether they are approaching or receding. The effect of any oscillator discrepancy will not be detectable by comparison of approaching and receding beat frequencies. However, when the satellites pass on the opposite side of the earth, the relative direction of the solar wind is reversed, so that measurements of the frequency differences on both sides of the earth can be used to eliminate systematic frequency errors.

Since it is desirable to maintain this experiment over a period of several years, if possible, it appears necessary also to monitor the oscillators directly. The oscillator frequencies can be telemetered directly to earth from each satellite on the same channel used to transmit the Doppler frequencies. Thus the actual frequency can be monitored regularly, say at 100-hour intervals. This procedure should provide an independent determination of the frequency differences.

## Conclusions

The analysis of frequency differences and variations in electromagnetic signals close to the critical plasma frequency provides a useful tool for the study of the large scale properties of the solar wind. By the use of advanced techniques for generating stable frequencies and for the detection of small frequency differences, significant data can be obtained on density and velocity, and on the perturbations of the solar wind generated by solar flares. This method should also be useful to study the interaction between the geomagnetic field and the solar wind. These experiments require the use of two space vehicles to provide a signal path entirely outside of the interfering effects of the earth's ionosphere.

## Acknowledgment

The authors wish to thank Dr. W. N. Hess, of Lawrence Radiation Laboratory, for his support and encouragement of this work.

## References

1. Piddington, J. H., Phys. Rev, vol. 112, 1958, p. 589.

2. Unsold, A. and S. Chapman, Observatory, vol. 69, 1949, p.219.

3. Biermann, L., Observatory, vol. 107, 1957, p. 109.

4. Hibberd, F. H. and J. A. Thomas, J. Atmos. and Terr. Physics, vol. 17, 1959, p. 71.

5. Hutchinson, H. P. and P. R. Arendt. Proc. I.R.E., April 1960, p. 670.

6. Bell, W. E. (Varian Associates) - private communication.

# THE SCIENTIFIC RESULTS OF THE SATELLITE, EXPLORER VI*

Edward Smith and Alan Rosen
Space Technology Laboratories, Inc.
Los Angeles 45, California

ABSTRACT

The preliminary results of the scientific experiments flown on the earth satellite, Explorer VI, are reviewed. The discussion includes (1) the characteristics of the particle radiation as obtained from three different particle detectors: The University of Chicago Cosmic Ray Telescope, The University of Minnesota Ionization Chamber and Geiger tube, and the Space Technology Laboratories, Inc. Scintillation Counter; (2) the character of the extraterrestrial magnetic field as measured by the STL magnetometer; and (3) the determination of the electron density of the exosphere using a Doppler-difference, Faraday-rotation technique. The combined data from these experiments will be viewed in terms of the macroscopic and microscopic characteristics of the radiation belts, dynamic processes involving trapped and untrapped plasma, the existence of a toroidal ring current, and geomagnetic storm effects.

## The Explorer VI

On August 7, 1959 the Explorer VI payload was placed in an highly elliptical orbit by a three-stage booster consisting of a Thor first stage, an Aerojet 10-101 second stage, and an ABL 248 solid-propellant spin-stabilized third stage. The payload, weighing about 142 pounds, consisted of instruments for studying the space environment, a power supply with means of converting solar energy to electrical energy, a telemetry system to transmit the data to earth, and a five-pound solid propellant injection rocket which could be fired on command to increase perigee and thereby increase the payload's lifetime if perigee had been too low.

Figure 1 shows the payload with solar cells mounted on paddles so as to occupy a large surface area and still not

*This program was carried out under the direction of the National Aeronautics and Space Administration.

Fig. 1. Explorer VI Earth Satellite.

heat up the payload to an intolerably high temperature. Approximately 8000 silicon solar cells were carried by the vehicle; however, because of attitude and spin of the vehicle, only 1000 solar cells received solar energy at one time. The current output of the cells was used to charge storage batteries of 50 watt-hour capacity at 16.8 volts. These batteries were the primary power source for the telemetry system and scientific instruments in the payload.

The internal view of the payload is shown in Figure 2. A simplified block diagram of the Explorer VI electrical system is shown in Figure 3. Besides the analog telemetry systems shown in Figure 3, the Explorer VI communication system included a payload receiver to permit the reception of earth-transmitted commands which, when interconnected coherently with a third transmitter, form a transponder capable of providing velocity and range information as an aid in tracking the payload. The primary use of the third transmitter was as a digital telemetry system. It was carried aboard Explorer VI principally to evaluate its usefulness in transmitting information over extremely large distances. Since the digital telemetry system conveyed the same information as the analog system, it was possible to monitor the performance of the new digital system developed by STL.

The twelve signal inputs correspond to three groups of experiments. The first group consisted of four radiation experiments. These were a scintillation counter, Geiger counter, ionization chamber, and a proportional counter telescope. The primary objective of these experiments was to study the intensity, energy spectrum, extent, and time variation of the terrestrial radiation belts discovered as a result of experiments carried on the previous Explorer satellites (1) and Pioneer space probes (2),(3). The second group consisted of a magnetometer system, employing a search coil magnetometer, a flux-gate magnetometer, and an aspect indicator which could be used to determine the direction of the magnetic field vector. The third set of experiments involved a measure of temperatures, voltages, micrometeorites and various radio propagation experiments which could yield information on electron concentrations and whistler mode propagation in extraterrestrial space.

## Trajectory

The orientation of the Explorer VI orbit relative to the earth and sun is shown in Figure 4 where ecliptic coordinates have been employed. The Explorer VI orbit was highly elliptic with an apogee of 48,800 km (7.5 earth radii) and a perigee of 6620 km. The period of rotation was 12-3/4 hours. The plane of the orbit was inclined at an angle of 47$^{\circ}$ with respect to the geographic equatorial plane. The semimajor axis was

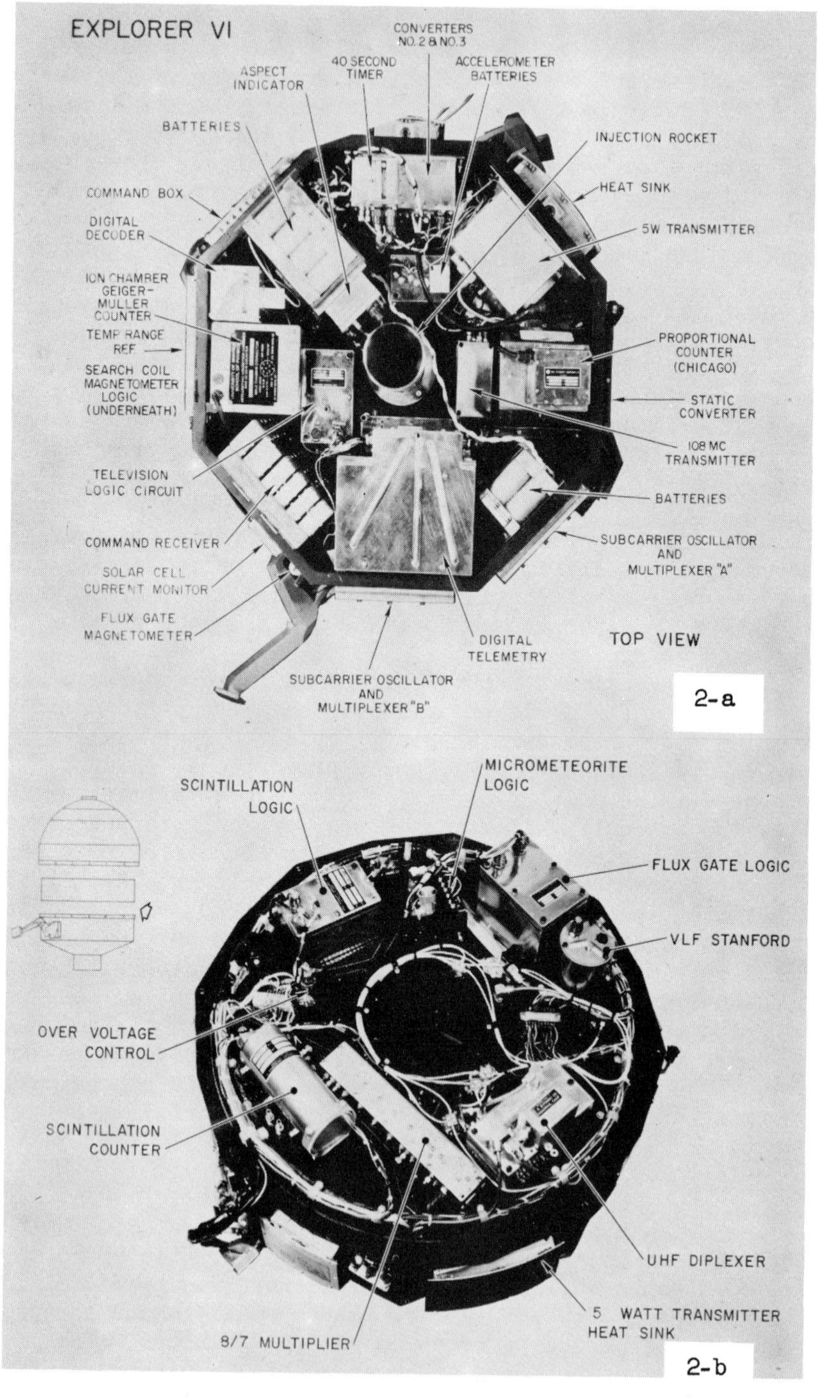


Fig. 2. Internal View of Explorer VI Payload.

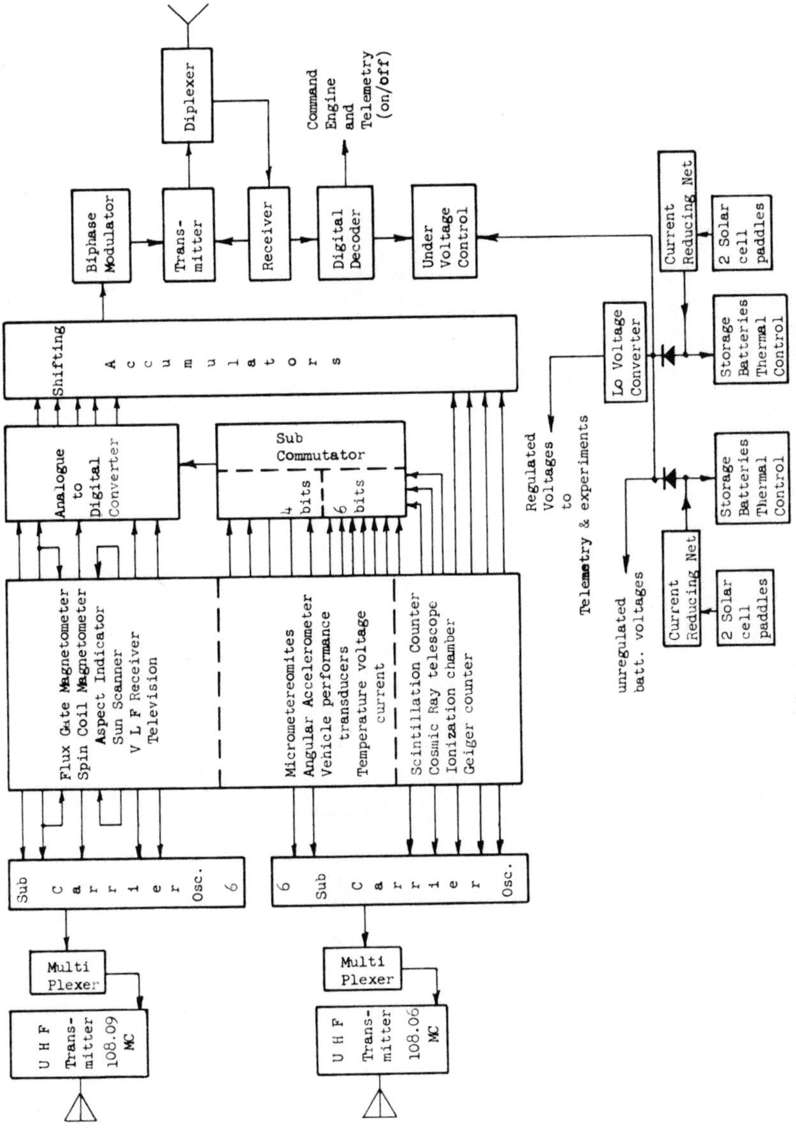


Fig. 3. Simplified Block Diagram of Explorer VI Instrumentation.

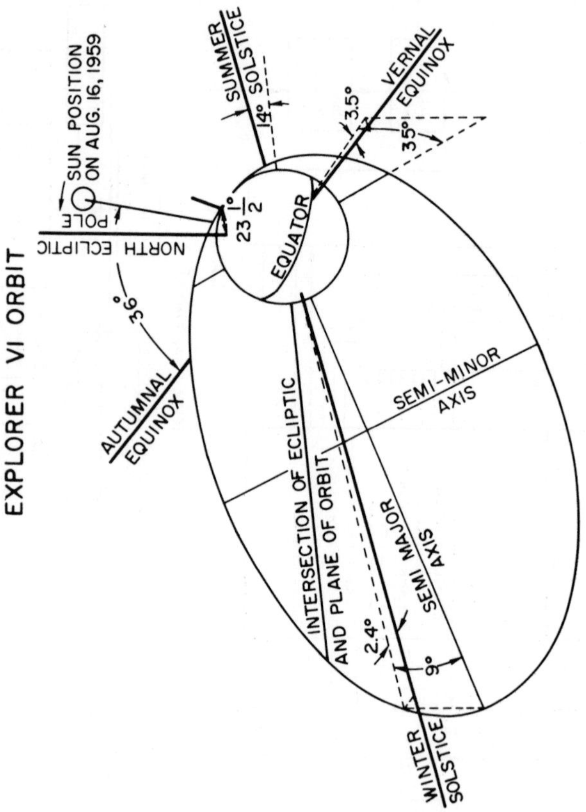


Fig. 4. The Orbit of Explorer VI.

inclined downward below the equatorial plane at an angle of 33° so that the payload spent most of its period at southerly latitudes. With respect to the earth-sun direction, apogee was located on the evening side of the earth at approximately 2100 hours local time.

This orbit had the advantage of an extremely high apogee which greatly exceeded those of previous earth satellites. This enabled measurements to be made twice daily throughout most of the trapped radiation region. In addition, particle and field measurements carried out at high altitudes were in a region where a transition to interplanetary conditions might be expected.

## Particle Radiation Experiments

Four detectors, on the Explorer VI payload, were used to determine the characteristics of the particles trapped in the radiation belt. The Geiger counter - ionization chamber combination responded to low energy electrons (energies greater than 30 kev). The scintillation counter was sensitive to electrons in the intermediate range of energies (greater than 200 kev). The proportional counter telescope responded to electrons of energy greater than 500 kev. The response of two of these instruments, the proportional counter telescope and the Geiger counter-ionization chamber combination, was indirect in that the bremsstrahlung produced by the electrons was detected. The scintillation counter responded to the electrons directly. These instruments were also sensitive to protons. The scintillation counter was most sensitive to low energy protons (energy greater than 2 Mev). The Geiger counter was next with an energy threshold at 25 Mev. By means of a triple coincidence system, the proportional counter telescope could be used to unambiguously identify protons of energy greater than 75 Mev.

A block diagram of the University of Minnesota experiment* is shown in Figure 5a. The Geiger counter measures the number of particles impinging on the sensitive volume of the chamber. The ionization chamber measures the number of ion pairs produced within its sensitive volume per unit time. The minimum energy to which these sensors respond is determined by the shielding around the sensors and the efficiency of the sensors for detection of bremsstrahlung radiation. Since the shielding around

---

*The Geiger counter - ionization chamber experiment was conducted under the direction of Prof. J. R. Winckler of the University of Minnesota. Material for the BMD Symposium was obtained from References (4) and (5).

BLOCK DIAGRAM OF ION CHAMBER AND GEIGER COUNTER

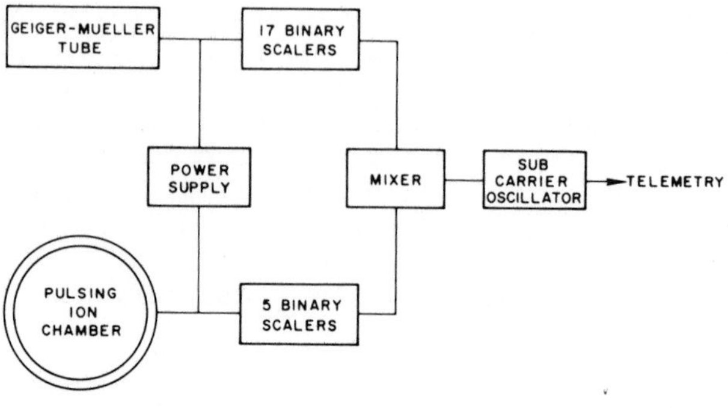


5-a

BLOCK DIAGRAM OF PROPORTIONAL COUNTER EXPERIMENT

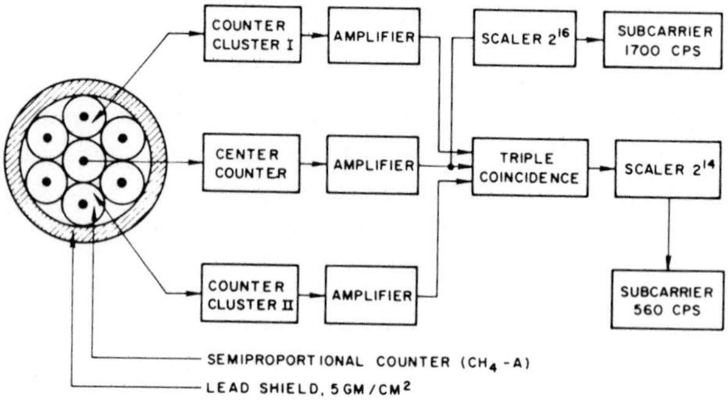


5-b

BLOCK DIAGRAM OF THE SCINTILLATION COUNTER EXPERIMENT

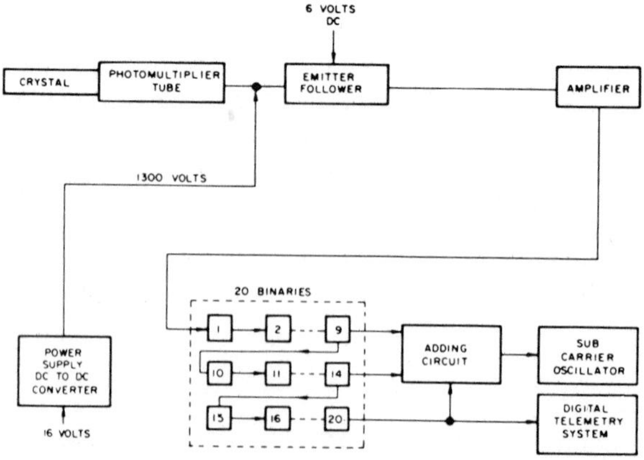


5-c

Fig. 5. Block Diagram of Radiation Experiments.

the two detectors is almost identical, it is possible to take the ratio of the outputs of the two sensors and thus obtain a measure of the mean number of ion pairs produced by each particle per centimeter of path. For a single charged particle the mean specific ionization is directly related to the particle velocity and may be used to determine the energy if the mass of the particle is known.

The proportional counter telescope* consisted of a group of seven discharge tubes, operating in a semiproportional region, and arranged in a closely packed array of six tubes surrounding the seventh. A three-fold coincidence telescope was formed by dividing the outer tubes into two groups of three. The center tube formed the third element of the coincidence system. A block diagram of the system is shown in Figure 5b. The whole assembly was surrounded by a shield 5 $gms/cm^2$ thick so that a true three-fold coincidence would occur only for protons of energy greater than 75 Mev, or electrons of energy greater than 13 Mev. In addition to the triple coincidence count rate, the count rate observed by the single central counter was telemetered to earth. The single counter was sensitive to bremsstrahlung radiation arising from electrons of energy greater than about 500 kev, whereas the triple coincidence system was quite insensitive to bremsstrahlung.

The scintillation counter experiment** consisted of a plastic scintillator which was cemented to a Dumont 6467 photomultiplier tube. The output pulses of the photomultiplier tube were amplified, fed into a 20-bit binary register, three of which were used to modulate a subcarrier oscillator, so that transitions between these states could be used to determine the counting rates. A block diagram of the instrument is shown in Figure 5c. The minimum energy of detectable particles was determined by the mass distribution around the crystal and an adjusted electronic bias of 100 kev. The purpose of the scintillation counter experiment on the Explorer VI earth satellite was to make direct observations of electrons in both the inner and outer radiation zones with a detector relatively insensitive to bremsstrahlung.

A summary of the relative response of the radiation sensors to electrons, protons and gamma rays is as follows: The Geiger

---

* The proportional counter telescope experiment was conducted under the direction of Prof. J. Simpson of the University of Chicago, Midway Laboratory. Material for the BMD Symposium presentation was from References (6), (7) and (8).

**The scintillation counter experiment was conducted by one of the authors (A.R.) and Thomas A. Farley of Space Technology Laboratories, Inc. Material for the BMD Symposium was obtained from References (9) and (10).

counter and proportional counter telescope do not respond to the low energy electrons directly, but by means of their bremsstrahlung. It is to be noted that the geometrical factor for detection of these low energy electrons drops rapidly with energy, because of the very low detection efficiency for soft gammas. The proportional counter telescope is characterized by a slower rate of change of geometrical factor with energy and a relatively high geometrical factor at intermediate electron energies compared to low energies. The scintillation counter is relatively insensitive to the bremsstrahlung radiation and responds to electrons and protons directly.

## Magnetometer Instrumentation

The search coil magnetometer* consisted of a solenoid wound on a high permeability core. It was attached to the shell of the spin-stabilized payload. The spinning of the vehicle generated a sinusoidal voltage in the coil with amplitude proportional to $|B_\perp|$, the component of the magnetic field perpendicular to the spin axis (See Figure 6). The coil was coupled to a low frequency amplifier tuned to the spin rate. Details of this equipment are the same as the Pioneer I magnetometer which have been reported elsewhere (11).

In addition to the search coil, the magnetometer contained a magnetic field aspect indicator or phase comparator. The purpose of this supplementary equipment was to provide information concerning the direction of extraterrestrial magnetic fields. This was accomplished by measuring the time delay between two signals: (1) a pulse from a sun-seeking photodiode and (2) a pulse coincident with the zero voltage crossing of the search coil signal. The data from the phase comparator is most easily visualized in terms of the phase angle, $\phi$, between $B_\perp$ and $S_\perp$, where $S_\perp$ represents the projection of a unit vector, pointing in the direction of the sun, into the payload equatorial plane (Figure 6).

## Doppler-difference, Faraday-rotation measurements**

The experimental method used to measure the electron density in the exosphere was similar to that employed by Seddon (15)

---

* The magnetometer experiment was conducted under the direction of Dr. C. P. Sonett of Space Technology Laboratories, assisted by D. L. Judge and P. J. Coleman. Material for the BMD Symposium was obtained from References (11),(12),(13), and (14).

**This experiment was carried out under the direction of Dr. C. D. Graves of Space Technology Laboratories.

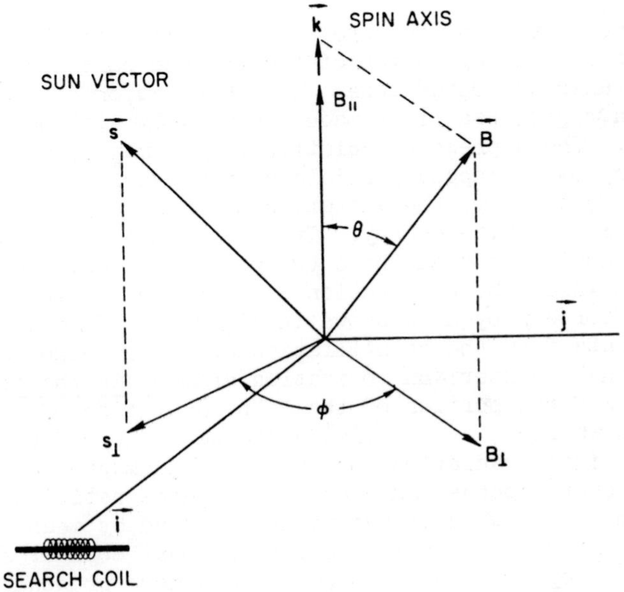


Fig. 6. The Coordinate System for Magnetometer Experiments.

to make similar measurements in the ionosphere. The method is based upon measuring the doppler frequency difference between two coherent signals transmitted to the ground from the satellite. The two transmitters used were one of the analog VHF transmitters (108 Mc/s) and the digital UHF transmitter (378 Mc/s). Because of time variation in the electron content along the propagation path, it was necessary to make supplementary measurements of the time rate of change of the Faraday rotation of one of the polarized signals (108 Mc/s).

## Scientific Results

### Characteristics of the Radiation Zones

The most striking feature of the geomagnetically trapped particles is the separation of the trapped particle regions into an inner and outer zone. The observation of a depressed radiation region was first made exclusively with Geiger counters. The depressed radiation region may be accounted for by either lower trapped particle energy density or an instrumental effect due to the variation of detection sensitivity of the Geiger tube with energy. It is not possible to make a definite choice between these two possibilities. However, the extent to which the observation of depressed regions depend on the detector employed is shown in Figure 7. Here the simultaneous data from the scintillation counter, Geiger counter, proportional counter and ionization chamber in the outer zone is plotted for a portion of the 17th revolution of the payload around the earth. At a radial distance of 10,000 km the payload is in the outer radiation zone at 25$^{\circ}$ N geomagnetic latitude heading toward apogee and crosses the geomagnetic equator at 31,000 km. The two distinct peaks observed by means of the Geiger counter are seen by the proportional counter as a slight change in slope at the first peak and a more pronounced increase at the second peak. It is interesting that the ionization chamber, like the proportional counter, is just barely able to distinguish between the two peaks so clearly seen by the Geiger counter. The response of the scintillation counter is vastly different from the other detectors. At the first Geiger counter peak the scintillation counter responds by showing a very slight change in slope. The first scintillation counter peak does not coincide with the peaks observed by the other instruments. It is, however, closer to the second than the first Geiger counter peak. The second scintillation counter peak occurs almost one earth radius further out than the second peak observed by other instruments. It is precisely in the scintillation counter valley, between the two peaks, that the Geiger counter second peak appears.

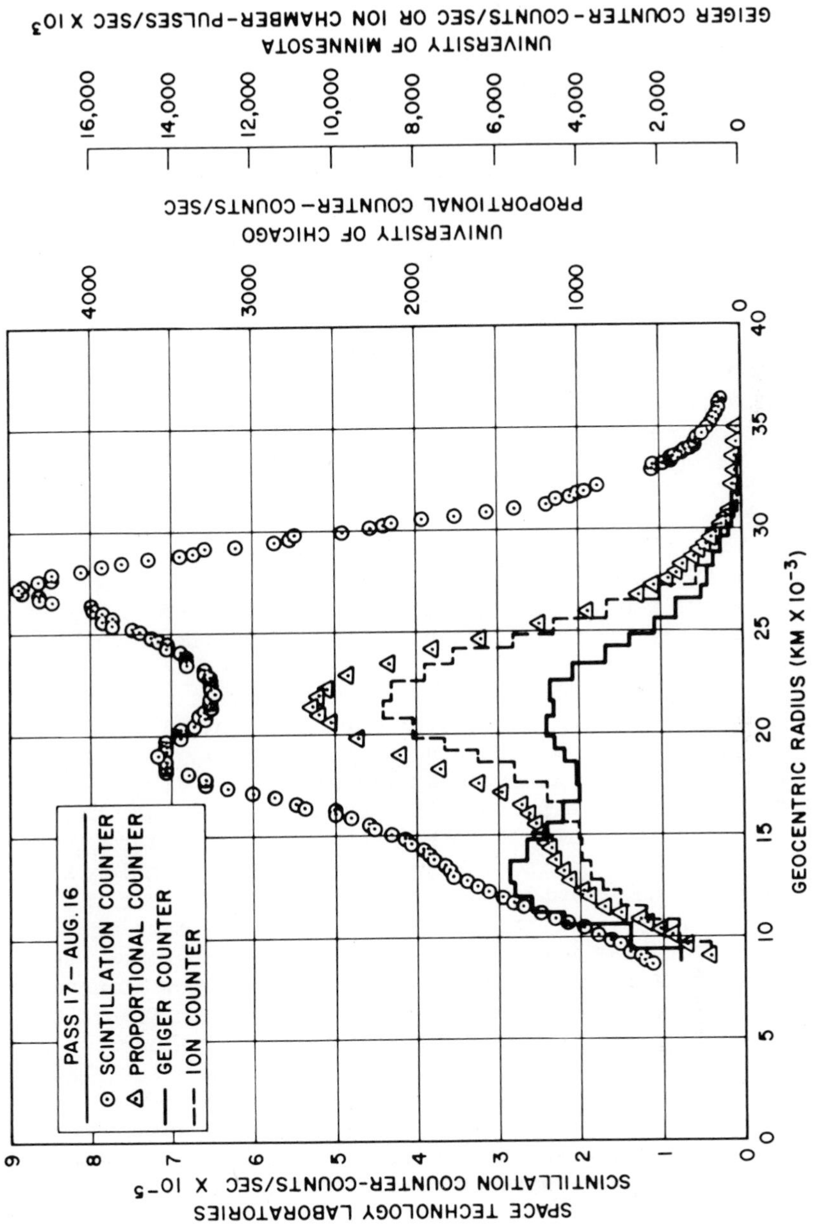


Fig. 7. Comparison of Quiet Day Structure of the Outer Zone.

It should be noted that the scintillation counter peak occurs at higher altitudes than peaks observed by the other radiation sensors. Since the scintillation counter responds to the lower energy component of the radiation, a softening of the radiation with altitude is implied. This result has been anticipated on theoretical grounds (16).

If a unique explanation of these results is not possible, new insight into the structure of the radiation belt is apparent. The energy spectrum as a function of position is an important factor in predicting the results obtained by a given radiation sensor. By keeping this fact in mind and considering the results obtained by the individual sensors, it is possible to reach some important conclusions about the structure of the trapped radiation.

Protons which penetrate the triple coincidence system of the proportional counter telescope were found at altitudes below 3500 km with an intensity of 1400 protons per $cm^2$ per second at the peak (6). Figure 8 shows the region in which these protons are observed. Bremsstrahlung from electrons produced the peak on the right which has been identified with the inner Van Allen zone. Only as the satellite approaches perigee from high southerly latitudes does it traverse the region of the inner Van Allen zone. Figure 8 shows that the proton belt is located at the lower altitude edge of the inner zone. The two peaks shown in Figure 7 are observed in the region which has been previously identified as the second Van Allen zone.

The structure of the Van Allen radiation regions as determined by means of a Geiger counter during August of 1959 is shown in Figure 9b. Figure 9a shows isointensity contours which were previously observed by Van Allen (3) with the Pioneer III deep space probe. It should be noted that the same instrument was used in both cases in order to facilitate such a comparison. It is to be noted that the radiation zones have shrunken considerably during the interval between the Pioneer III flight (December, 1958) and the time that the Explorer VI data was taken (August, 1959). Furthermore, the University of Minnesota Geiger counter results show structure in the outer Van Allen zone. This is best seen in Figure 7 where two Geiger counter peaks appear at high altitudes.

The isointensity contours as observed by the scintillation counter are shown in Figure 10. During the operation of the analog transmitter broadcasting the scintillator data, the satellite completed more than 60 circuits around its trajectory. However, because there were gross fluctuations in the outer zone associated with enhanced solar activity and magnetic storms, the isointensity plot shown in Figure 10 includes only data from the period between August 7 and August 15, 1959, when there was a minimum of such activity. In spite of this

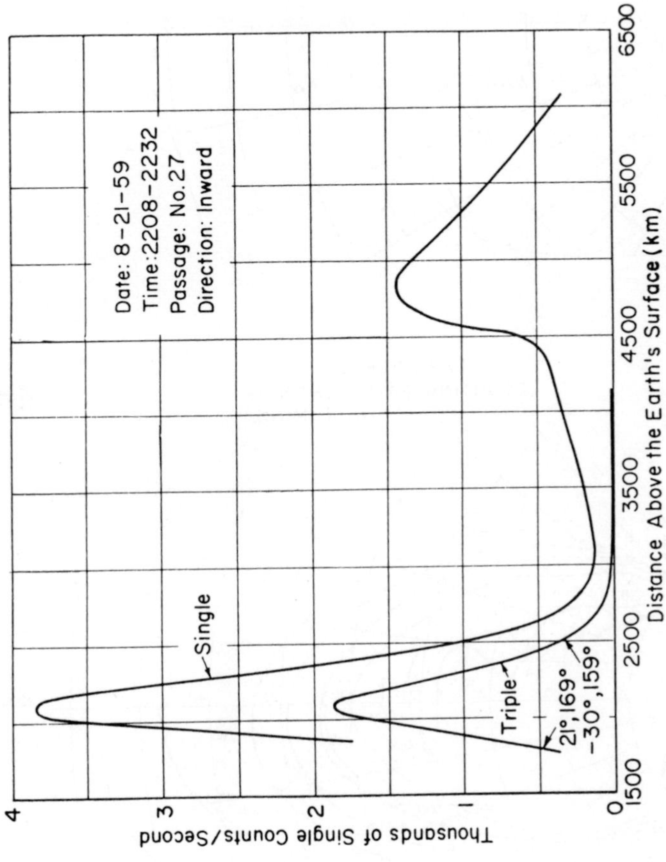


Fig. 8. Evidence of Protons in the Inner Zone.

VAN ALLEN RADIATION REGIONS

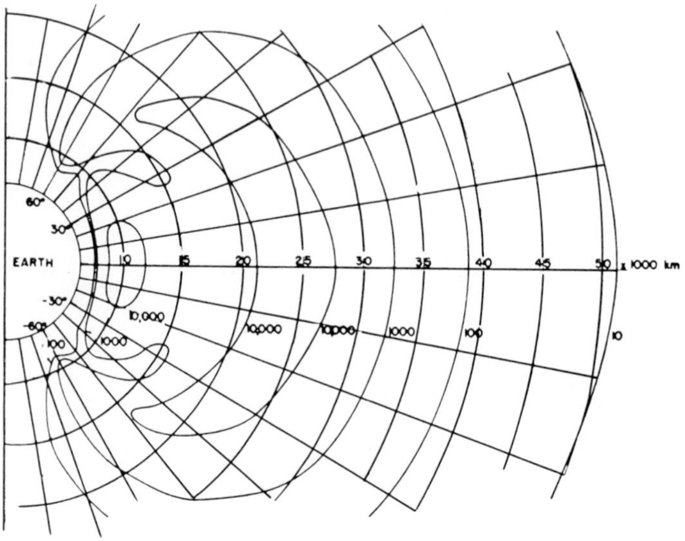


9-a

EXPLORER VI
COUNTING RATE CONTOURS
(U. OF MINN.)

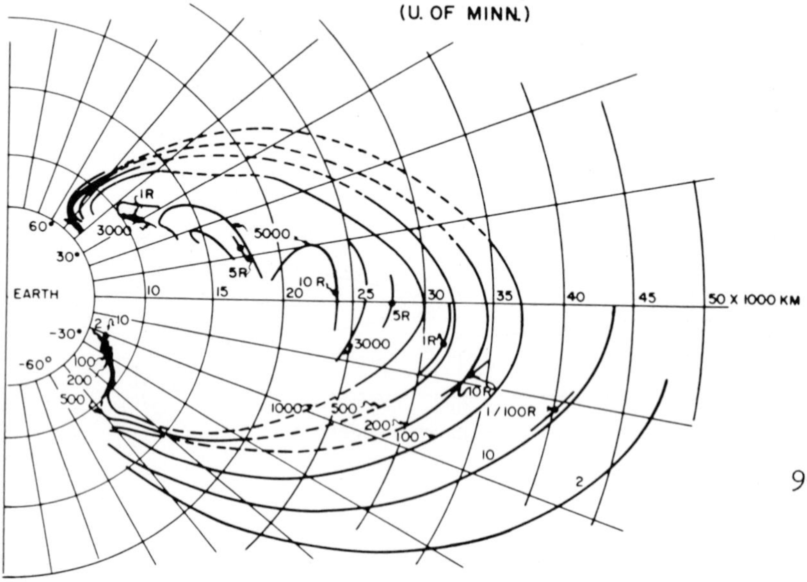


9-b

Fig. 9. Comparison of Iso-intensity Contours (Pioneer III and Explorer VI).

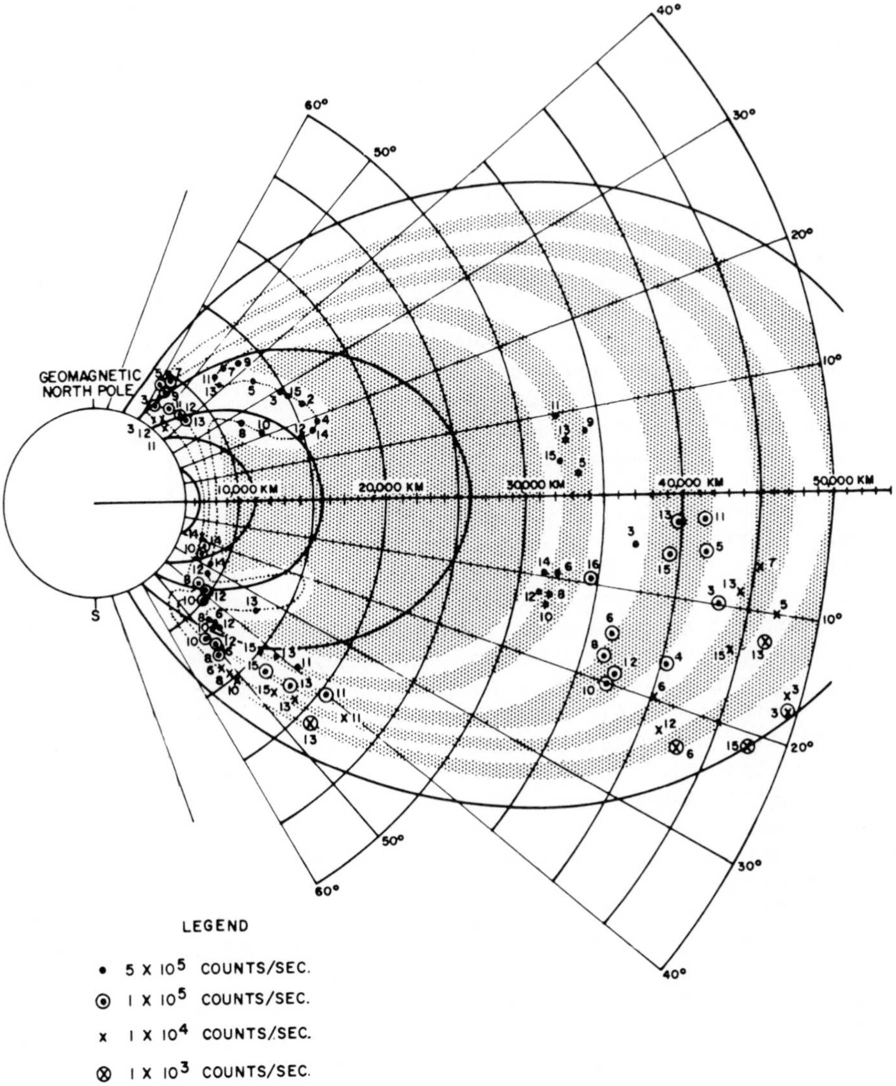


Fig. 10. Radiation Intensity Contours According to Scintillation Counter.

selection, there are daily variations in the outer zone and the isointensity lines in this region have been broadened into bands to include the daily variation of the contours. The number beside each point represents the revolution of the satellite during which the data was taken, numbered consecutively after launch. The innermost shaded area represents the region in space in which the scintillation counter was in saturation and the bands represent decreasing count rate levels as shown in the legend. The location of the bands where no points are available have been estimated from symmetry considerations. Since the saturation characteristics of the scintillation counter were determined in the laboratory prior to launch, it is possible to deduce the true count rate during the time that the scintillation counter is in saturation. This has been done and isointensity contours in the inner most shaded regions are now under construction. Data points at $5 \times 10^5$ counts per second were obtained inside the slot with the vehicle at northern latitudes at approximately 10,000 to 17,000 km. The data illustrate the stability of this feature when compared with the width of bands at radial distances greater than 30,000 kilometers. Data point number 3, for example, is consistent with the other data points defining the boundary of the slot. At radial distances greater than 30,000 km, however, the points of the third revolution fall a few thousand kilometers further out of each isointensity band than the other points defining that band. Evidently the outer zone contained more particles on August 9 (a mildly disturbed day) during the third revolution, while the inner zones remained essentially unchanged. A detailed correlation of these occurrences with solar activity has not yet been completed.

Consideration of the above data shows that the structure of the outer Van Allen zone varies markedly with time. In addition to long-term secular variations, there are violent changes associated with magnetic storms. There is evidence also of daily fluctuations. The scintillation counter, which presumably detects the lower energy particles, also reveals most noticeably the occurrence of short-term fluctuations. This suggests that the density of the low energy component of the terrestrial radiation is more variable than that of the higher energy component. Consequently, the low energy particles may be more susceptable to the influences of solar activity.

## The Magnetic Field within the Van Allen Zones

In the region of the most intense radiation (at altitudes less than 30,000 km) the quiet-day magnetic field appears to be only slightly affected by the trapped particles. Figure 11 presents representative amplitude data from three days as a function of geocentric altitude. There is a general corresponden

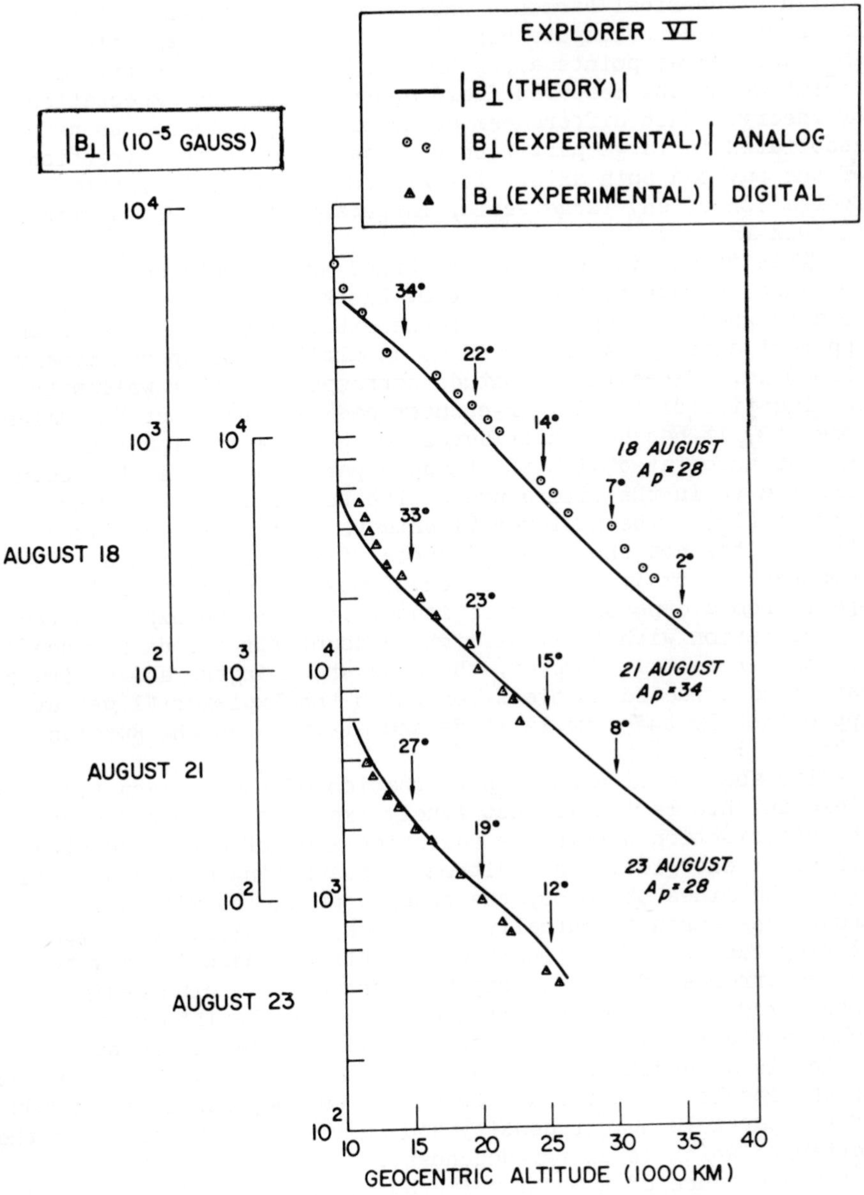


Fig. 11. Magnetic Field in the Vicinity of Intense Radiation of Outer Zone.

between the observed field and the extrapolated surface geomagnetic field. For the sake of comparison, an 8-coefficient, spherical harmonic expansion of the surface field has been used to compute expected values of the magnetic field ($B_\perp$ and $\phi$) at points along the trajectory. The altitude variation of the measured field approximates the expectation of theory. Such differences as occur are considered to be associated in large part with uncertainties in the direction of the payload spin axis. If this is so, there is little indication of any large-scale, large-amplitude field deviations in this region.

This result is in direct contrast to the data obtained by the Russians during the flight of Lunik I (17). In addition to a large-scale depression of the extraterrestrial field, an apparent anomaly was observed at an altitude of approximately 20,000 km. Since this altitude corresponds rather well with the location of the Geiger-counter peak in the outer Van Allen zone (3), it has been attributed to the effects of a ring current associated with the trapped particles. This has been referred to in the literature as the Dolganov-Pushkov ring current (18). The Explorer VI data which has been analyzed thus far has not shown any evidence of either this or a comparable anomaly in the region of most intense radiation. Apart from a dependence on altitude, it might be expected that the variation with latitude might account for the difference in these results. However, the data shown in the above figure have been selected at times for which the Explorer VI was at approximately the same latitude and altitude as the Russian vehicle.

The absence of a major perturbation of the geomagnetic field in this region is most likely explainable in terms of the distribution within the radiation zone of particles with different energies. In addition to travelling back and forth along the lines of force, the trapped particles will drift around the earth azimuthally and, thus, constitute one type of ring current. The longitudinal drift is associated with the occurrence of two centripetal forces: the dipole-dipole force exerted on the spiraling particle by the inhomogeneous geomagnetic field, and the force required to keep the particle moving in a curved orbit along the line of force. The magnitude of the resulting westward-flowing current depends on the product of the particle number density and on the drift velocity of the particles which is energy-dependent.

The absence of a major perturbation of the field suggests that the number density of the particle radiation is low. Furthermore, the energetic particles in the outer zone have been identified as being predominantly electrons with energies of approximately 100 kev. Because of their small mass, electrons are much less effective in producing drift currents than protons.

In addition to the radiation particles, it is expected that the earth's outer atmosphere contains upward of 100 protons per $cm^3$. But, while the number density of such exosphere particles is larger, their energies are essentially thermal and consequently they contribute very little to the expected current flow. This experimental result establishes the internal self-consistency of calculations of individual particle motion which neglect the effect of an aggregate of such motions on the primary field.

## The Extraterrestrial Current System

Large-scale currents flowing around the earth at great altitudes has been postulated in the past to account for a variety of geophysical phenomena: (1) the deflection of charged solar particles into the auroral zone (19); (2) the main phase decrease of the geomagnetic field accompanying magnetic storms (20),(21),(22); and (3) termination of the geomagnetic field by interplanetary or coronal gases (23),(24). Evidence for the existence of a localized current system lying outside the Van Allen radiation zones is provided by the Explorer VI magnetometer data (12). Figure 12 is representative of data for both $B_{\perp}$ and $\bar{\phi}$. Note the existence of a region in which the observed field undergoes a large-scale deviation from the geomagnetic field. Figure 13 shows an expanded view of the deviation region using data obtained on the previous day. Also included are the results of a model calculation (13) which was intended to establish the macroscopic characteristics of the current responsible for the perturbing magnetic field. The characteristics of the model which fit the data as shown are: (1) the total current is 5 million amperes and flows westward; (2) the center of the current system is located at an altitude of 60,000 km ($\sim$10 $R_e$); and (3) the cross section of the current (which was assumed to be circular) has a radius of approximately 3 $R_e$ so that it extends over the region from 7 to 13 $R_e$.

In addition to establishing the existence of such a current, the Explorer VI data has provided evidence that the current system is a persistent feature of the distant geomagnetic field. It occurs when conditions at the earth's surface are either magnetically quiet or magnetically disturbed. Furthermore, the current shows a time variation such that the magnitude and location of the field deviation varies from day to day.

The origin of this current in the outer atmosphere is considered to be due to trapped low energy particles (e.g., 10 kev protons). That these particles have such low energies may be inferred from the fact that they have not been observed by the radiation particle detectors, which have relatively high energy-thresholds.

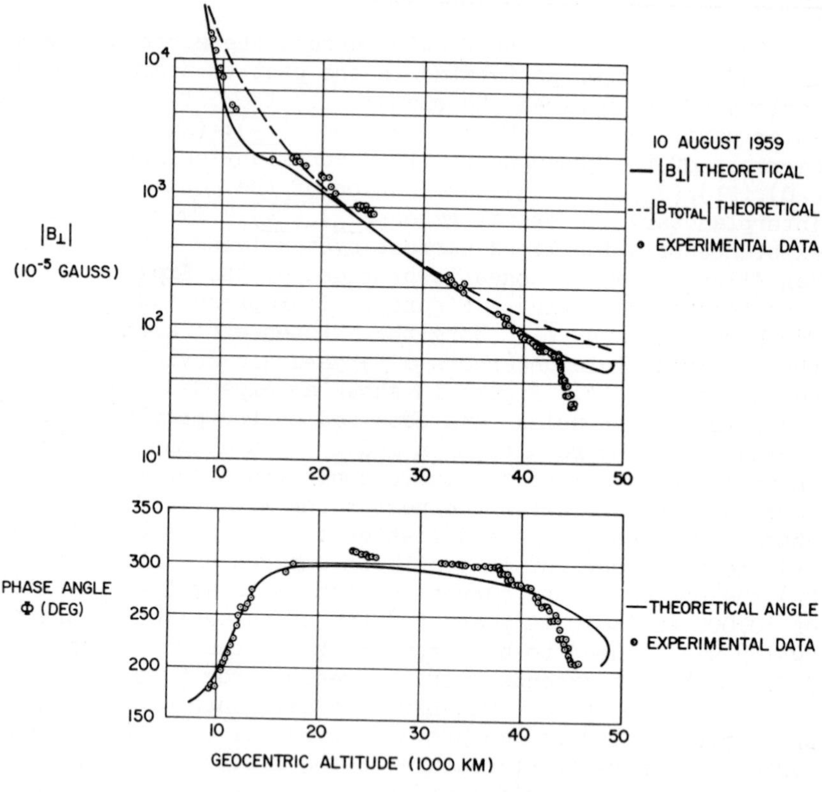


Fig. 12. Amplitude and Direction of the Extraterrestrial Magnetic Field.

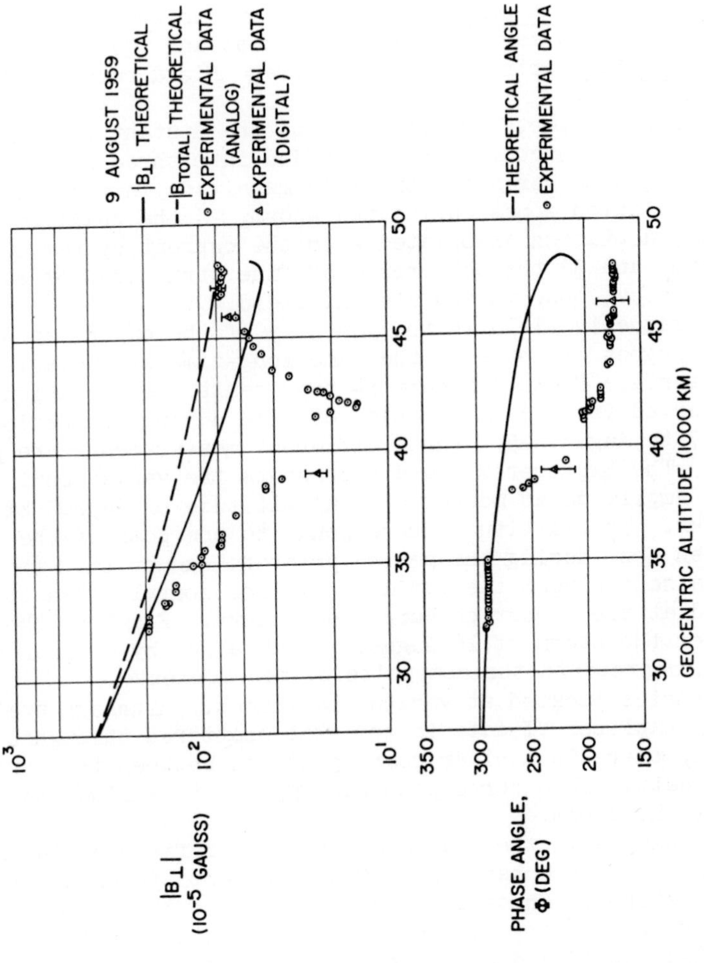


Fig. 13. Amplitude and Direction of the Magnetic Field in the Deviation Region.

## Magnetic Storm Effects

The occurrence of large amplitude fluctuations in the field is the characteristic feature of magnetic storms at the surface of the earth. In addition, the surface field undergoes certain long period changes which have been classified: (1) during the initial phase of the storm (of several hours duration), the average field magnitude is increased above its quiescent value; (2) during the main phase (usually of one to two days duration), the average field magnitude is depressed; and (3) there is a recovery period during which the average field returns to its quiescent value.

The storm effects associated with the distant geomagnetic field (14) may be conveniently divided into three categories: 1) the long-time variation of field magnitude in the vicinity of the radiation zones during the storm; 2) the character of the far field deviation associated with the current system during the storm; and 3) the occurrence of fine structure, or rapid field fluctuations, in the distant field.

The magnetic field in the vicinity of the outer Van Allen zone undergoes essentially the same long-time storm variations as the surface field. Figure 14 represents the variation of the observed field as a function of time during the period from August 7 to August 25. Three different measurements are presented. The Explorer VI data represents the variation in average amplitude as measured at an altitude of 24,000 km ± 1000 km. This altitude corresponds to one peak of the outer Van Allen zone during the period prior to August 16. The figure also includes the variation in horizontal intensity as measured at the Fredericksburg Observatory. Finally, the $D_{st}$ curve for the storm of 16 August, as obtained by Chapman and Akasofu, represents the composite of measurements at 12 observatories located at various latitudes. Although preliminary Explorer VI data is somewhat scattered throughout this interval, there is a clear correspondence between the three sets of data. This correspondence appears to include the initial phase of the storm.

The changes in the character of the far field deviation region suggest an enhancement of the current system during magnetic storms. Phase data shown in Figure 15 contrasts the character of the large-scale field perturbation during magnetic storms (August 17 and September 4) and during magnetically quiet periods (August 27). The $A_p$ indices, which are a measure of surface storminess, have been included for the sake of comparison. Although not reproduced here, the Explorer VI phase-angle data obtained during the storm period of August 15 through 18 shows the regular evolution of the deviation region during this interval. The deviation increases in amplitude and becomes noticeable at lower altitudes as the storm progresses

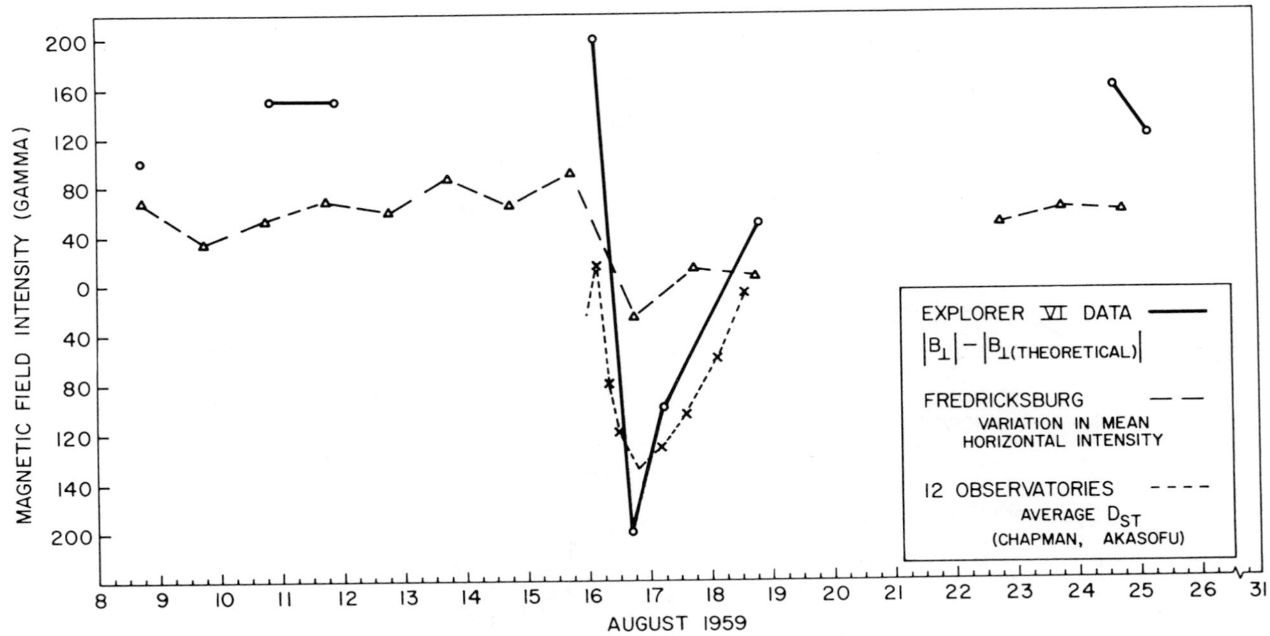


Fig. 14. Storm-time Variation of the Magnetic Field in the Vicinity of Outer Radiation Zone.

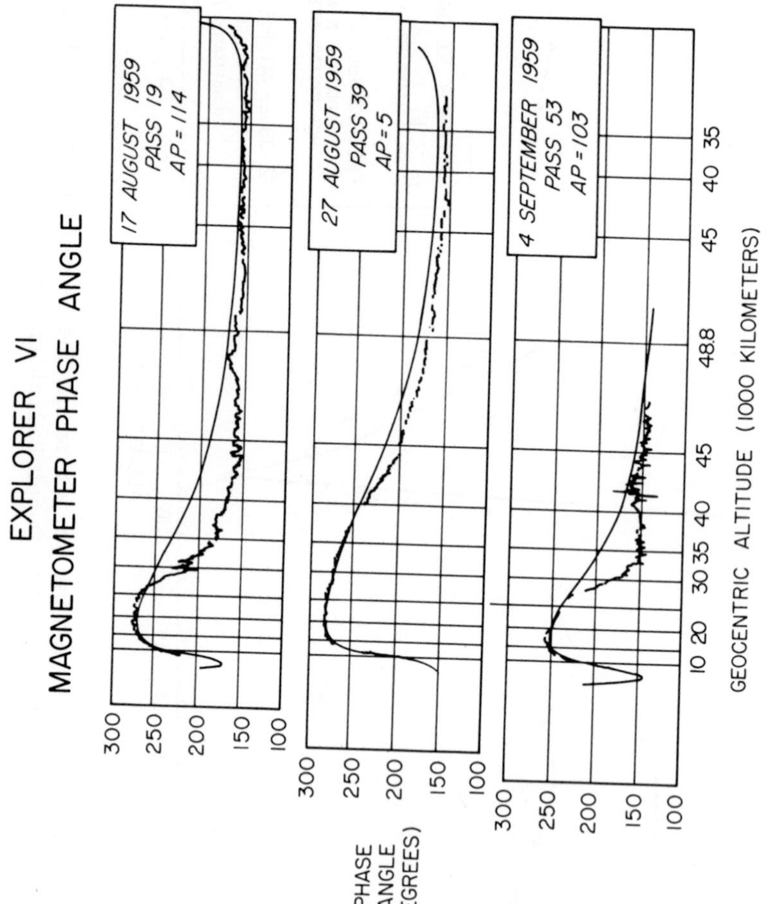


Fig. 15. Variation of the Extraterrestrial Field with Magnetic Activity at the Earth's Surface.

and then retreats to its prestorm magnitude and location during the recovery period. Similar changes are observed in the amplitude of the perturbation field (i.e., $B_{\perp}$). Small-scale, rapid fluctuations of rather large amplitude occur during storm periods, particularly in the far field. Figure 15 shows evidence of large amounts of fine structure. These rapid fluctuations in the field will be further discussed below in connection with an observed correlation between the Explorer VI magnetometer and scintillator.

From the point of view of the trapped radiation, magnetic storms produce a distinct history of large-scale variation in addition to violent fluctuations. The geomagnetic storm on August 16, 1959 produced intense and unusual fluctuations in the particle intensity measured by the Explorer VI scintillation counter. Figure 16 shows the fluctuations which were first observed during pass 17 at about 0600 GMT, some two hours after the storm's sudden commencement. These fluctuations, rising and falling by as much as three orders of magnitude within a few minutes, were observed while the vehicle was traveling at a speed of less than 1-1/2 kilometers/sec with respect to the earth.

Figure 17 shows the intensities observed with a scintillation counter before and after the geomagnetic storm. Twelve hours after the sudden commencement fluctuations in intensity are observed at radial distances greater than three earth radii and the intensity at the peaks is almost twice the prestorm value. A continual buildup in peak intensity was observed until the twenty-first pass when the intensity was twenty times the prestorm value.

This observation may be contrasted with the Geiger counter results on the same vehicle. Figure 18 shows the intensities observed with the Geiger counter and ionization chamber before and after the disturbance. The ion chamber rate drops from a maximum of 9 pulses/sec to about 2 pulses/sec after the beginning of the disturbance and the Geiger counter counting rate from 4800 counts/sec to about 1800 counts/sec. Arnoldy, et al.,(5) conclude from this data that nearly 3/4 of the radiation contained in the outer zone during pass 17 was lost during the first day of the geomagnetic storm. It is postulated by the authors that a large fraction of the trapped radiation is precipitated or 'dumped' during the main phase of the geomagnetic storm. On the night of August 16-17 J. R. Winckler observed a very strong aurora at approximately 57° latitude over the State of Minnesota. It was a typical strong storm aurora with ray structure and visible form extending as far south as 54° or 55° geomagnetic latitudes. Such an aurora has generally been correlated with the observations of strong X-ray bursts at the top of the atmosphere.

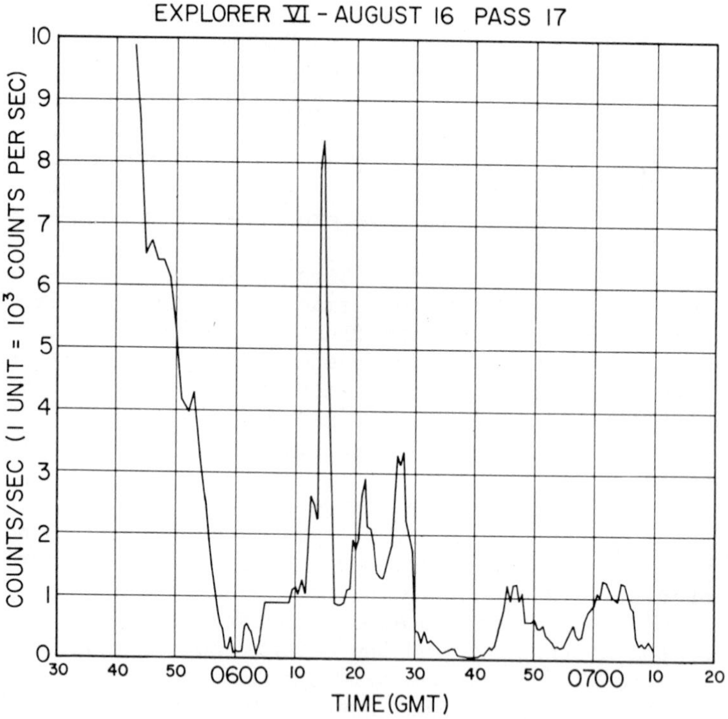


Fig. 16. Rapid Fluctuations in Particle Intensity during a Magnetic Storm.

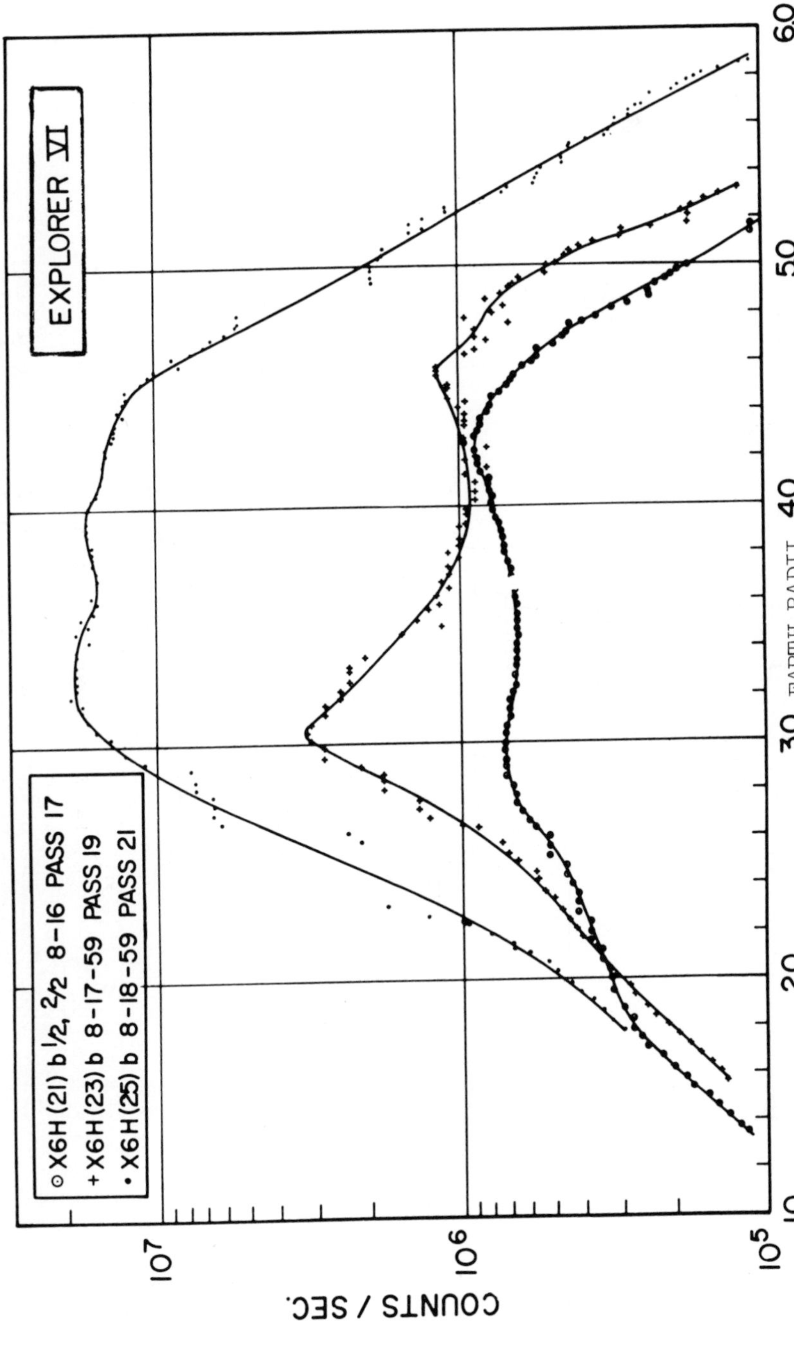


Fig. 17. Changes in the Structure of the Outer Zone during a Magnetic Storm (Scintillation Counter).

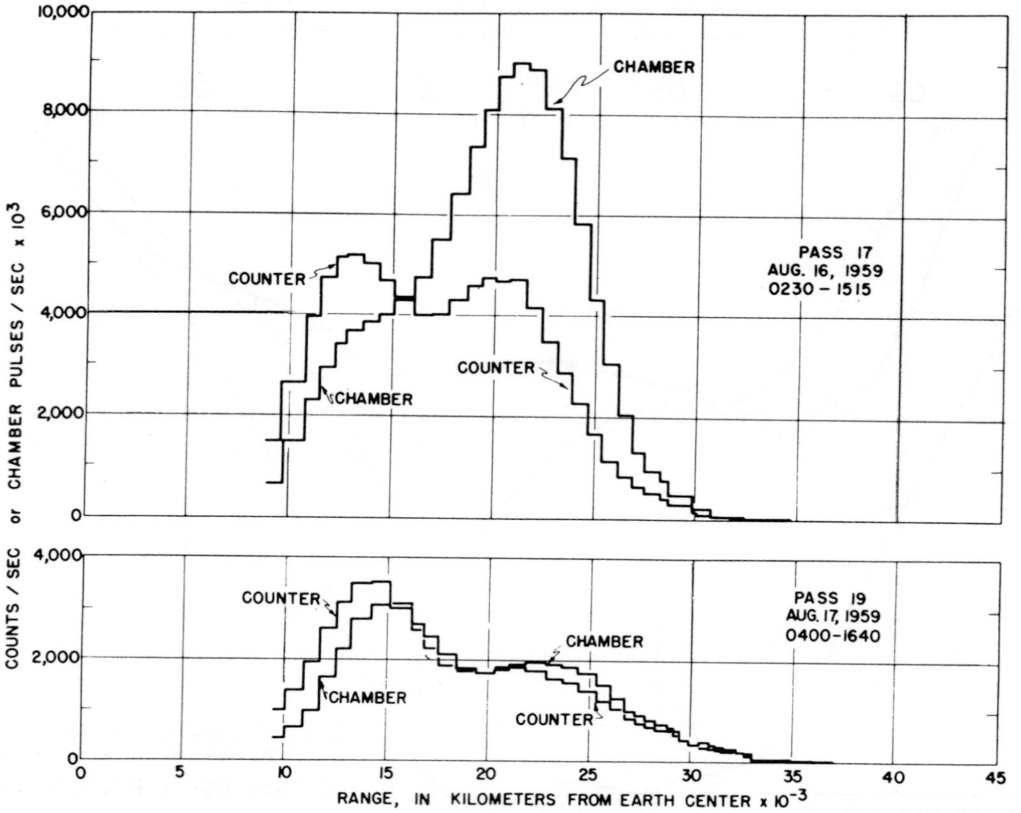


Fig. 18. Changes in the Structure of the Outer Zone during a Magnetic Storm (Ion Chamber and Geiger Counter).

The ratio of the ion chamber and counter suggests that the particles in the outer radiation zone are electrons with 40 to 50 kev energy. The authors suggest that these electrons impinging at the top of the atmosphere generate the X-rays that have been observed on numerous occasions in balloon flights flown near the latitudes of Minneapolis.

On August 18, pass 21, the intensity of radiation observed by the Geiger counter showed a very large increase in the outer region to a value much higher than that which was characteristic of prestorm conditions. The effect of a decrease in the early phases of the storm followed by an increase during the recovery period was also observed by the proportional counter telescope. In contrast, the scintillation counter showed a continual buildup in intensity. Whether this intensity increase at the end of the storm is due to solar injection or a local acceleration mechanism cannot be clearly decided at present. However, it is clear that if the Geiger tube response is predominantly to soft electrons, as the ion chamber to Geiger tube ratio seems to indicate, then the increase in scintillation counter intensity, while the other instruments show a decrease, must be due to the injection of protons of energy greater than 2 Mev. If, on the other hand, the Geiger tube response is predominantly to hard electrons and the scintillation counter to softer electrons, then either a loss of electrons or a lowering of the energy of the harder component, would explain the observation. In the latter case, it would not be necessary to postulate the injection of new particles into the radiation zones since the scintillation counter results could also be explained in terms of an acceleration of low energy particles to energies above the bias level. It is unlikely that a deceleration of the harder component could occur at the same time as an acceleration of the soft component above the scintillation counter bias level. It seems more probable that a dumping of the harder component occurs at about the same time as an acceleration of the softer component, or that a deceleration of the harder component occurs at about the same time as solar injection of new particles.

Preliminary studies of the magnetic field during the storm, correlated with scintillation counter intensity measurements, have been undertaken in order to determine the effect of the particle flux on the geomagnetic field. Figure 19 shows a portion of the detailed correlations made at 44,000 km on August 16 (pass 18) of the satellite. The scintillation counter intensity fluctuations are observed to be 180$^{\circ}$ out of phase with the magnetometer fluctuation. These observations indicate that there is a magnetic field associated with the particles seen by the scintillation counter, which is capable of substantially reducing the geomagnetic field at that distance. This magnetic field depression may possibly be the result of an intrusion of diamagnetic gas clouds into the geomagnetic field caused by the

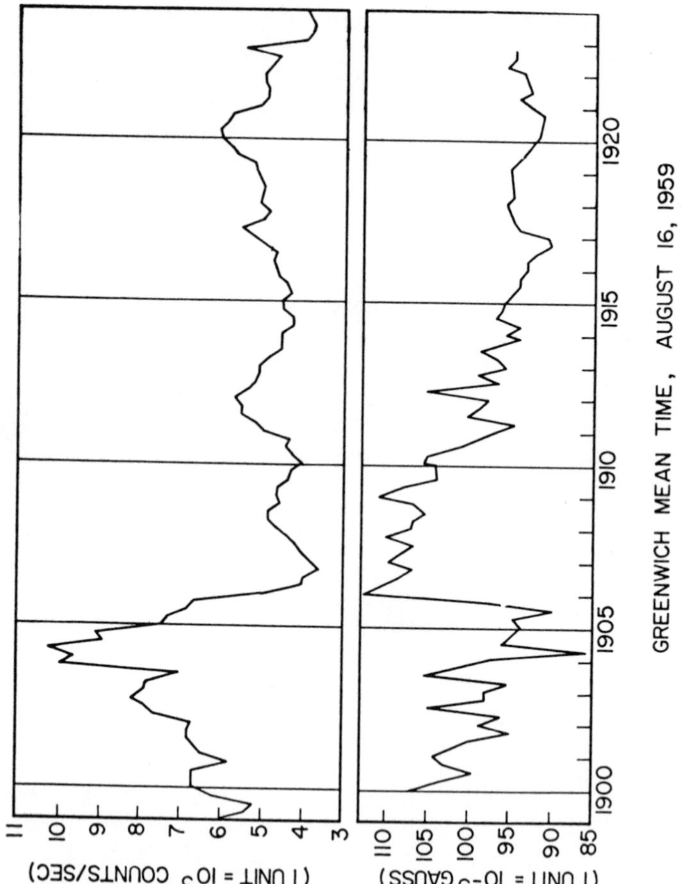


Fig. 19. Out-of-phase Correlations between Variations in Particle Flux and Magnetic Field.

increased pressure of the storm-day solar wind, or by the arrival of a cloud of solar gas in the vicinity of the earth. The particles in these ragged gas clouds may have disordered internal motions which become ordered as the particles take up internal orbits which will exclude the geomagnetic field. The field outside the clouds is increased because some of the lines of force are excluded from the interior of the bubbles. The field inside the clouds is not zero, since the geomagnetic field lines are not completely excluded, or else because the clouds have some internal fields of their own.

The local time on this satellite at seven earth radii is always about 7 P.M., and the satellite is, therefore, always on the side of the earth away from the sun at this distance. Whether these gas clouds ever penetrate to distances less than seven earth radii on this side of the earth has not yet been determined.

The particles seen by the scintillation counter at this time may be either electrons or protons. If they are electrons above 500 kev, which seems likely, and if the particle flux is isotropic, a count rate of $10^4$ per second corresponds to a flux of approximately $3 \times 10^5$ electrons/$cm^2$ sec. This flux of 500 kev electrons has an energy density of about $10^{-11}$ ergs/$cm^3$. The magnetic energy density in a field of 100 gamma ($10^{-3}$ gauss) is $4 \times 10^{-8}$ ergs/$cm^3$. Even if the particles are protons, the particle fluxes measured by the scintillation counter are inadequate to cause the observed variations in the magnetic field, and there must be large numbers of low energy particles associated with the particles seen by the scintillation counter.

It is interesting to note that this observation corresponds to the apparent enhancement of the extraterrestrial current system whose origin has been attributed to low energy particles.

The anti-correlated observation of the scintillation counter and magnetometer, combined with the storm observations of the other radiation instruments, may be summarized as follows: Since the instruments on this satellite sensitive to bremsstrahlung from electrons see a decrease in peak intensity, and the Geiger counter response is predominantly to soft electrons (as the ion chamber to Geiger tube ratio seems to indicate), the increase in peak intensity seen by the scintillation counter must be the result of an increase in the number of protons above 2 Mev in the geomagnetic field. The evidence presented here does not settle the question of the origin of these protons. They may enter the field in diamagnetic gas clouds. If so, the geomagnetic field may diffuse almost immediately into these clouds (22), trapping a fraction of the newly arrived particles along the lines of force of the geomagnetic field.

## Acceleration Mechanisms

An acceleration mechanism, or mechanisms, may be required to account for the large decreases and increases in intensity seen by the various radiation sensors. The large decrease in intensity seen by the University of Minnesota and Chicago sensors would be accounted for, if the magnetic field in the vicinity of the outer zone participates in the initial phase increase as the data suggest. Particles may be lost due to lowering of the mirror points associated with the field increase. Also, the irregular structure of the outer Van Allen zone, and the rapid field fluctuations observed with the magnetometer at this time, suggests the presence of hydromagnetic waves which may cause some scattering loss of particles already trapped in the field. At least part of the effect may be instrumental. Since a generalized depression of the field is also present at this time, this will cause a large-scale betatron deceleration of trapped particles. This may explain the decreased count rate in the satellite instruments sensitive to bremsstrahlung.

The question has been raised (5),(6),(10),(25) whether the intensity fluctuations seen by the scintillation counter and other fluctuations might be the result of a betatron mechanism, which would alternately raise and lower the energies of large numbers of particles above and below the threshold of the instrument as the magnetic field alternately increases and decreases. Accordingly, a close correlation has been made between the scintillator count rate and the magnetometer. A number of intervals have been found, covering a considerable period of time in each case, in which the magnetic field shows a very good in-phase correlation with the scintillation counter.

Figure 20 shows a comparison of the Explorer VI magnetometer and scintillation counter on August 9, 1959. The in-phase correlation between the two instruments has been interpreted as an acceleration and deceleration of particles above and below the scintillation counter bias level by a time-varying geomagnetic field. Calculations to determine the exponent $\gamma$ on an assumed $E^{-\gamma}$ energy spectrum, and a detailed study of this phenomenon, have been undertaken by Judge and Coleman (26). The correlations illustrated by Figure 20 may be compared to the anti-correlations observed during the geomagnetic storm (Figure 19). In a betatron acceleration mechanism the geomagnetic field is in control of the particles, whereas, in the case of anti-correlations the opposite situation exists.

## Primary Cosmic Radiation

One of the scientific objectives of the proportional counter telescope experiment was to investigate the electromagnetic phenomenon which leads to modulation of the primary cosmic ray

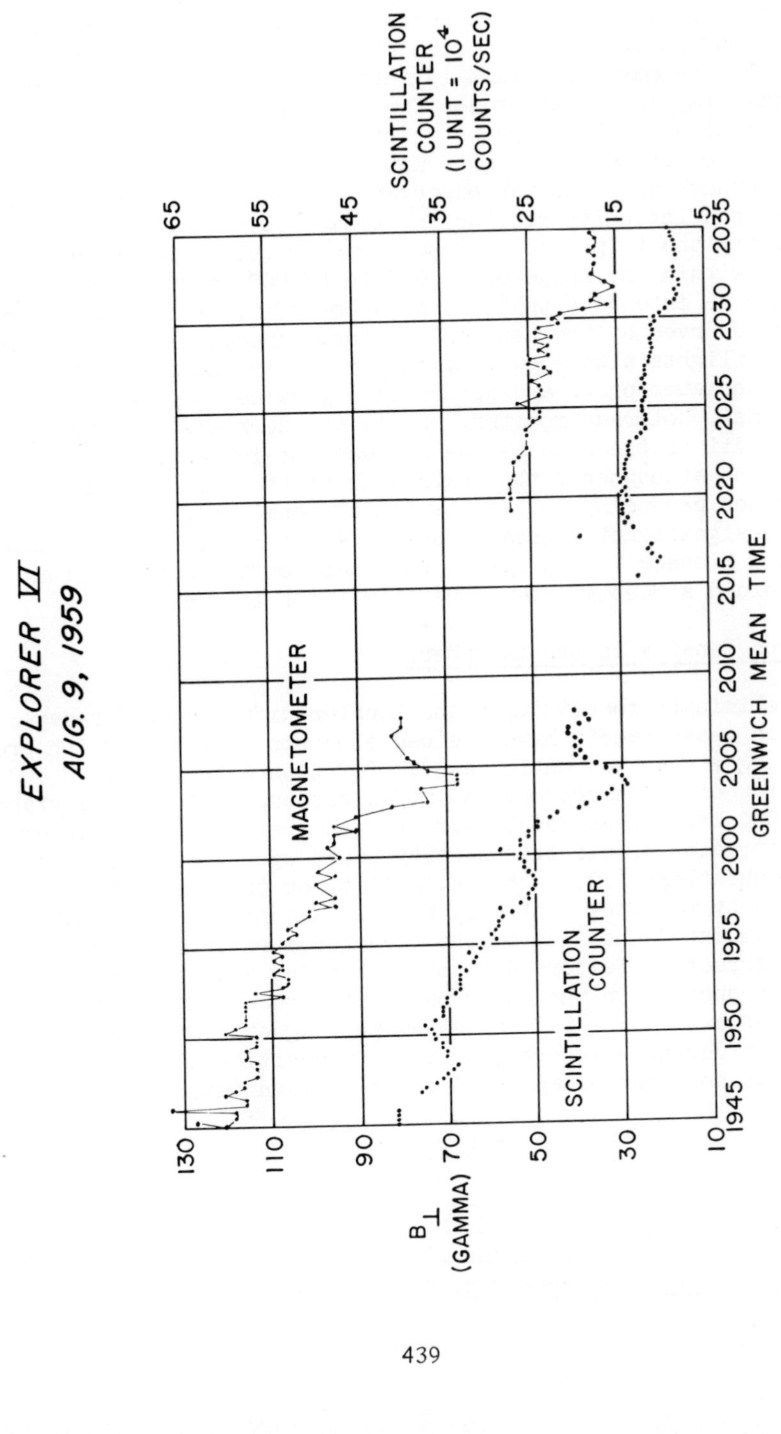


Fig. 20. In-phase Correlations between Variations in Particle Flux and Magnetic Field.

intensity. These sharp decreases in the cosmic ray intensity were first observed by Forbush and were shown to be associated with geomagnetic storms (27). Simpson (28) has shown that the modulation is produced by magnetic fields. The question has been raised as to the scale size of the modulating mechanism. Either the geomagnetic field is responsible for the decrease in cosmic ray intensity or the field is heliocentric. The events following the geomagnetic storms of August 16 provided evidence concerning these alternatives.

A forbush decrease was observed on the earth by means of the neutron intensity monitor in Climax, Colorado. At the same time, the triple coincidence counter telescope which was located within the range of 37,000 to 48,000 km showed a decrease in intensity that was a factor of 2.2 larger than the change observed by the neutron monitor. Independent data from balloon flights also show that the intensity changes at the top of the atmosphere are approximately twice as large as at the Climax, Colorado, monitor. Since the decrease at 6 to 7 earth radii is the same as the decrease of intensity at the top of the atmosphere, the scale size of the electromagnetic phenomenon producing the modulation of cosmic ray intensity must be significantly greater than 6 earth radii. Recent data from the Pioneer V deep space probe has confirmed this result and yielded a much greater lower limit for the scale size.

## Electron Density in the Exosphere

Preliminary results from the Doppler-difference, Faraday-rotation measurements have yielded electron densities which are much larger than was anticipated. The data have yielded densities of $10^4$ electrons/$cm^3$ at an altitude above the surface of 20,000 km. These results are an order of magnitude larger than estimates of electron density based upon the propagation of VLF whistlers (29). The reliability of these results is affected by the fact that only a small amount of useful data was accumulated and also by the occurrence of unexpectedly large correction factors due to ray bending and the effects of the ionosphere. On the other hand, it should be noted that these results may be influenced by the magnetic storm of August 16 during which the particle intensities in the outer Van Allen zone increased by an order of magnitude.

## References

1. Van Allen, J. A., C. E. McIlwain and G. H. Ludwig, "Radiation Observations with Satellite 1958 ε," Journal of Geophysical Research, vol. 64, p. 271, (1959).

2. Rosen, Alan, C. P. Sonett and P. J. Coleman, Jr., "Ionizing Radiation at Altitudes of 3,500 to 36,000 Kilometers; Pioneer I," Journal of Geophysical Research, vol. 64, p. 709, (1959).

3. Van Allen, J. A. and L. A. Frank, "Survey of Radiation Around the Earth to A Radial Distance of 107,400 Kilometers," Nature, vol. 183, p. 430, (1959).

4. Arnoldy, R., R. Hoffman and J. R. Winckler, "Observations of Van Allen Radiation Regions During Geomagnetic Storms," Proceedings of the COSPAR Space Symposium, North Holland Publishing Company, Amsterdam, (1960).

5. Arnoldy, R. L., R. A. Hoffman and J. R. Winckler, "Observations of Van Allen Radiation Regions During Geomagnetic Storms," Journal of Geophysical Research, vol. 65, p. 1331, (1960).

6. Fan, C. Y., P. Meyer and J. A. Simpson, "Trapped and Cosmic Radiation Measurements from Explorer VI," Proceedings of the COSPAR Space Symposium, North Holland Publishing Company, Amsterdam, (1960).

7. Fan, C. Y., P. Meyer and J. A. Simpson, "Preliminary Results from the Space Probe, Pioneer V," Journal of Geophysical Research, vol. 65, no. 6, p. 1862, June, 1960.

8. Fan, C. Y., P. Meyer and J. A. Simpson, "Cosmic Radiation Intensity Decreases Observed at the Earth and In Nearby Planetary Medium," Physical Review Letters, vol. 4, p. 421, (1960).

9. Rosen, A., T. A. Farley and C. P. Sonett, "Soft Radiation Measurements on Explorer VI Earth Satellite," Proceedings of the COSPAR Space Symposium, North Holland Publishing Company, Amsterdam, (1960).

10. Farley, T. A. and Alan Rosen, "Charged Particle Variations in the Outer Van Allen Zone During A Geomagnetic Storm," Journal of Geophysical Research, In press, October, 1960.

11. Sonett, C. P., D. L. Judge, A. R. Sims and J. M. Kelso, "A Radial Rocket Survey of the Distant Geomagnetic Field," Journal of Geophysical Research, vol. 65, p. 55, (1960).

12. Sonett, C. P., E. J. Smith, D. L. Judge and P. J. Coleman, "Current Systems in the Vestigial Geomagnetic Field," Physical Review Letters, vol. 4, p. 161, (1960).

13. Judge, D. L. and C. P. Sonett, "Characteristics of the Extraterrestrial Current System: Explorer VI and Pioneer V," Journal of Geophysical Research, vol. 65, p. 1858, (1960).

14. Smith, E. J., P. J. Coleman, Jr., J. L. Judge and C. P. Sonett, "The Existence of A Large Scale Geomagnetic Ring Current," Presented at IUGG Meeting at Helsinki, Finland, July, 1960.

15. Seddon, J. C., "Propagation Measurements in the Ionosphere with the Aid of Rockets," Journal of Geophysical Research, vol. 58, p. 323, (1953).

16. Singer, S. F., "Cause of the Minimum in the Earth's Radiation Belt," Physical Review Letters, vol. 3, p. 188, (1959).

17. Dolganov, S. and N. Pushkov, Doklady, Academy of Sciences, AN-SSSR 129, 1, (1959). Also Space Technology Laboratories translation No. RU-14, "Result of the Earth's Magnetic Field Measurement by the Cosmic Rocket".

18. Van Allen, J. A., and L. A. Frank, "Radiation Measurements to 658,300 Kilometers with Pioneer IV," Nature, vol. 184, p. 219, (1959).

19. Stormer, C., "Sur les Trajectoires des Corpuscles E'lectrise dans l'espace Sous l'action du Magnetisme Terrestre avec Application aux Aurores bore'ales," Arch. Sci. Phys., et Nat., vol. 32, pp. 117, 190, 277, 415, 501, (1911).

20. Chapman, S., and V.C.A. Ferraro, "The Geomagnetic Ring Current," Terr. Mag. and Atmos. Elec., vol. 46, p. 1, (1941).

21. Singer, S. F., "A New Model of Magnetic Storms and Aurorae," Trans. Am. Geophys. Union, vol. 38, p. 175, (1957).

22. Dessler, A. J. and E. N. Parker, "Hydromagnetic Theory of Geomagnetic Storms," Journal of Geophysical Research, vol. 64, p. 2239, (1959).

23. Dungey, J. W., Cosmic Electrodynamics, Chapter 8, Cambridge University Press, London, (1958).

24. Parker, E. N., "Interaction of the Solar Wind with the Geomagnetic Field," Physical Fluids, vol. 1, p. 171, (1958).

25. Dessler, A. J. and R. Karplus, "Some Properties of the Van Allen Radiation," Physical Review Letters, vol. 4, 271, (1960).

26. Judge, D. L. and P. J. Coleman, Jr., Private Communication.

27. Forbush, S. E., "World-Wide Changes In Cosmic-Ray Intensity," Physical Review, vol. 54, p. 975, (1938).

28. Simpson, J. A., "Cosmic-Radiation Intensity-Time Variations and Their Origin. Part III, The Origin of 27-Day Variations," Physical Review, vol. 94, p. 426, (1954).

29. Storey, L.R.O., "An Investigation of Whistling Atmospherics," Phil. Trans. Roy. Soc., vol. 246, p. 113, (1953).

# THE DYNAMIC STABILITY OF THE UPPER ATMOSPHERE OF VENUS*

Jean I. F. King
Missile and Space Vehicle Department
General Electric Company
Philadelphia, Pennsylvania

## Abstract

The far-infrared limb darkening curve measured by Sinton and Strong is used to determine the thermal stability of the optically accessible Venus atmosphere. It is found that the atmosphere above the obscuring layer is convectively stable with a lapse-rate about half that of the Venus adiabatic lapse-rate. The observed temperature decrease with height together with the radiative heating pattern shows similarities to the upper terrestrial troposphere and, conversely, argues against the presence of a low, warm, ozone-generated stratosphere. These results which are inferred from hard-won telescopic data point up the need and usefulness of near-Venus radiation probe measurements.

## Introduction

As is shown elsewhere (1), (2), (3), it is possible to deduce the vertical thermal structure of a remotely viewed celestial object by means of the variation of the radiant intensity across the disk. Although this method has been used primarily in the stellar context, it is equally applicable to the limb-darkening observed in the thermal emission of planetary atmospheres.

In particular we shall apply this method to the limb-darkening observed by Sinton and Strong (4) in scanning across

*This work has been supported by the Air Force Ballistic Missile Division under Contract No. AF 04(647)-269.

the disk of Venus. We shall see how, under reasonable assumptions, it is possible to deduce quite specific results regarding the lapse-rate and the cooling pattern of the optically accessible Venus atmosphere. The importance of the lapse-rate lies in the fact that it is the thermal gradient rather than the absolute temperature which determines the dynamic stability of an atmosphere.

## Theory and Results

Sinton and Strong found that the self-emissive power of Venus in the far-infrared observed from center to edge fit closely the curve

$$I(\mu) = I(1)\,\mu^{\frac{1}{2}} \tag{1}$$

where $I(\mu)$ is the radiant intensity emitted at an angle $\theta = \cos^{-1}\mu$, with $\theta$ the angle formed by the planetary vertical and the line of sight. Thus I (1) would be the radiation emitted from the apparent center of the disk.

The emergent intensity for a gray, semi-infinite atmosphere, assumptions reasonably valid for this case, is the Laplace transform of the Planck radiation temperature. Thus

$$I(\mu) = \int_0^{\infty} B(\tau)\, e^{-\frac{\tau}{\mu}}\, d\frac{\tau}{\mu} = \mathcal{L}_{\frac{1}{\mu}}\left[B(\tau)\right] \tag{2}$$

where $\tau = \mathcal{H}\mu$ is the optical depth of the atmosphere. Upon taking the inverse transform of relation (1), we have at once

$$B(\tau) = \mathcal{L}^{-1}_{\frac{1}{\mu}}\left[I(\mu)\right] = \frac{2}{\sqrt{\pi}}\, I(0,1)\, \tau^{\frac{1}{2}} \tag{3}$$

Here it is convenient to express the radiation temperature in terms of the effective temperature of the disk by means of the emergent flux relation

$$\pi F = 2\pi \int_0^1 I(\mu)\, \mu\, d\mu = \frac{4}{5}\pi I(1) = \pi B_{eff} \tag{4}$$

yielding

$$B(\tau) = \frac{5}{2\sqrt{\pi}} B_{eff} \tau^{\frac{1}{2}} \tag{5}$$

Continuing with the gray atmosphere assumption, we have the temperature given as the following function of the optical depth,

$$T(\tau) = \left(\frac{5}{2\sqrt{\pi}}\right)^{\frac{1}{4}} T_{eff} \tau^{\frac{1}{8}} \tag{6}$$

We see that the temperature increases slowly with depth, equal to the effective temperature near $\tau = 0.5$.

If we assume the concentration of radiating gases is constant with height as is the case, for example, with carbon dioxide in the terrestrial atmosphere, we can readily derive the lapse-rate in the Venus upper atmosphere. Since

$$\tau = \tau_0 e^{-\int_{z_0}^{z} \frac{mg}{RT} dz} \tag{7}$$

we have the lapse-rate

$$-\frac{dT}{dZ} = -\frac{dT}{d\tau}\frac{d\tau}{dZ} = +\frac{dT}{d\tau}\frac{g}{R/m}\frac{\tau}{T} = +\frac{g}{R/m}\frac{d\ln T}{d\ln \tau} \tag{8}$$

Upon substitution of relation (6) into Eq. (8), we find

$$-\frac{dT}{dZ} = \frac{1}{8}\frac{g}{R/m} = \frac{1}{8}\frac{\gamma}{\gamma-1}\frac{g}{C_p} \tag{9}$$

where $\gamma = C_p/C_v$ is the ratio of specific heats and $g/C_p$ is the adiabatic lapse-rate.

A convenient criterion for stability is the ratio of the "observed" lapse-rate to that of the dry adiabatic. If we assume a diatomic atmosphere for Venus ($\gamma = 7/5$) we find from Eq. (9) that

$$\frac{\left(-dT/dZ\right)_{♀}}{\left(-dT/dZ\right)_{♀ad.}} = \frac{1}{8}\frac{\gamma}{\gamma-1} = \frac{7}{16} \tag{10}$$

We can therefore infer that the long wave radiation reaching us from Venus arises from an atmosphere which is convectively stable whose temperature decrease with height is about half that of the adiabatic lapse-rate. This thermal stratification is similar to the terrestrial troposphere, where the observed lapse-rate of $6^{\circ}K/km$ is 0.6 of the dry adiabatic lapse-rate of $10^{\circ}K/km$.

It is of interest to calculate the heating pattern which arises from the deduced radiative temperature distribution, Eq. (5). From the Milne-Schwarzschild equation of radiative heat transfer we have

$$\frac{1}{4}\frac{dF}{d\tau} = \frac{1}{2}\int_{\tau}^{\infty} B(t)\, e^{-(t-\tau)}\, dt + \frac{1}{2}\int_{0}^{\tau} B(t)\, e^{-(\tau-t)}\, dt - B(\tau) \tag{11}$$

Since the heating rate is proportional to the flux divergence, i.e.

$$\frac{\partial T}{\partial t} = \frac{2\pi \mathcal{H} \omega}{3 C_p}\frac{dF}{d\tau}$$

we can write from Eq. (5)

$$\text{const.}\frac{\partial T}{\partial t} = Q(\tau) = \frac{1}{2}\int_{\tau}^{\infty} t^{\frac{1}{2}} e^{-(t-\tau)}\, dt + \frac{1}{2}\int_{0}^{\tau} t^{\frac{1}{2}} e^{-(\tau-t)}\, dt - \tau^{\frac{1}{2}}$$

From Table 1, a plot of Q vs. $\tau$ , we see that the long wave radiative exchange heats the top of the atmosphere while below $\tau = 0.4$, radiation cooling takes place. Since the observed lapse-rate represents a steady-state thermal configuration, non-radiative thermal sources, presumably convection, must counterbalance this pattern. This implies that vertical mass transfer is cooling the top of the Venus atmosphere, while it is being heated convectively from below. Once again this pattern is reminiscent of the upper terrestrial troposphere, where forced mixing gives rise to a cooling at tropopause heights while convective heating occurs in the lower reaches of the atmosphere.

Table 1. Radiative Heat Exchange of the Venus Atmosphere

| $\tau$ (optical depth) | $Q(\tau)$* |
|---|---|
| 0 | +0.44 |
| 0.2 | +0.089 |
| 0.4 | +0.001 |
| 0.6 | -0.043 |
| 0.8 | -0.067 |
| 1.0 | -0.080 |
| 1.2 | -0.085 |
| 1.4 | -0.086 |
| 1.6 | -0.084 |
| 1.8 | -0.081 |
| 2.0 | -0.077 |
| 2.2 | -0.073 |
| 2.4 | -0.068 |
| 2.6 | -0.063 |
| 2.8 | -0.059 |
| 3.0 | -0.055 |

*plus sign indicates radiative heating, minus sign radiative cooling in relative units.

## Conclusions

From the observed Venus limb-darkening curve in the thermal emission spectrum, we have deduced that the atmosphere giving rise to this radiation is convectively stable with a temperature decreasing with height. The atmosphere appears to be convectively heated from below, which together with the lapse-rate, gives it a character similar to the upper terrestrial troposphere. The observed radiative heating pattern and the absence of limb-brightening would argue against a stratosphere of the terrestrial type, suggesting that ozone is perhaps absent here.

Although we have perhaps overloaded our long inference chain anchored to one observed curve, nevertheless the deduced results are plausible and self-consistent. Two conclusions emerge: the usefulness of the inversion technique and the need for near-Venus probe measurements.

## References

1. Ambartsumyan, V., Theoretical Astrophysics, Pergamon Press, 1951.

2. King, J.I.F., Scientific Uses of Earth Satellites, Chap. 14, ed. J.A. Van Allen, U. of Michigan Press, 1956.

3. King, J.I.F., Proceedings of the Fourth AFBMD/STL Symposium on Ballistic Missile and Space Technology, 24-27 August 1959, Vol. III, Pergamon Press, 1960.

4. Sinton, W.M. and Strong, J.D., Radiometric Observations of Venus, Ap. J., 131, 470, March 1960.